بسم الله الرحمن الرحيم

ABOUT THE AUTHOR

Under the pen-name HARUN YAHYA, the author has published many books on political and faith-related issues. An important body of his work deals with the materialistic world view and the impact of it in world history and politics. (The pen-name is formed from the names 'Harun' [Aaron] and 'Yahya' [John] in the esteemed memory of the two Prophets who struggled against infidelity.)

His works include The 'Secret Hand' in Bosnia, The Holocaust Hoax, Behind the Scenes of Terrorism, Israel's Kurdish Card, A National Strategy for Turkey, Solution: The Morals of the Qur'an, Darwin's Antagonism Against the Turks, Articles 1, Articles 2, The Calamities Darwinism Caused Humanity, The Evolution Deceit, Perished Nations, The Prophet Musa, The Golden Age, Allah's Artistry in Colour, Glory is Everywhere, The Truth of the Life of This World, Confessions of Evolutionists, The Blunders of Evolutionists 1, The Blunders of Evolutionists 2, The Dark Magic of Darwinism, The Religion of Darwinism, The Qur'an Leads the Way to Science, The Real Origin of Life, The Consciousness of the Cell, The Creation of the Universe, Miracles of the Qur'an, The Design in Nature, Self-Sacrifice and Intelligent Behaviour Models in Animals, Eternity Has Already Begun, Children Darwin Was Lying!, The End of Darwinism, Deep Thinking, Timelessness and the Reality of Fate, Never Plead Ignorance, The Secrets of DNA, The Miracle of the Atom, The Miracle in the Cell, The Miracle of the Immune System, The Miracle in the Eye, The Creation Miracle in Plants, The Miracle in the Spider, The Miracle in the Ant, The Miracle in the Gnat, The Miracle in the Honeybee, The Miracle of Seed, The Miracle in the Termite, The Miracle of the Human Body, The Miracle of Birth.

Among his booklets are The Mystery of the Atom, The Collapse of the Theory of Evolution: The Fact of Creation, The Collapse of Materialism, The End of Materialism, The Blunders of Evolutionists 1, The Blunders of Evolutionists 2, The Microbiological Collapse of Evolution, The Fact of Creation, The Collapse of the Theory of Evolution in 20 Questions, The Biggest Deception in the History of Biology: Darwinism.

The author's other works on Quranic topics include: Ever Thought About the Truth?, Devoted to Allah, Abandoning the Society of Ignorance, Paradise, The Theory of Evolution, The Moral Values of the Qur'an, Knowledge of the Qur'an, Qur'an Index, Emigrating for the Cause of Allah, The Character of Hypocrites in the Qur'an, The Secrets of the Hypocrite, The Names of Allah, Communicating the Message and Disputing in the Qur'an, The Basic Concepts in the Qur'an, Answers from the Qur'an, Death Resurrection Hell, The Struggle of the Messengers, The Avowed Enemy of Man: Satan, Idolatry, The Religion of the Ignorant, The Arrogance of Satan, Prayer in the Qur'an, The Importance of Conscience in the Qur'an, The Day of Resurrection, Never Forget, Disregarded Judgements of the Qur'an, Human Characters in the Society of Ignorance, The Importance of Patience in the Qur'an, General Information from the Qur'an, Quick Grasp of Faith 1-2-3, The Crude Reasoning of Disbelief, The Mature Faith, Before You Regret, Our Messengers Say, The Mercy of Believers, The Fear of Allah, The Nightmare of Disbelief, Prophet Isa Will Come, Beauties Presented by the Qur'an for Life, Bouquet of the Beauties of Allah 1-2-3-4, The Iniquity Called "Mockery", The Secret of the Test, The True Wisdom According to the Qur'an, The Struggle with the Religion of Irreligion, The School of Yusuf, The Alliance of the Good, Slanders Spread Against Muslims Throughout History, The Importance of Following the Good Word, Why Do You Deceive Yourself?, Islam: The Religion of Ease, Enthusiasm and Vigor in the Qur'an, Seeing Good in Everything, How does the Unwise Interpret the Qur'an?, Some Secrets of the Qur'an, The Courage of Believers, Being Hopeful in the Qur'an.

THE SIGNS IN THE
HEAVENS AND THE EARTH

FOR MEN OF UNDERSTANDING

In the heavens and the earth
there are certainly signs for the believers.
And in your creation and all the creatures
He has scattered about there are signs
for people with certainty.

(Surat al-Jathiyah: 3-4)

HARUN YAHYA

Ta-Ha Publishers Ltd.
1 Wynne Road London SW9 OBB

First Published by Vural Yayıncılık, İstanbul, Turkey in January 1995

First English Edition published in December 1999
Second English Edition published in January 2001
Third English Edition published in April 2003

Published by:
Ta-Ha Publishers Ltd.
1 Wynne Road
London SW9 OBB

Website: http://www.taha.co.uk
E-Mail: sales @ taha.co.uk

By Harun Yahya
Translated By: Mustapha Ahmad
Edited By: Abdassamad Clarke

A catalog record of this book is available from the British Library
ISBN 1-84200-003-9

Printed and bound by:
Secil Ofset in İstanbul
Address: Yüzyıl Mahallesi MAS-SIT Matbaacılar Sitesi
4. Cadde No:77 Bağcılar- İstanbul / TURKEY

Website:
www.harunyahya.com

TO THE READER

The reason why a special chapter is assigned to the collapse of the theory of evolution is that this theory constitutes the basis of all anti-spiritual philosophies. Since Darwinism rejects the fact of creation, and therefore the existence of Allah, during the last 140 years it has caused many people to abandon their faith or fall into doubt. Therefore, showing that this theory is a deception is a very important duty, which is strongly related to the religion. It is imperative that this important service be rendered to everyone. Some of our readers may find the chance to read only one of our books. Therefore, we think it appropriate to spare a chapter for a summary of this subject.

In all the books by the author, faith-related issues are explained in the light of the Qur'anic verses and people are invited to learn Allah's words and to live by them. All the subjects that concern Allah's verses are explained in such a way as to leave no room for doubt or question marks in the reader's mind. The sincere, plain and fluent style employed ensures that everyone of every age and from every social group can easily understand the books. This effective and lucid narrative makes it possible to read them in a single sitting. Even those who rigorously reject spirituality are influenced by the facts recounted in these books and cannot refute the truthfulness of their contents.

This book and all the other works of the author can be read individually or discussed in a group at a time of conversation. Those readers who are willing to profit from the books will find discussion very useful in the sense that they will be able to relate their own reflections and experiences to one another.

In addition, it will be a great service to the religion to contribute to the presentation and reading of these books, which are written solely for the good pleasure of Allah. All the books of the author are extremely convincing. For this reason, for those who want to communicate the religion to other people, one of the most effective methods is to encourage them to read these books.

It is hoped that the reader will take time to look through the review of other books on the final pages of the book, and appreciate the rich source of material on faith-related issues, which are very useful and a pleasure to read.

In these books, you will not find, as in some other books, the personal views of the author, explanations based on dubious sources, styles that are unobservant of the respect and reverence due to sacred subjects, nor hopeless, doubt-creating, and pessimistic accounts that create deviations in the heart.

CONTENTS

THE ABILITY TO SEE THE SIGNS OF ALLAH...

Say: "Praise be to Allah. He will show you His Signs and you will recognise them. Your Lord is not heedless of anything you do." (Surat an-Naml: 93)

In many societies today, the Qur'an is assessed very differently from what is the real purpose of its revelation. In the Islamic world, in general, very few people know the contents of the Qur'an.

Some Muslim people often hang the Qur'an on the walls of their houses within a decorative cover and elderly people read it from time to time. They assume that the Qur'an protects those who read it from "misfortune and trouble". According to this superstition, they consider the Qur'an a sort of amulet against misfortunes.

The Qur'anic verses, however, inform us that the purpose of the Qur'an's revelation is entirely different from what is mentioned above. For instance, in the 52nd verse of Surah Ibrahim, Allah states: **"This is a communication to be transmitted to mankind so that they can be warned by it and so that they will know that He is One God and so that people of intelligence will pay heed."** In many other verses, Allah emphasises that one of the most crucial purposes of the Qur'an's revelation is to invite people to ponder.

In the Qur'an, Allah invites people to reject blindly accepting the beliefs and values society imposes on them and to ponder by pushing aside all the prejudices, taboos and constraints on their minds.

Man must think on how he came into being, what is the purpose of his life, why he will die and what awaits him after death. He must question how he himself and the whole universe came into existence and how they continue to exist. While doing this, he must relieve himself of all constraints and prejudices.

By thinking, while isolating his conscience from all social, ideological and psychological obligations, the person should eventually perceive that the entire universe, including himself, is created by a superior power. Even when he examines his own body or any other thing in nature, he will see an impressive harmony, plan and wisdom at work within its design.

At this point again, the Qur'an guides man. In the Qur'an, Allah guides us as to what we should reflect on and investigate. With the methods of reflection given in the Qur'an, he who has faith in Allah will better perceive Allah's perfection, eternal wisdom, knowledge and power in His creation. When a believing person starts to think in the way shown in the Qur'an, he soon realises that the whole universe is a sign of Allah's power and art, and that, "nature is a work of art, not the artist itself". Every work of art exhibits the exceptional skills of the one who has made it and conveys his messages.

In the Qur'an, people are summoned to contemplate numerous events and objects that clearly testify to the existence and uniqueness of Allah and His attributes. In the Qur'an, all these beings that bear witness are designated as "signs", meaning "tested evidence, absolute knowledge and expression of truth". Therefore, the signs of Allah comprise all the beings in the universe that disclose and communicate the being and attributes of Allah. Those who can observe and remember will see that the entire universe is only composed of the signs of Allah.

This, indeed, is the responsibility of mankind; to be able to see the signs of Allah... Thus, such a person will come to know the Creator Who created him and all other things, draw closer to Him, discover the meaning of his existence and his life and so prosper.

This book can never adequately show the innumerable signs of Allah, nor can any other work. Each thing, the breaths a human takes, political and social developments; the cosmic harmony in the universe, the atom, which is one of the smallest pieces of matter, is each a sign of Allah and they all operate under His control and knowledge, abiding by His laws. Recognising and knowing the signs of Allah calls for personal effort. Everyone will recognise and know the signs of Allah in accordance with his own wisdom and conscience.

Undoubtedly, some guidelines may also help. As the first step, one can investigate certain points stressed in the Qur'an in order to acquire the mentality that perceives the whole universe as an articulation of the things Allah created.

This book is written to draw attention to some of the subjects that we are advised to ponder in the Qur'an. Allah's signs in nature are emphasised in Surat an-Nahl:

> **It is He Who sends down water from the sky. From it you drink and from it come the shrubs among which you graze your herds. And by it He makes crops grow for you and olives and dates and grapes and fruit of every kind. . There is certainly a sign in that for people who reflect. He has made the night and the day subservient to you, and**

the sun, the moon and the stars, all subject to His command. There are certainly signs in that for people who use their intellect. And also the things of varying colours He has created for you in the earth. There is certainly a sign in that for people who pay heed. It is He Who made the sea subservient to you so that you can eat fresh flesh from it and bring out from it ornaments to wear. And you see the ships cleaving through it so that you can seek His bounty, and so that perhaps you may show thanks. He cast firmly embedded mountains on the earth so it would not move under you, and rivers and pathways so that perhaps you might be guided, and landmarks. And they are guided by the stars. Is He Who creates like him who does not create? So will you not pay heed? (Surat an-Nahl: 10-17)

In the Qur'an, Allah invites men of understanding to think about the issues which other people overlook, or just dismiss using such barren terms as "evolution", "coincidence", or "a miracle of nature".

In the creation of the heavens and the earth, and the alternation of night and day, there are Signs for people of intelligence: those who remember Allah standing, sitting and lying on their sides, and reflect on the creation of the heavens and the earth: "Our Lord, You did not create this for nothing. Glory be to You! So guard us from the punishment of the Fire. (Surah Ali-'Imran: 190-191)

As we see in these verses, people of understanding see the signs of Allah and try to comprehend His eternal knowledge, power and art by remembering and reflecting on them, for Allah's knowledge is limitless, and His creation flawless.

For men of understanding, everything around them is a sign of this creation.

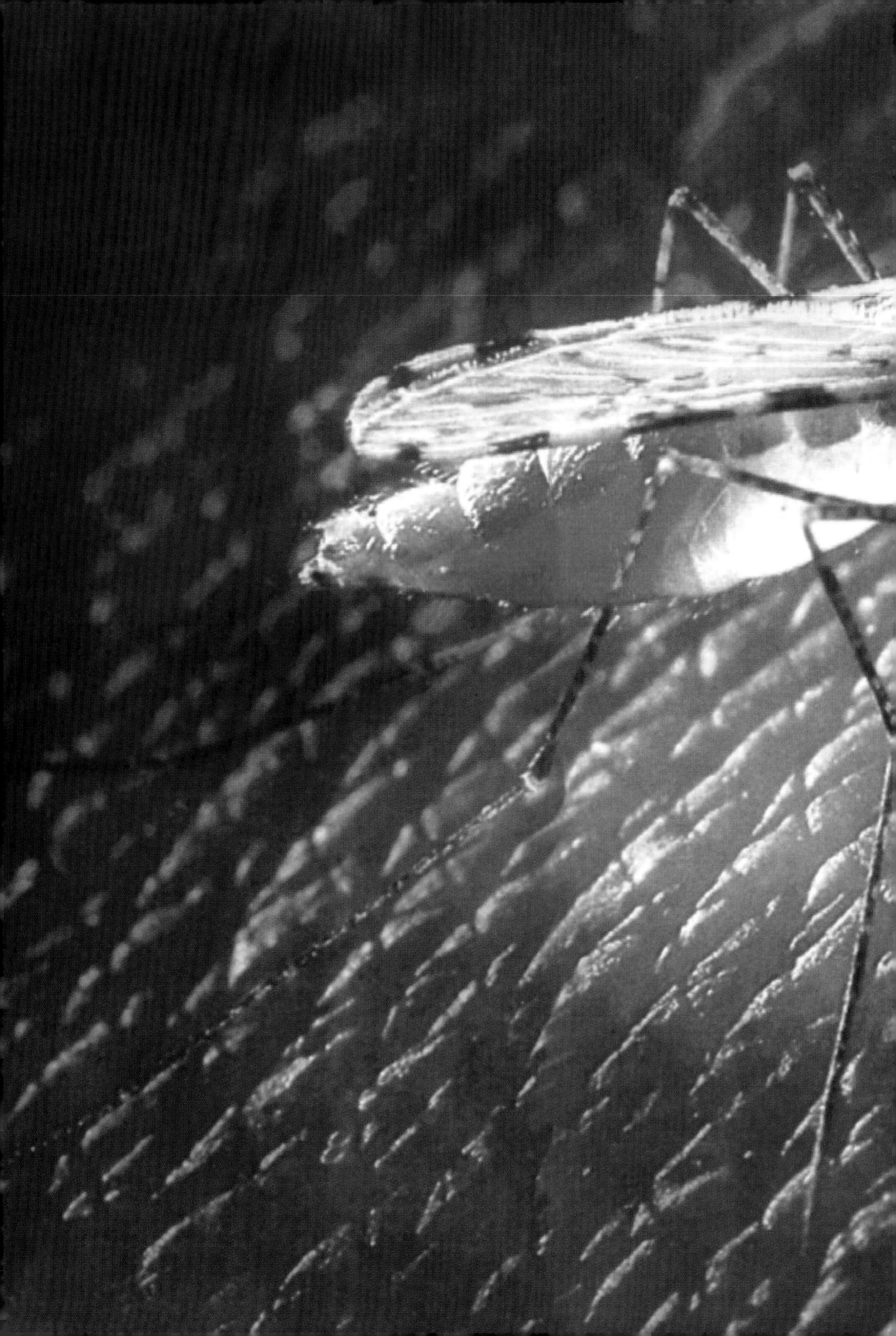

Allah is not ashamed to make the example of a gnat or of an even smaller thing. As for those who believe, they know it is the truth from their Lord. But as for those who reject, they say, "What does Allah mean by this example?" He misguides many by it and guides many by it. But He only misguides the degenerate.
(Surat al-Baqarah: 26)

THE GNAT

In the Qur'an, as mentioned in earlier pages, Allah frequently summons people to investigate nature and see the "signs" therein. All animate and inanimate beings in the universe are full of signs revealing that they are "made", and they demonstrate the power, knowledge and art of their "maker". Man is responsible for identifying these signs by using his wisdom, and for paying reverence to Allah.

While all living beings bear these signs, there are some to which Allah specifically refers in the Qur'an. The gnat is one of these animals. In the 26th verse of Surat al-Baqarah, the gnat is mentioned:

Allah is not ashamed to make the example of a gnat or of an even smaller thing. As for those who believe, they know it is the truth from their Lord. But as for those who reject, they say, "What does Allah mean by this example?" He misguides many by it and guides many by it. But He only misguides the degenerate.

Considered as an ordinary, insignificant living being, even the gnat is worthy of being examined and pondered since it bears the signs of Allah. This is why "Allah is not ashamed to make the example of a gnat or of an even smaller thing".

The main food source for male and female gnats is nectar.

SPECIAL PINCERS FOR MATING

A male gnat mature enough to mate uses its antennae, i.e. its hearing organs, to find its female. The antennae of male gnats have different functions from those of females. Thin feathers at the end of their antennae are highly sensitive to sounds emitted by female gnats. Right beside the sexual organs of the male gnat, there are appendages, which help him to grab the female while mating in the air. Male gnats fly in groups that seem like clouds and when a female gnat enters the group, the male who succeeds in grabbing the female mates with her during flight. Mating does not take long and the male gnat goes back to his group after mating. From that moment, the female gnat needs blood for the development of her eggs.

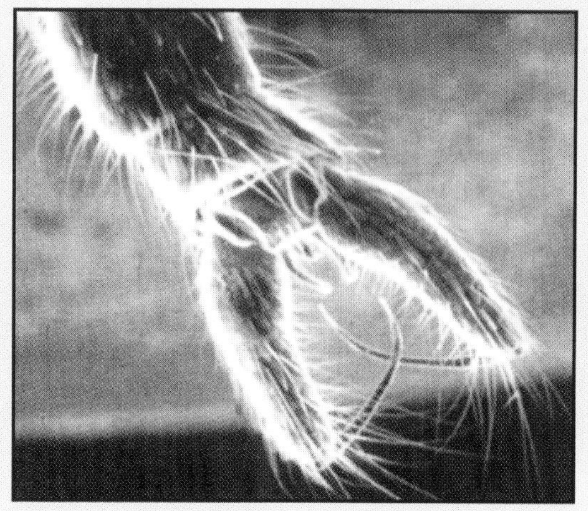

THE EXTRAORDINARY ADVENTURE OF THE GNAT

What is generally known about gnats is that they are bloodsuckers and feed on blood. This, however, is not quite correct, because not all gnats suck blood but only females. Besides, the females suck blood not because of their need for food. Both male and female gnats feed on the nectar from flowers. The only reason female gnats, unlike the males, suck blood is their need for the proteins found in blood which help their eggs to develop. In other words, the female gnat sucks blood just to secure the perpetuation of its species.

The developmental process is one of the most amazing and admirable sides of the gnat. The short story of the transformation of a living being from a tiny larva through many different phases into a gnat is as follows:

Gnat eggs, which are fed by blood to develop, are deposited on damp leaves or dried ponds by the female gnat during summer or autumn. Prior to this, the mother initially inspects the ground thoroughly by using the delicate receptors under her abdomen. Upon finding a convenient place, she starts to deposit her eggs. The eggs, which are less than 1 mm in length, are arranged

In some gnat species, the female lines up hundreds of eggs like a raft.

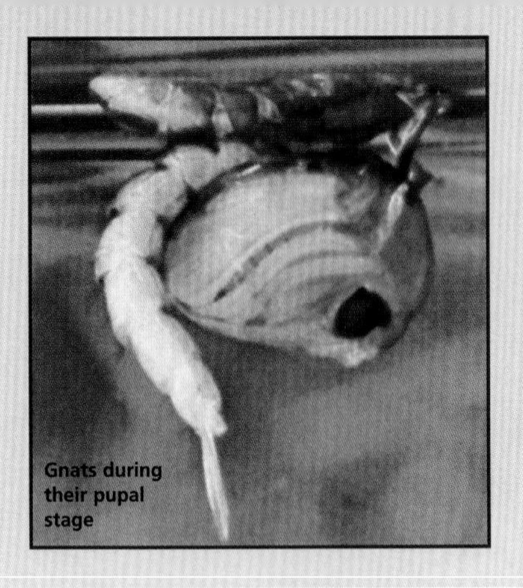
Gnats during their pupal stage

RESPIRATORY SYSTEM:

The respiratory system of the larva is based on a method whereby the larva breathes air by means of a hollow tube pushed up above the water surface. Meanwhile, larvae hang upside down under the water. A viscous secretion prevents water from leaking into the openings through which larvae breathe.

in a row either in groups or one by one. Some species deposit their eggs in a form, which is joined together like a raft. Some of these egg groups contain about 300 eggs.

The neatly placed white eggs soon start to darken, and they turn completely black in a couple of hours. This dark colour provides protection for the larvae by preventing them from being noticed by other insects and birds. Apart from the eggs, the skin colours of some other larvae also change according to their surroundings, and this helps to protect them.

The larvae change colours by making use of certain factors after quite complicated chemical processes. No doubt, neither the eggs, nor the larvae, nor the mother gnat is aware of the processes behind the colour changes during the gnat's different developmental stages. It is out of the question for these living beings themselves to make this system or for this system to form by coincidence. Gnats have been created with these systems from the moment they first appeared.

COMING OUT OF THE EGG

When the incubation period is complete, larvae start to come out of the eggs almost simultaneously. The larvae, which feed continuously, grow quickly. Soon, their skins become too tight, not allowing them to grow any further. This indicates that it is time for the first change of skin. In this phase, the hard and brittle skin breaks easily.

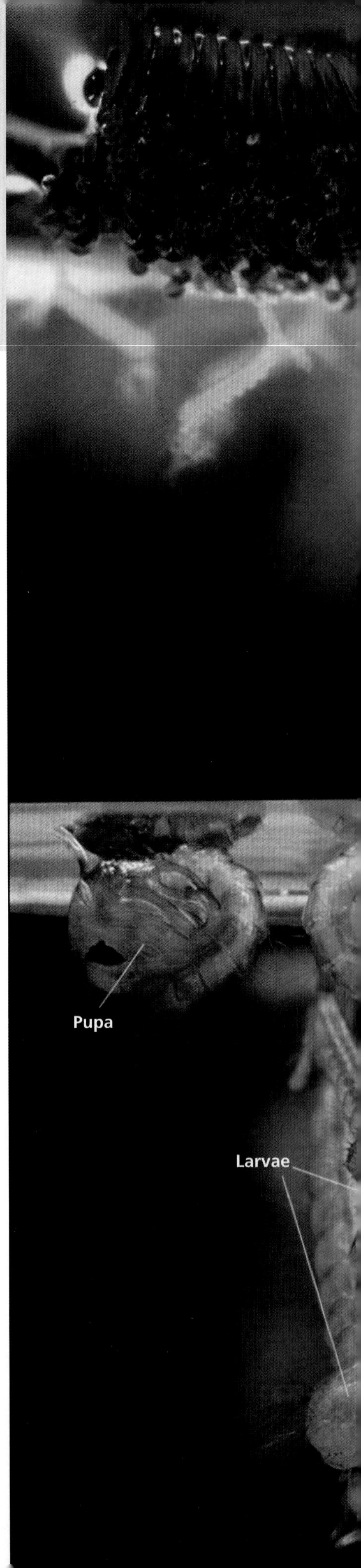

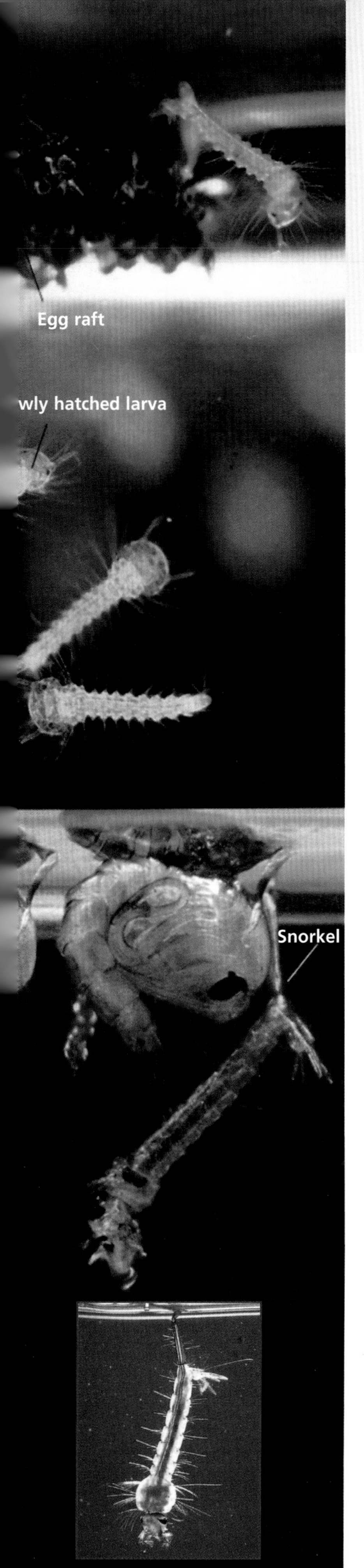

Before the gnat larva fully completes its development, it changes its skin two more times.

The method used for feeding the larvae is rather astonishing. The larvae make small whirlpools in the water with their two fan-shaped appendages made up of feathers, and thus make bacteria and other micro-organisms flow towards their mouths. The respiration of the larvae, which repose upside down in water, takes place through an aerial tube similar to the "snorkel" used by divers. A viscous solution secreted by their bodies prevents water from leaking into the openings through which they breathe. Briefly, this living being survives through the inter-relationship and interplay of many delicate balances. If it did not have an aerial tube, it could not survive; if it did not have a viscous secretion, its respiratory tube would fill with water. The formation of these two systems at two different times would cause the animal to die at this stage. This proves that the gnat has all its systems intact, that is, it was created.

The larvae change their skin once more. The last change of skin is rather different from the others. In this stage, larvae pass onto the final stage of their maturation, the "pupal stage". The shell they are placed in becomes quite tight. This shows that it is time for the larvae to emerge from this shell. Such a different creature comes out of the shell that it is indeed hard to believe that these two are different developmental phases of the same being. As seen, this transformation process is far too complicated and delicate to have been designed either by the larva or by the female gnat...

During this last stage of transformation, the animal faces the danger of being choked, as its respiratory openings, reaching above the water through an aerial tube, would be closed. However,

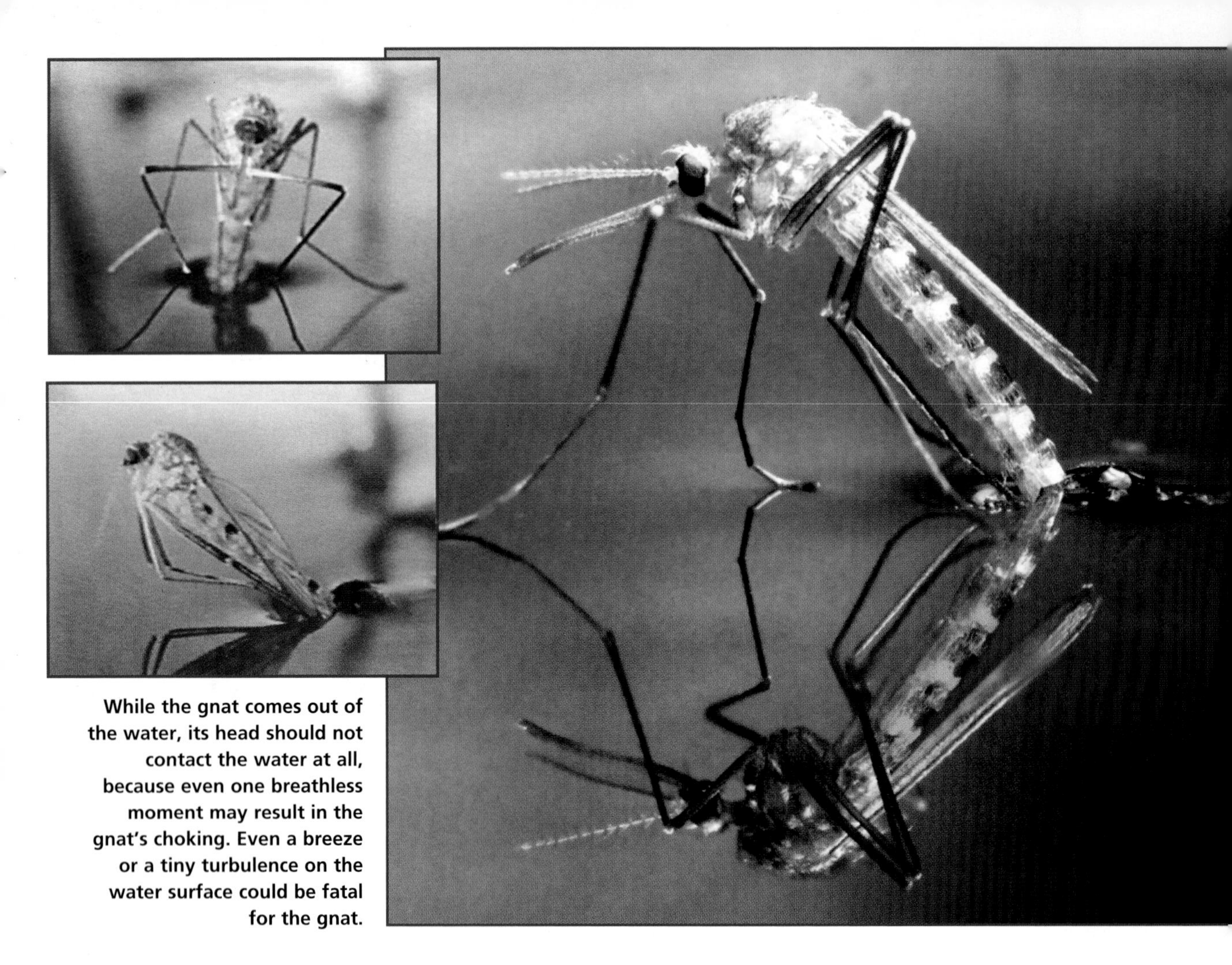

While the gnat comes out of the water, its head should not contact the water at all, because even one breathless moment may result in the gnat's choking. Even a breeze or a tiny turbulence on the water surface could be fatal for the gnat.

from that stage on, respiration will not be done by means of these holes, but by means of two tubes newly emerging on the anterior of the animal. This is why these tubes rise to the surface of the water prior to the change of skin. The gnat in the pupa cocoon has now become mature. It is ready to fly with all its organs and organelles such as antennae, trunks, feet, chest, wings, abdomen and its large eyes.

The pupa cocoon is torn at the top. The greatest risk at this stage is the leakage of water into the cocoon. However, the torn top of the cocoon is covered with a special viscous liquid protecting the gnat's head from contact with the water. This moment is extremely important. Because even a soft wind may bring its death by causing it to fall into the water, the gnat has to climb on the water with its feet only touching the water surface. It succeeds.

How is it that the first gnat attained the "ability" to go through such a transformation? Could it be that a larva "decided" to transform into a gnat after changing skin three times? Absolutely not! It is quite evident that this tiny living being, which Allah gives as an example, has specifically been created this way.

HOW GNATS PERCEIVE THE OUTSIDE WORLD

Gnats are equipped with extremely sensitive heat receptors. They perceive the things around them in different colours depending on their heat, as in the picture on the right. As its perception is not dependent on light, it is quite easy for the gnat to spot blood vessels even in a dark room. The heat receptors of the gnat are sensitive enough to detect heat differences as small as 1/1,000º C.

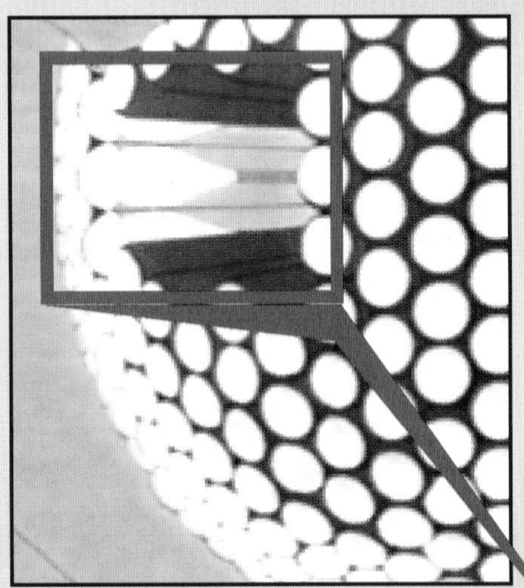

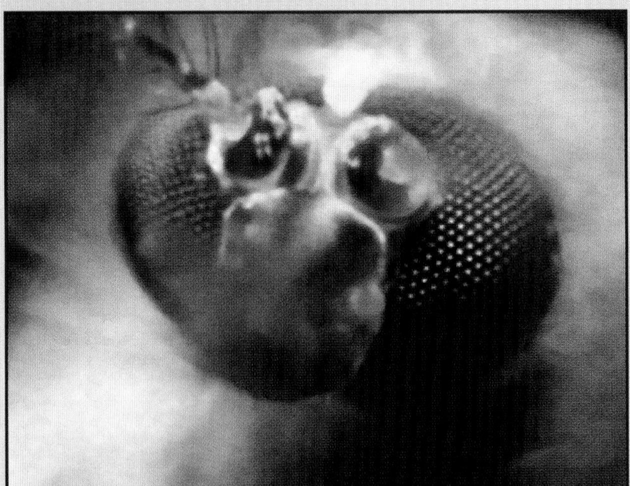

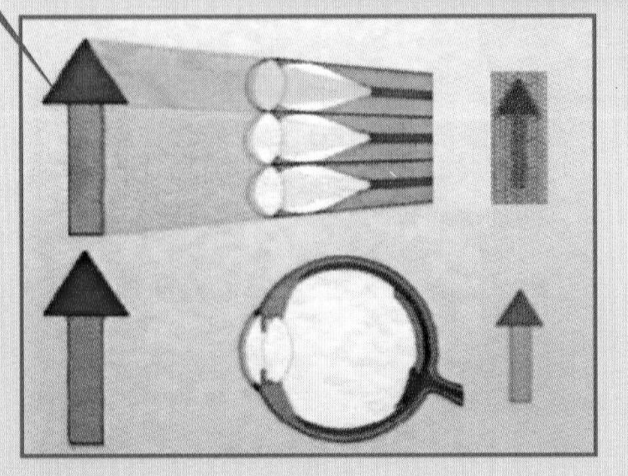

The gnat has nearly one hundred eyes. As compound eyes, these are placed on the top of its head. In the picture above, the cross-sections of three of these eyes are shown. On the right, we see how the image of an object is transmitted to the brain from the eye.

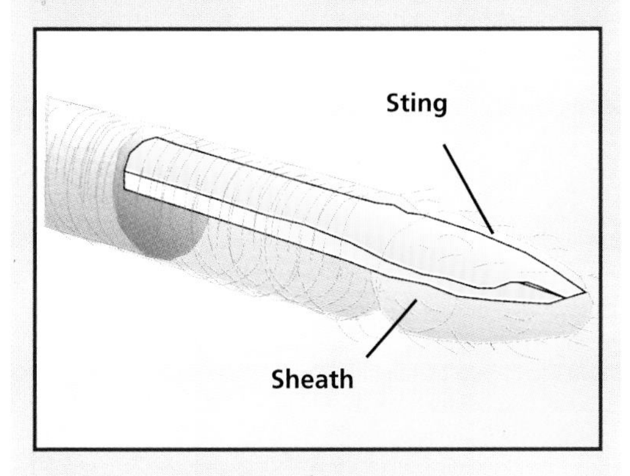

AMAZING TECHNIQUE OF BLOOD SUCKING

The gnat's technique of "blood-sucking" depends on a complex system in which unbelievably detailed structures work together.

After the gnat lands on its target, it first detects a spot by means of the lips in its proboscis. The syringe-like 'sting' of the gnat is protected by a special sheath, which is stripped back during the blood-sucking process.

The gnat does not pierce the skin, as assumed, by thrusting its proboscis into it with pressure. Here, the main task falls to the upper jaw, which is as sharp as a knife, and the mandible on which there are teeth bent backwards. The gnat moves its mandible forwards and backwards like a saw and cuts the skin with the help of the upper jaws. When the sting, inserted through this cut in the skin, reaches to the blood vessel, the drilling ends. Now it is time for the gnat to suck blood.

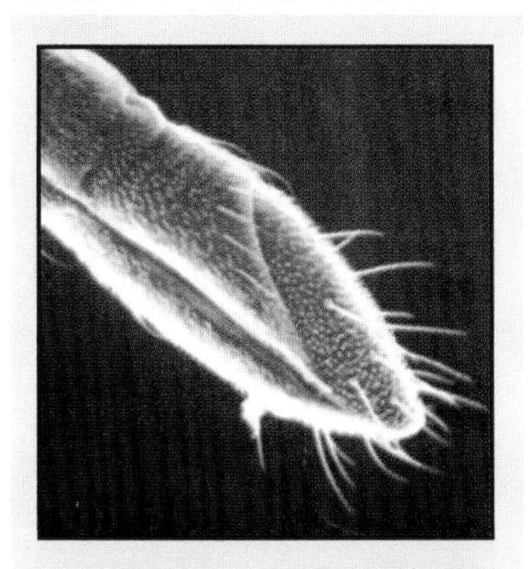

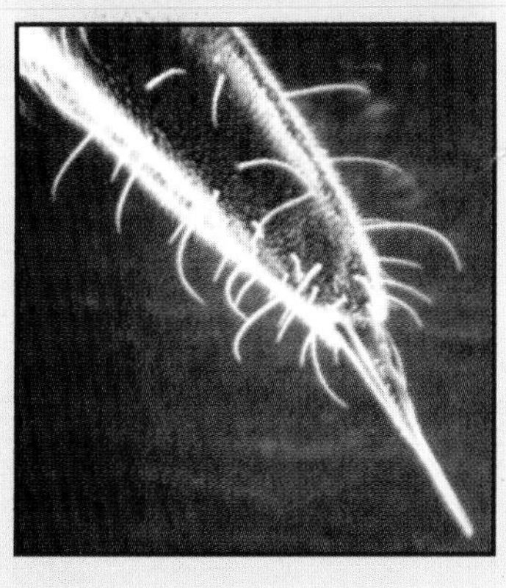

However, as we know, the slightest harm to the vessels causes the human body to secrete an enzyme that makes the blood clot and stops its leakage. This enzyme should create a problem for the gnat, because the body should also react to the hole opened by the gnat, causing the blood at this spot to clot immediately and the wound to be repaired. That would mean that the gnat could not suck any blood.

But the problem is eliminated for the gnat. Before the gnat starts sucking blood, it injects a special liquid secreted in its body into the cleavage opened in the living being it has stung. This liquid neutralises the enzyme that causes the clot-

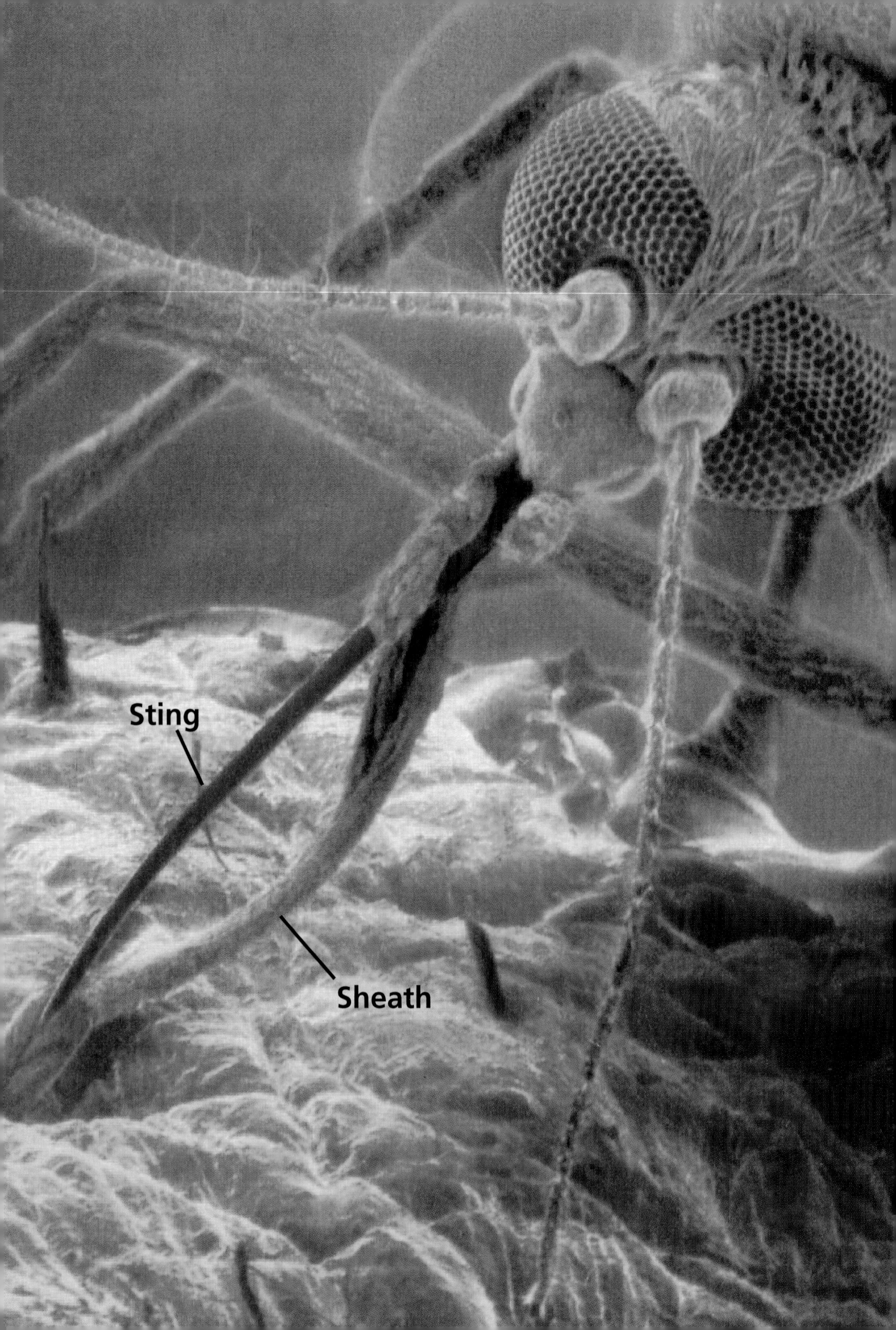
Sting
Sheath

The photograph is of a tiny animal that lives as a parasite on gnats.
When we consider that apart from the excellent systems of the gnat, such as feeding, reproduction, respiration and blood circulation, only a small part of which we could examine here, this lice also has complex systems and organic functions, we can better comprehend the boundlessness of the signs of Allah.

ting of blood. Thus, the gnat sucks the blood it needs without the problem of clotting. The itching and swelling formed on the spot bitten by the gnat is caused by this liquid that prevents clotting.

This is surely an extraordinary process and it brings the following questions to mind:

1) How does the gnat know that there is a clotting enzyme in the human body?

2) In order to produce a neutralising secretion in its own body against that enzyme, it needs to know the chemical structure of the enzyme. How could this be possible?

3) Even if it somehow attained such knowledge (!), how could it produce the secretion in its own body and make the "technical rigging" needed to transfer it to its proboscis?

The answer to all these questions is obvious: it is not possible for the gnat to perform any of the above. It neither has the required wisdom, knowledge of chemistry, or the "laboratory" environment to produce the secretion. What we talk about here is only a gnat of a few millimetres in length, without consciousness or wisdom, that is all!

It is quite clear that Allah, "Lord of the heavens and of the earth, and of all that is between them", has created both the gnat and man, and donated such extraordinary and marvellous features to the gnat.

> *Everything in the heavens and the earth glorifies Allah. He is the Almighty, the All-Wise. The sovereignty of the heavens and the earth belongs to Him. He gives life and causes to die. He has power over everything.*
> *(Surat al-Hadid: 1-2)*

"Your Lord inspired the bees ..."

Your Lord inspired the bees: "Build dwellings in the mountains and the trees, and also in the structures which men erect. Then eat from every kind of fruit and travel the paths of your Lord, made easy for you to follow." From their bellies comes a drink of varying colours, containing healing for mankind. There is certainly a sign in that for people who reflect. (Surat an-Nahl: 68-69)

THE HONEY BEE

It is well known by almost everyone that honey is a fundamental food source for the human body, whereas only a few people are aware of the extraordinary qualities of its producer, the honeybee.

As we know, the food source of bees is nectar, which is not found during winter. For this reason, they combine the nectar collected in summer time with special secretions of their body, produce a new nutrient - honey - and store it for the coming winter months.

It is noteworthy that the amount of honey stored by bees is much greater than their actual need. The first question that comes to mind is why do the bees not give up this "excess production", which seems a waste of time and energy for them? The answer to this question is hidden in the "inspiration" stated in the verse to have been given the bee.

Bees produce honey not only for themselves but also for human beings. Bees, like many other natural beings, are also dedicated to the service of man, just as the chicken lays at least one egg a day although it does not need it, and the cow produces much more milk than its offspring needs.

EXCELLENT ORGANISATION IN THE HIVE

The bees' lives in the hive and their honey production are fascinating. Without going into too much detail, let us discover the basic features of the "social life" of bees. Bees must carry out numerous "tasks" and they manage all of them with excellent organisation.

Regulation of humidity and ventilation: The humidity of the hive, which gives honey its highly protective quality, must be kept within certain limits. If humidity is over or under those limits, then the honey is spoiled and loses its protective and nutritious qualities. Similarly, the temperature in the hive has to be 35° C throughout 10 months of the year. In order to keep the temperature and humidity of the hive within certain limits, a special group takes charge of "ventilation".

On a hot day, bees can easily be observed ventilating the hive. The entrance of the hive fills with bees and clamping themselves to the wooden structure, they fan the hive with their wings. In a standard hive, air entering from one side is forced to leave from the other side. Extra ventilator bees work within the hive to push the air to all corners of the hive.

This ventilation system is also useful in protecting the hive from smoke and air pollution.

Health system: The efforts of the bees to preserve the quality of honey are not limited to the regulation of humidity and heat. A perfect healthcare system exists within the hive to keep all events that may result in the production of bacteria under control. The main purpose of this system is to remove all substances likely to cause bacteria production. The basic principle of this health system is to prevent foreign substances from entering the hive. To secure this, two guardians are always kept at the entrance of the hive. If a foreign substance or insect enters the hive despite this precaution, all bees act to remove it from the hive.

For bigger foreign objects that cannot be removed from the hive, another protection mechanism is used. Bees "embalm" these foreign objects. They produce a substance called "propolis (bee resin)" with which they carry out the "embalming" process. Produced by adding special secretions to the resins they collect from trees like pine, poplar and acacia, the bee resin is also used to patch cracks in the hive. After being applied to the cracks by the bees, the resin dries as it reacts with air and forms a hard surface. Thus, it can stand against all kinds of external threats. Bees use this substance in most of their work.

At this point, many questions spring to mind. Propolis has the feature of not allowing any bacteria to live in it. This makes propolis an ideal substance for embalming. How do bees know that this substance is an ideal substance for embalming? How do bees produce a substance, which man can only produce in laboratory conditions and with the use of technology if he has a certain level of knowledge of chemistry? How do they know that a dead insect causes bacteria production and that embalming will prevent this?

It is evident that the bee has neither any knowledge on this subject, nor a laboratory in its body. The bee is only an insect 1-2 cm in size and it only does that with which its Lord has inspired it.

MAXIMUM STORAGE WITH MINIMUM MATERIAL

Bees construct hives in which 80,000 bees can live and work together by shaping small portions of beeswax.

The hive is made up of beeswax-walled honeycombs, which have hundreds of tiny cells on each of their faces. All honeycomb cells are exactly the same size. This engineering miracle is achieved by the collective work of thousands of bees. Bees use these cells for food storage and the maintenance of young bees.

Bees have been using the hexagonal structure for the construction of honeycombs for millions of years. (A bee fossil has been found dating from 100 million years ago). It is astonishing that they have chosen a hexagonal structure rather than an octagonal, or pentagonal. Mathematicians give the reason: "the hexagonal structure is the most suitable geometric form for the maximum use of unit area." If honeycomb cells were constructed in another form, then there would be areas left unused; thus, less honey would be stored, and fewer bees would be able to benefit from it.

As long as their depths are the same, a triangular or quadrangular cell would hold the same amount of honey as a hexagonal cell. However, among all these geometric forms, the hexagonal has the shortest circumference. Whilst they have the same volume, the amount of wax required for hexagonal cells is less than the amount of wax required for a triangular or quadrangular one.

The conclusion: hexagonal cells require minimal amounts of wax in terms of construction while they store maximal amounts of honey. Bees themselves surely cannot have calculated this result, obtained by man after many complex geometrical calculations. These tiny animals use the hexagonal form innately, just because they are taught and "inspired" so by their Lord.

The hexagonal design of cells is practical in many respects. Cells fit to one another and they share each other's walls. This, again, ensures maximum storage with minimum wax. Although the walls of the cells are rather thin, they are strong enough to carry a few times their own weight.

As well as in the walls of the sides of the cells, bees also take the maximum saving principle into consideration while they construct the bottom edges.

Combs are built as a slice with two rows lying back to back. In this case, the problem of the junction point of two cells occurs. Constructing the bottom surfaces of cells by combining three equilateral quadrangles solves this problem. When three cells are built on one face of the comb, the bottom surface of one cell on the other face is automatically constructed.

As the bottom surface is composed of equilateral quadrangular wax plaques, a downward deepening is observed at the bottom of those cells made by this method. This means an increase in the volume of the cell and, thus, in the amount of honey stored.

OTHER CHARACTERISTICS OF HONEY COMB CELLS

Another point that bees consider during the construction of the honeycomb is the inclination of cells. By raising cells 13° on both sides, they prevent the cells from being parallel to the ground. Thus, honey does not leak out from the mouth of the cell.

While working, worker bees hang onto each other in circles and congregate together in bunches. By doing this, they provide the necessary temperature for wax production. Little sacks in their abdomens produce a transparent liquid, which leaks out and hardens the thin wax layers. Bees collect the wax with the little hooks on their legs. They put this wax into their mouths, and chew and process it until it softens enough and so give it shape in the cells. Many bees work together to ensure the required temperature for the work place in order to keep the wax soft and malleable.

There is another interesting point to note: the construction of the honeycomb starts from the upper side of the hive and continues simultaneously in two or three separate rows downward. While a honeycomb slice expands in two opposite directions, first the bottom of its two rows join. This process is realised in an astonishing harmony and order. Therefore, it is never possible to understand that the honeycomb actually consists of three separate parts. The honeycomb slices, which started simultaneously from different directions, are so perfectly arranged that, although there are hundreds of different angles in its structure, it seems like one uniform piece.

For such a construction, bees need to calculate the distances between the starting and connection points in advance and then design the dimensions of the cells accordingly. How can such a delicate calculation be done by thousands of bees? This has always impressed scientists.

It is obviously irrational to assume that bees have solved this task, which man can hardly manage. There is such a delicate and detailed organisation involved that it is impossible for them to carry it out on their own.

So how do they achieve this? An evolutionist would explain that this event

And in your creation and all the creatures He has scattered about there are signs for people with certainty.
(Surat al-Jathiyah: 4)

has been achieved by "instinct". However, what is the "instinct" that can address thousands of bees at the same time and make them perform a collective task? It would not be sufficient even if each bee acted on its own "instinct", since what they do would necessarily have to be in concordance with each other's instincts in order to achieve this astonishing result. Due to this, they must be directed by an "instinct" coming from a unique source. Bees, who start constructing the hive from different corners and then combine their separate tasks without leaving any gaps and having all the cells constructed equally in a perfect hexagonal structure, must certainly be receiving "instinctive" messages from the very same source!...

The term "instinct" used above is "only a name" as mentioned in the Qur'an, in the 40th verse of Surah Yusuf. It is of no use insisting on such "mere names" in order to conceal clear truths. Bees are guided from a unique source and thus they successfully come to perform tasks which they otherwise would not be able to. It is not instinct, a term with no definition, that guides bees but the "inspiration" mentioned in Surat an-Nahl. What these tiny animals do is implement the programme that Allah has particularly set for them.

HOW THEY DETERMINE THEIR DIRECTION

Bees usually have to fly long distances and scan large areas to find food. They collect flower pollens and the constituents of honey within a range of 800m of the hive. A bee, which finds flowers, flies back to its hive to let others know about their place, but how will this bee describe the location of the flowers to the other bees in the hive?

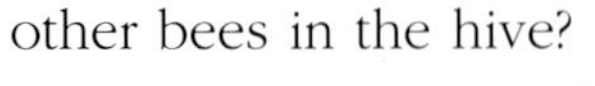

By dancing!... The bee returning to the hive starts to perform a dance. This dance is a means of expression, which it uses to tell the other bees the location of the flowers. This dance, repeated many times by the bee, includes all the information about the inclination, direction, distance and other details of the food source that enable other bees to reach it.

This dance is actually a figure "8" constantly repeated by the bee (see picture above). The bee forms the middle part of the figure "8" by wagging its tail and performing zigzags. The angle between the zigzags and the line between the

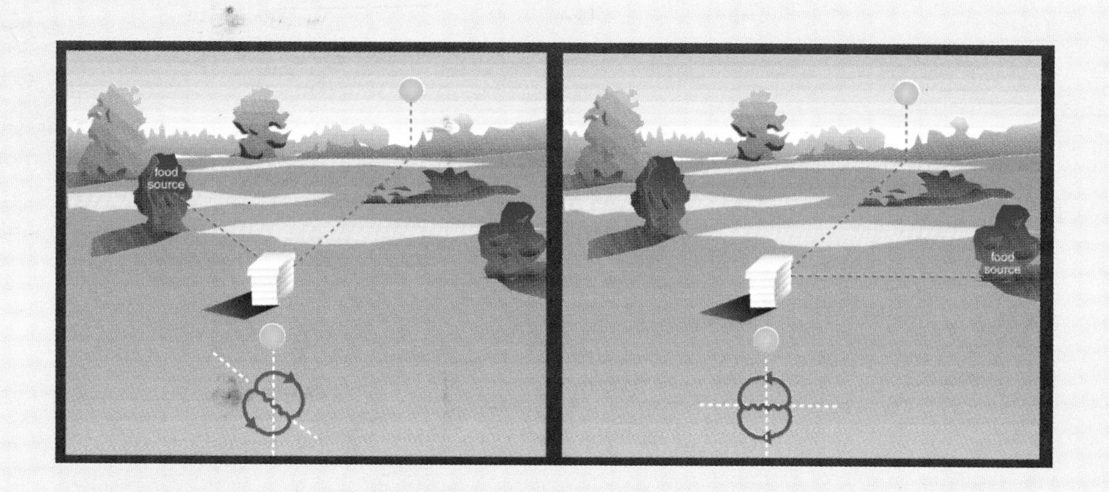

sun and the hive gives the exact direction of the food source (see picture above).

However, knowing only the direction of the food source is not enough. Worker bees also need to "know" how far they have to travel to collect the ingredients for the honey, so, the bee returning from the flower source, "tells" the other bees the distance of the flower pollens by means of certain body movements. It does this by wagging the bottom part of its body and creating air currents. For example, in order to "describe" a distance of 250m, it wags the bottom part of its body 5 times in half a minute. This way, the exact location of the source is made clear in detail, both with respect to its distance and its orientation.

A new problem awaits the bee in those flights where the round trip to the food source takes a long time. As the bee, who can only describe the food source according to the direction of the sun, goes back to its hive, the sun moves 1 degree every 4 minutes. Eventually, the bee will make an error of 1 degree for each four minutes it spends on the way about the direction of the food source of which it informs the other bees.

Astonishingly, the bee does not have such a problem! The bee's eye is formed of hundreds of tiny hexagonal lenses. Each lens focuses on a very narrow area just like a telescope does. A bee looking towards the sun at a certain time of the day can always find its location while it flies. The bee is reckoned to do this calculation by making use of the change in the light emitted by the sun depending on the time of the day. Consequently, the bee determines the direction of the target location without mistake by making corrections in the information it gives in the hive as the sun moves forward.

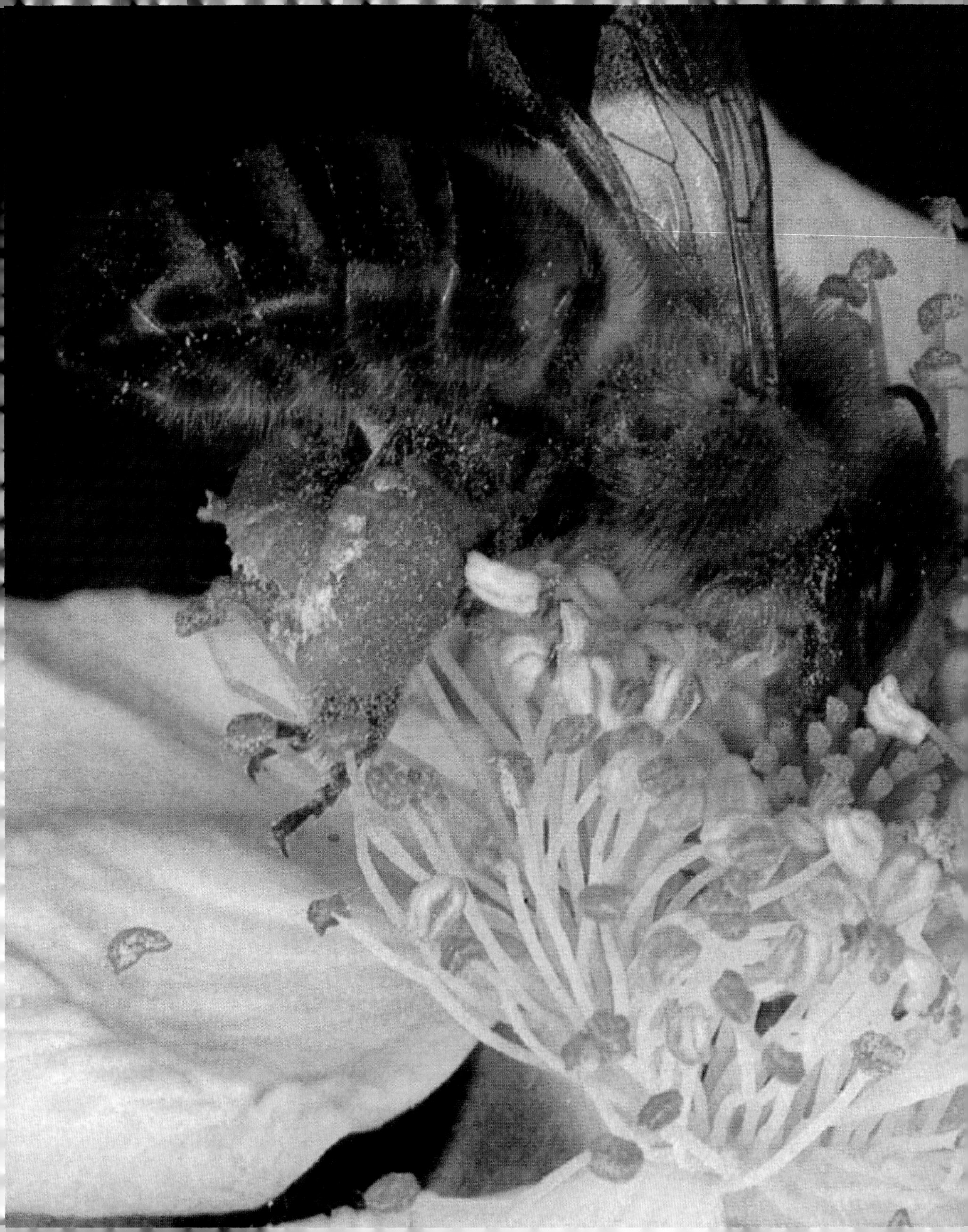

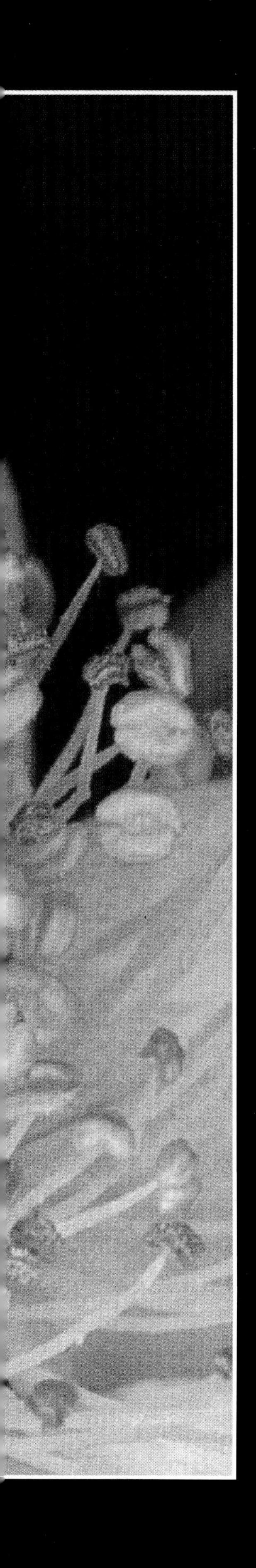

METHOD OF MARKING FLOWERS

When a flower has already been visited, the honeybee can understand that another bee has earlier consumed the nectar of that flower, and leave the flower immediately. This way, it saves both time and energy. Well, how does the bee understand, without checking the flower, that the nectar has earlier been consumed?

This is made possible because the bees which visited the flower earlier marked it by leaving a drop on it with a special scent. Whenever a new bee looks in on the same flower, it smells the scent and understands that the flower is of no use and so goes on directly towards another flower. Thus, bees do not waste time on the same flower.

THE MIRACLE OF HONEY

Do you know how important a food source the honey is, which Allah offers man by means of a tiny insect?

Honey is composed of sugars like glucose and fructose and minerals like magnesium, potassium, calcium, sodium chlorine, sulphur, iron and phosphate. It contains vitamins B1, B2, C, B6, B5 and B3 all of which change according to the qualities of the nectar and pollen. Besides the above, copper, iodine, and zinc exist in it in small quantities. Several kinds of hormones are also present in it.

As Allah says in the Qur'an, honey is a "healing for men". This scientific fact was confirmed by scientists who assembled during the World Apiculture Conference held from 20-26 September 1993 in China. During the conference, treatments with honey derivatives were discussed. American scientists in particular said that honey, royal jelly, pollen and propolis (bee resin) cure many diseases. A Romanian doctor stated that he tried honey on cataract patients, and 2002 out of his 2094 patients recovered completely. Polish doctors also informed the conference that bee resin helps to cure many diseases such as haemorrhoids, skin problems, gynaecological diseases and many other disorders.

Nowadays, apiculture and bee products have opened a new branch for research in countries advanced in sci-

...From their bellies comes
a drink of varying colours,
containing healing for mankind...
(Surat an-Nahl: 69)

ence. Other benefits of honey may be described as below:

Easily digested: Because sugar molecules in honey can convert into other sugars (e.g. fructose to glucose), honey is easily digested by the most sensitive stomachs, despite its high acid content. It helps kidneys and intestines to function better.

Has a low calorie level: Another quality of honey is that, when it is compared with the same amount of sugar, it gives 40% less calories to the body. Although it gives great energy to the body, it does not add weight.

Rapidly diffuses through the blood: When accompanied by mild water, honey diffuses into the bloodstream in 7 minutes. Its free sugar molecules make the brain function better since the brain is the largest consumer of sugar.

Supports blood formation: Honey provides an important part of the energy needed by the body for blood formation. In addition, it helps in cleansing the blood. It has some positive effects in regulating and facilitating blood circulation. It also functions as a protection against capillary problems and arteriosclerosis.

Does not accommodate bacteria: This bactericide (bacteria-killing) property of honey is named "the inhibition effect". Experiments conducted on honey show that its bactericide properties increase twofold when diluted with water. It is very interesting to note that newly born bees in the colony are nourished with diluted honey by the bees responsible for their supervision - as if they know this feature of the honey.

Royal Jelly: Royal jelly is a substance produced by worker bees inside the beehive. Inside this nutritious substance are sugar, proteins, fats and many vitamins. It is used in problems caused by tissue deficiency or body frailty.

It is obvious that honey, which is produced in much higher amounts than the requirements of the bees, is made for the benefit of man. And it is also obvious that bees cannot perform such an unbelievable task "on their own."

And He has made everything in the heavens and everything in the earth subservient to you. It is all from Him. There are certainly signs in that for people who reflect.
(Surat al-Jathiyah: 13)

THE CAMEL

"Have they not looked at the camel how it was created?..."

***Have they not looked at the camel - how it was created? and at the sky - how it was raised up? and at the mountains - how they were embedded? and at the earth - how it was smoothed out? So remind them! You are only a reminder.* (Surat al-Ghashiyah: 17-21)**

It is beyond doubt that al beings, with the features the possess, reflect the unbound ed power and knowledge of thei Creator. Allah expresses this in numer ous verses in the Qur'an, where H points out that everything He create is actually a sign, that is, a symbol anc warning.

In the 17th verse of Surat al Ghashiyah, Allah refers to an animal which we are to examine carefully anc think about: the "camel".

In this section, we will study thi living being to which Allah has callec our attention in the following expres sion in the Qur'an, "Have they no looked at the camel - how it was cre ated?"

What makes the camel "a specia living being" is its body structure which is not affected even by the mos severe conditions. Its body has such features that allow it to survive fo days without water or food, and it car travel with a load of hundreds of kilo grams on its back for days.

The characteristics of the camel which you will learn in detail in the following pages, prove that this anima is brought into being particularly fo dry climatic conditions, and that it is given to the service of mankind. This is an evident sign of creation for men of understanding.

"In the alternation of night and day and what Allah has created in the heavens and the earth there are signs for people who are godfearing." (Surah Yunus: 6)

HEAD PROTECTED FROM THE SAND:

• The eyelashes have an interlocking system. In case of danger, they are automatically shut. The interlocking eyelashes do not let any dust particles enter the eyes of the animal.
• The nose and the ears are covered with long hairs to protect the animal from sand and dust.
• Its long neck enables the animal to reach and feed on leaves three metres above the ground.

FEET SUITABLE FOR ALL TYPES OF LAND:

• The feet comprise two toes joined with an elastic pad. This structure, which enables the animal to firmly grasp the earth, consists of four fatty balls. It is totally suitable for all kinds of land conditions.
• The toenails protect the feet from potential damage resulting from a bump.
• The knees are covered with callus, which is composed of skin as hard and thick as a horn. When the animal lies down on hot sand, this callused structure protects the animal from being injured by the extremely hot ground.

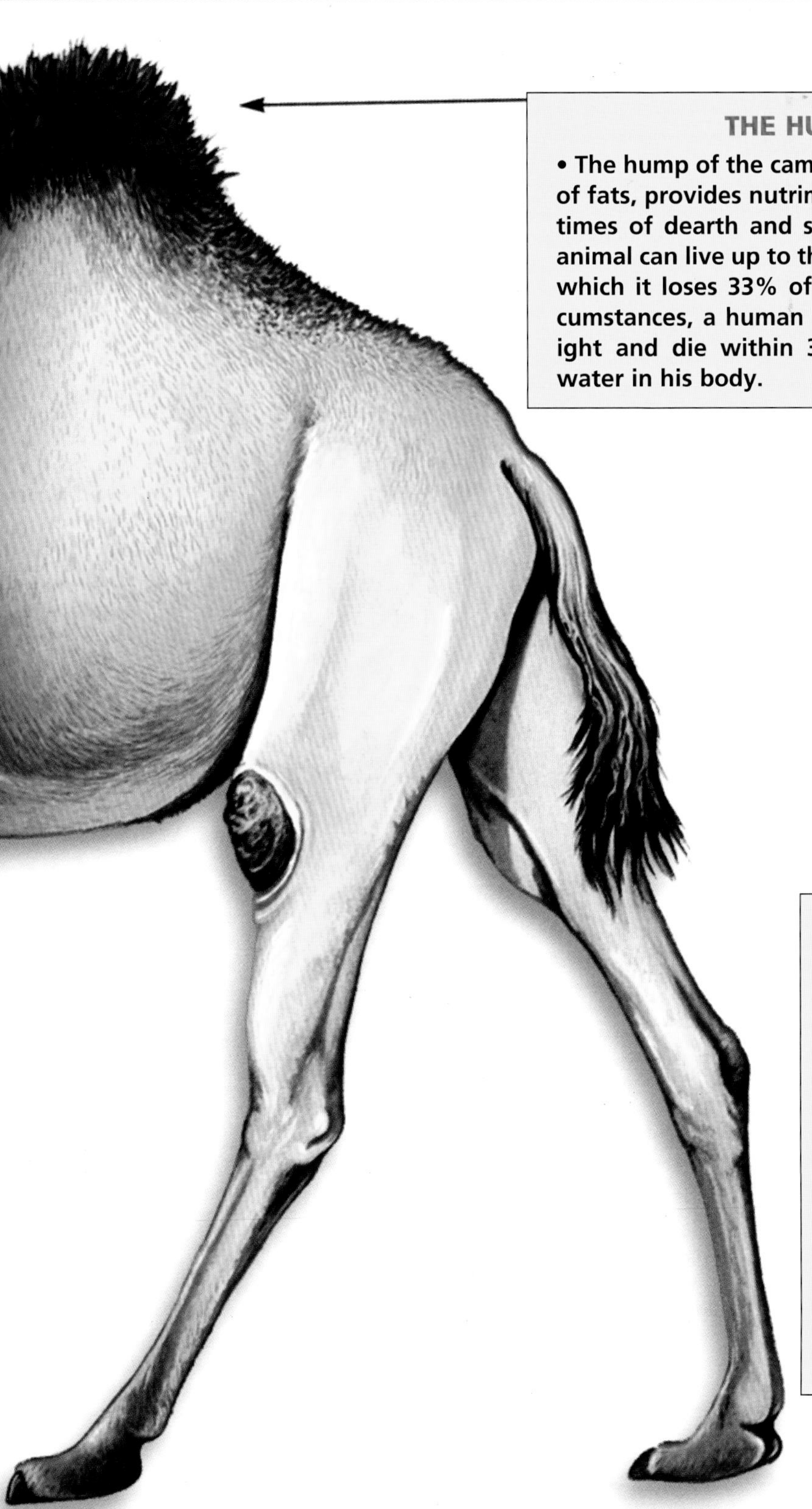

THE HUMP AS A STOCK OF FOOD:

• The hump of the camel, which is in the form of a mass of fats, provides nutriment to the animal periodically in times of dearth and starvation. With this system, the animal can live up to three weeks without water during which it loses 33% of its weight. Under the same circumstances, a human being would lose 8% of his weight and die within 36 hours, completely losing the water in his body.

HEAT INSULATING WOOL:

• This wool consists of thick and matted hair that not only protects the body of the animal against freezing and burning weather conditions, but also eliminates water loss from the body. The Dromedary camel can delay perspiration by increasing its body temperature to 41°C. In this way, it prevents water loss.

• With their thick wool, camels in Asia can survive temperatures up to +50°C in summer and down to -50°C in winter.

THEY CAN EVEN FEED ON THORNS
Dromedary camels can resist temperatures of -52°C in the highest areas of Middle Asia.

EXTRAORDINARY RESISTANCE TO THIRST AND HUNGER

The camel can survive without food and water for eight days at a temperature of 50°C. In this period, it loses 22% of its total body weight. While a man will be near death if he loses body water equivalent to about 12% of his body weight, a lean camel can survive losing body water equivalent to 40% of its body weight. Another reason for its resistance to thirst is a mechanism that enables the camel to increase its internal temperature to 41°C. As such, the animal keeps water loss to a minimum in the extreme hot climates of the desert daytime. The camel can also reduce its internal body temperature to 30°C in the cool desert nights.

IMPROVED WATER UTILISATION UNIT

Camels can consume up to 130 litres of water, which is around one third of their body weight, in almost 10 minutes. Besides, camels have a mucus structure in their nose that is 100 times larger than that of humans. With its huge and curved nose mucus, camels can hold 66% of the moisture in the air.

MAXIMUM BENEFIT FROM FOOD AND WATER

Most animals die by poisoning when accumulated urea in the kidneys diffuses into the blood. However, camels make maximum use of water and food by passing this urea numerous times through the liver. Both the blood and the cell structures of the camel are specialised in order to enable this animal to survive for long periods without water in desert conditions.

The cell walls of the animal have a special structure preventing extra water loss. Furthermore, blood composition is such that it does not let any deceleration in the blood circulation even when the water level in the camel's body is reduced to the minimum. In addition, albumin enzyme, which reinforces resistance to thirst, is found in much higher amounts in the camel's blood than in that of other living things.

The hump is the other support of the camel. One fifth of the camel's total body weight is stored as fat in its hump. The storage of the body fat in only one part of the camel's body prevents the excretion of water from all over its body - which is related to fat. This allows the camel to use the minimum of water.

Although a humped camel can take in 30-50 kilograms of food in a day, in tough conditions it is able to live up to one month with only 2 kg of grass a day. Camels have very strong and rubber-like lips that allow them to eat thorns sharp enough to pierce thick leather. Moreover, it has a four chambered stomach and a very strong digestive system with which it can digest everything it eats. It can even feed on materials like caoutchouc that cannot be looked upon as food. It is obvious enough how valuable this quality is in such dry climates.

PRECAUTION AGAINST TORNADOES AND STORMS

The eyes of camels have two eyelash layers. The eyelashes interlock like a trap and protect the eyes of the animal from harsh sandstorms. In addition, camels can close their nostrils so that no sand enters.

PROTECTION AGAINST BURNING AND FREEZING WEATHER CONDITIONS

The thick and impenetrable hairs on the camel's body prevent the scorching sun of the desert from reaching the skin of the animal. These also keep the animal warm in freezing weather. Desert camels are not affected by high temperatures up to 50°C, and double-humped Bactrian camels can survive in very low temperatures down to -50°C. Camels of this kind can survive even in high valleys, 4,000 metres above sea level.

PROTECTION AGAINST BURNING SAND

The camels' feet, which are large in proportion to its legs, are specially "designed" and enlarged to help the animal walk in the sand without becoming stuck. These feet possess a wide spread form and puffy qualities. In addition, the special thick skin under the soles is a protection against the burning desert sand.

Let us think in the light of these pieces of information: has the camel on its own adapted its own body to desert conditions? Has it by itself formed the mucus in its nose or the hump on its back? Has it by itself designed its own nose and eye structures in order to protect itself against tornadoes and storms? Has it by itself based its own blood and cell structures on the principle of conservation of water? Has it itself chosen the type of hair covering its body? Has it on its own converted itself to a "ship of the desert"?

Just as any other living being, the camel surely could not perform any of the above and make itself beneficial to mankind. The verse in the Qur'an stating, "Have they not looked at the camel - how it was created?" draws our attention to the creation of this excellent animal in the best way. Like all other creatures, the camel too is endowed with many special qualities and then placed on earth as a sign of the excellence of the Creator in creation.

Created with such superior physical features, the camel is decreed to serve mankind. As for humans, they are ordered to see like miracles of creation throughout the universe and revere the Creator of all beings: Allah.

"Do you not see that Allah has made subservient to you everything in the heavens and the earth and has showered His blessings upon you, both outwardly and inwardly? Yet there are people who argue about Allah without knowledge or guidance or any illuminating Book."

(Surah Luqman: 20)

THE FLY

"... (they) are not even able to create a single fly..."

O mankind! A likeness has been made, so listen to it carefully. Those you call upon apart from Allah are not even able to create a single fly, even if they were to join together to do it. And if a fly steals something away from them, they cannot get it back from it. How feeble are both the seeker and the sought! They do not measure Allah with His true measure. Allah is All-Strong, Almighty.

(Surat al-Hajj: 73-74)

Panoramic sight from thousands of lenses

The hexagonal shaped lenses constituting the eyes of a fly provide a much larger area of vision than an ordinary lens does. In some flies, the number of these lenses may sometimes be as many as 5,000. Additionally, the spherical structure of the eye also enables the fly to see its back, and thus gives it a great advantage over its enemies.

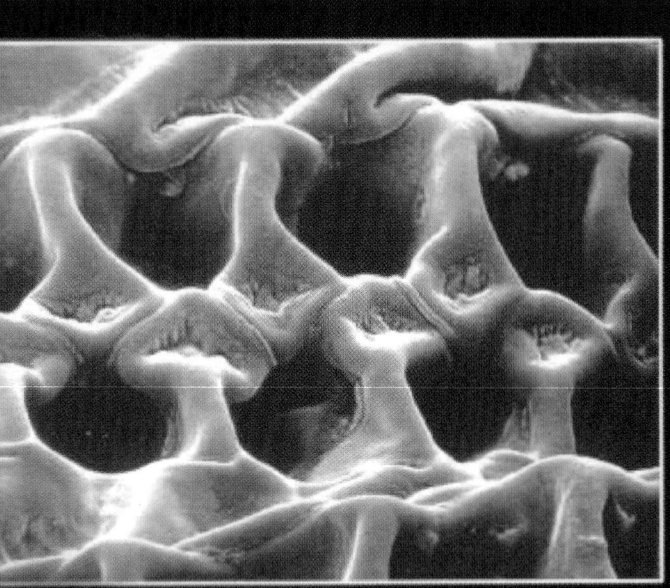

The absorbent pump of the fly: Proboscis

Another specific feature of flies is the way they digest food. Unlike many other living organisms, flies digest food not in their mouth, but outside their bodies. They pour a special liquid over the food by means of their proboscis, which puts the food in the proper degree of consistency for absorption. Then the fly absorbs the food with the absorbent pumps in its throat.

"Does not man recall
that We created him
before when he was
not anything?"
(Surah Maryam: 67)

CREATION IN THE UTERUS

If person does not use his common sense and ask himself the question "how did I come into being?" he will adopt an illogical attitude saying to himself, "I somehow came into being!...". With such reasoning, he will start to lead a life in which he will have no time to think on such issues.

However, a person with common sense should think how he was created and determine the meaning of his life accordingly. While doing this, he should not be afraid, as some people are, of ending up with the conclusion "I have been created". Those people mentioned above do not want to take any responsibility towards a Creator. They fear changing their lifestyles, habits, and the ideologies the have accepted in case they acknowledge that they are created. Therefore, they run away from obeying their Creator. Those who deny Allah and who "refuted them (His signs) wrongly and haughtily, in spite of their own certainty about them," (Surat an-Naml: 14) as described in the Qur'an, adopt this psychology.

On the other hand, a person who appraises his existence with wisdom and common sense will see nothing in himself but the signs of Allah's creation. He will acknowledge that his existence depends on the co-operation of thousands of complicated systems, none of which he creates or controls. He will grasp the fact that "he is created" and, by knowing our Creator, Allah, he will try to understand for what purpose He "created" him.

For anyone who tries to comprehend the meaning of His creation there is a guide book: the Qur'an. This book is a guide sent to him and to all created men on earth by our Creator, Allah.

That the phenomenon of creation takes place just as described in the Qur'an conveys significant meanings to the men of understanding.

Allah created you from dust and then from a drop of sperm and then made you into pairs. No female becomes pregnant or gives birth except with His knowledge. And no living thing lives long or has its life cut short without that being in a Book. That is easy for Allah. (Surah Fatir: 11)

The following pages include various pieces of information, for those with wisdom and common sense, exhibiting how "they were created" and the marvel of this creation.

The story of man's creation starts at two different locations very distant from each other. The human being steps into life by the union of two separate substances present in the bodies of women and men, which are created totally independently from each other yet in perfect harmony. It is certain that the sperm in the male body is not produced by the will and control of man, just as the egg in the female body is not formed by the will and control of woman. Indeed, they are not even aware of those occurrences.

We created you so why do you not confirm the truth? Have you thought about the sperm that you ejaculate? Is it you who create it or are We the Creator? (Surat al-Waqi'ah: 57-59)

Sperm and the inside view of testicles.

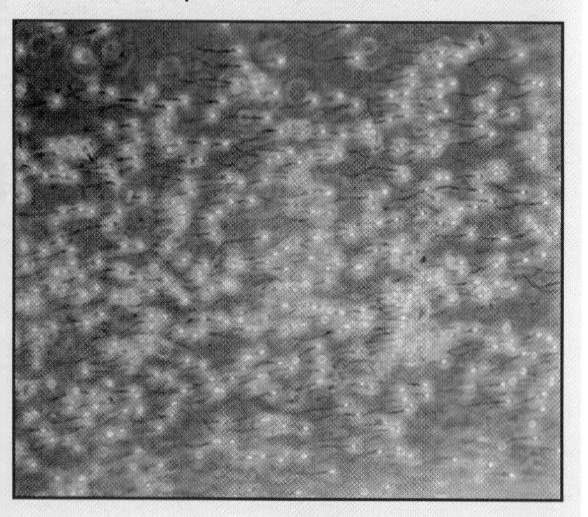

It is obvious that both the substances, that coming from the man and that from the woman, are created in accordance with one another. The creation of these two substances, their union and transformation into a human being are indeed great miracles.

THE TESTICLES AND THE SPERM

Sperm, which constitutes the first step in the creation of a new human being, is produced "outside" the man's body. The reason for this is that sperm production is only possible in an environment two degrees cooler than normal body temperature. In order to stabilise the temperature at this level there is special skin on the testicles. It shrinks in cold weather and expands in hot weather, keeping temperature constant. Does the male himself "regulate" and arrange this delicate balance? Certainly not. The male is not even aware of this. Those who keep on resisting the fact of creation can only say that this is "an undiscovered function of the human body". The definition of "undiscovered function" is nothing but a "mere name".

Produced in the testicles at the rate of 1,000 per minute, sperm has a special design made for its journey to the female ovaries, a journey that progresses as if it "knows" the place. The sperm is composed of a head, a neck and a tail. Its tail helps it move in the uterus like a fish.

Its head part, containing a portion of the baby's genetic code, is covered with a special protective shield. The function of this shield is revealed at the entrance to the mother's uterus: here, the environment is very acidic. It is clear that the sperm is covered with a protective shield by "someone" who is aware of this acidity. (The purpose of this acidic environment is the protection of the mother from microbes.)

It is not only millions of sperms that are ejaculated into the uterus. Semen is a mixture of various kinds of fluid. In the Qur'an this fact is emphasised in the verse below:

"Has man ever known a point of time when he was not something remembered? We created man from a mingled drop to test him, and We made him hearing and seeing." (Surat al-Insan: 1-2)

These fluids within the semen contain sugar, which is to provide the energy needed by the sperm. Besides, its basic composition has various tasks such as neutralising the acids at the entrance to the mother's uterus, and maintaining the slippery medium for the movement of the sperms. (Here, we again see that two different and independent beings are created in accordance with each other.) The spermatozoa make a difficult journey within the mother's body until they reach the ovum. No matter how much they defend themselves, approximately only a thousand out of the 200-300 million spermatozoa reach the ovum.

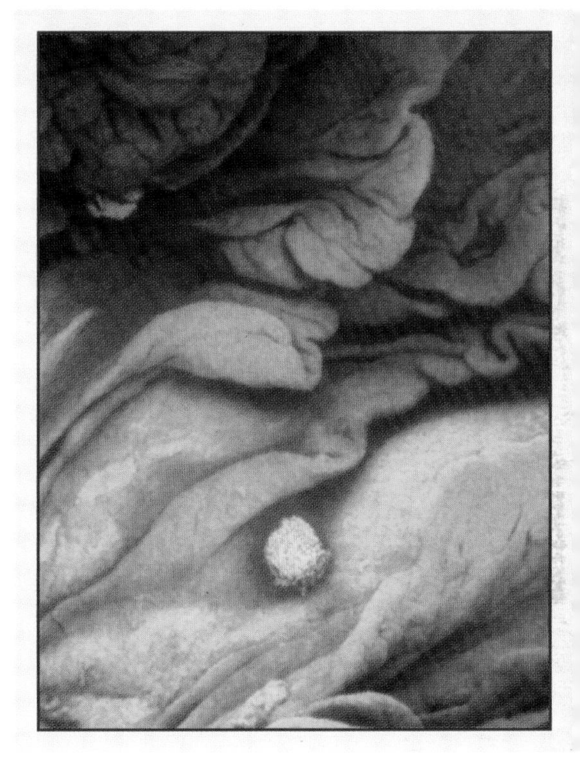

THE OVUM

While the sperm is designed according to the ovum, the ovum, on the other hand, is prepared to be the seed of life in a totally different medium.... While the woman is unaware, first, an egg matured in the ovaries is left in the abdominal cavity, and then it is caught in the arms placed at the end of the appendages called the fallopian tubes of the uterus. Following this, the egg starts to move on with the help of the movement of the cilia inside the fallopian tube. This egg is only as big as the half of a salt particle.

The place where the ovum and the sperm meet is the fallopian tube. Here, the ovum starts to secrete a special fluid. With the help of this secretion, the spermatozoa find the location of the ovum. We need to be aware: when we say that the ovum "starts to secrete", we are not talking about a man or a conscious being. It cannot be explained by coincidence that a microscopic protein mass "decides" on such an act "by itself" and then "prepares" and secretes a chemical compound to attract the spermatozoa to itself. There is evidently design at work.

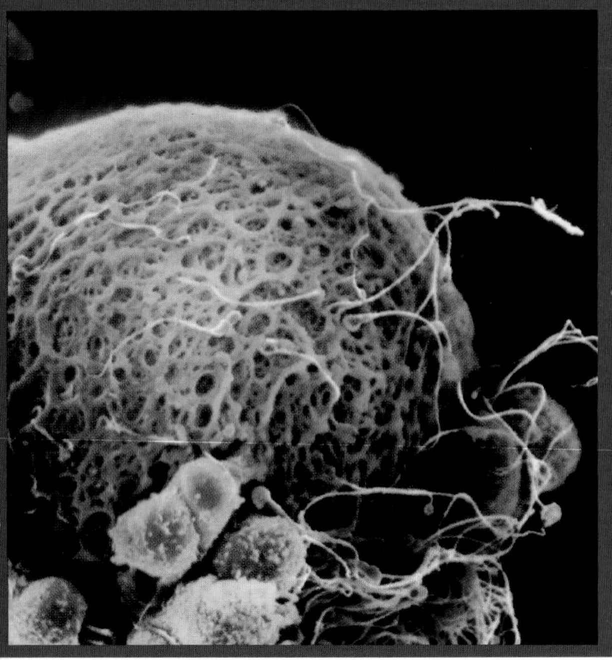

The spermatozoa around the ovum

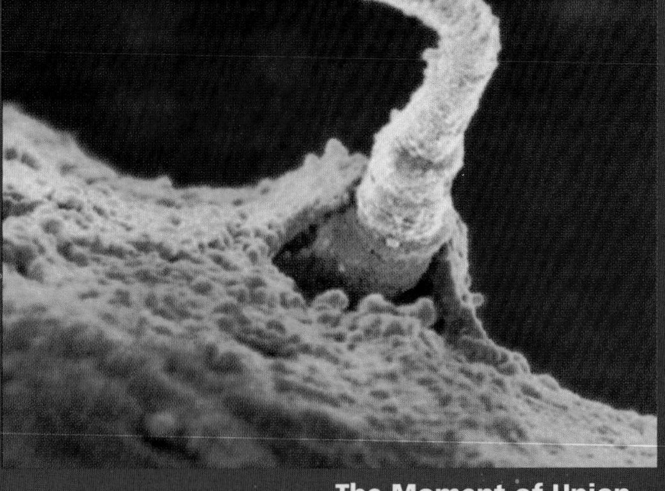

The Moment of Union
One of the spermatozoa enters the ovum to fertilise it after a long and difficult journey.

Briefly, the reproduction system of the body is designed to unite the ovum and the sperm. This means that woman's reproduction system is created in accordance with the needs of the spermatozoa and the spermatozoa are created in accordance with the needs of the environment within the woman's body.

MEETING OF THE SPERM AND THE OVUM

When the sperm, which will fertilise the egg, draws closer to the ovum, the egg again "decides" to secrete a special fluid, prepared particularly for the sperm, which dissolves the protective shield of the sperm. Consequently, the solvent enzyme sacks which are found at the end of the sperm and are especially made for the ovum are laid open. When the sperm reaches the ovum, these enzymes drill the membrane of the ovum allowing the sperm to enter. The spermatozoa around the ovum start to compete to break in, but in general, only one sperm fertilises the ovum.

The Qur'anic verses describing this stage are very interesting. In the Qur'an, it is stated that a human being is made from an extract of base fluid, that is, the semen.

"...then He produced his seed from an extract of base fluid" (Surat as-Sajda: 8)

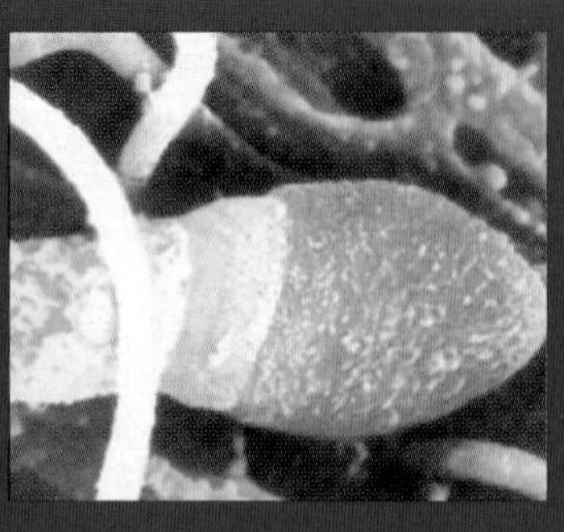

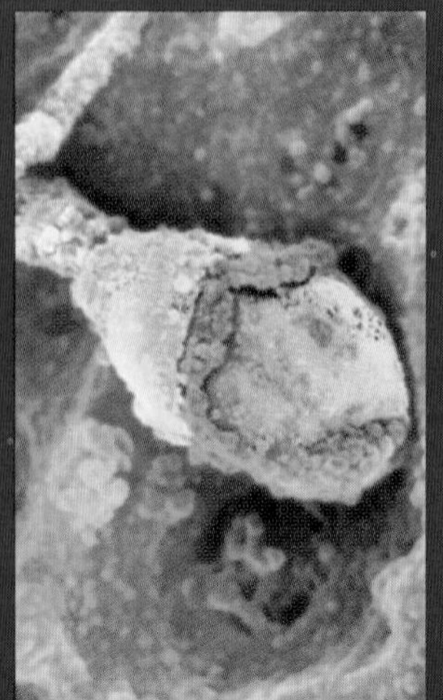

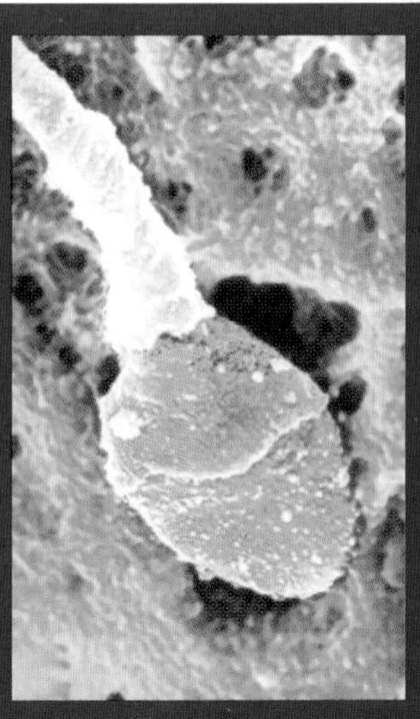

When the sperm that will fertilise the egg draws close to the egg, the egg suddenly secretes a special fluid that dissolves the protective shield of the sperm. Consequently, the solvent enzyme sacks at the tip of the sperm are laid open. As soon as the sperm reaches the egg, these enzymes pierce the egg membrane, thus letting the sperm enter.

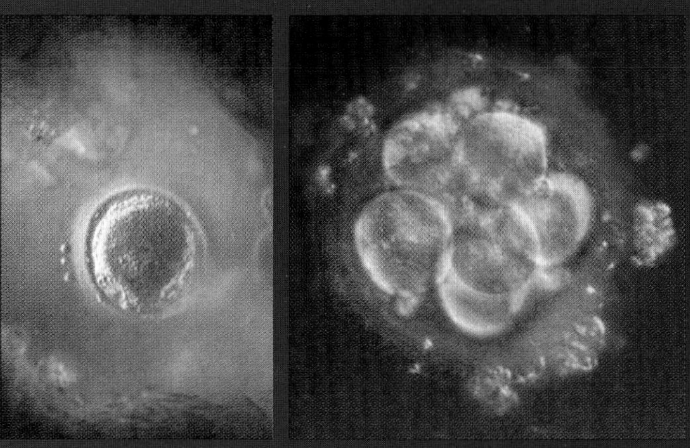

The growth that starts with a single cell continues with the constant multiplication of cells.

The zygote seen clinging to the mother's uterus.

As the verse informs us, it is not the fluid itself carrying the spermatozoa that fertilises the egg, but only an "extract" of it. A single sperm within it is the fertilising agent, and moreover, the chromosomes in the sperm which are "an extract" of it.

When an ovum allows one sperm in, it is not possible for another sperm to enter it. The reason for this is the electrical field that forms around the ovum. The area around the egg is (-) negatively charged, and as soon as the first sperm penetrates the ovum, this charge changes to (+) positive. Therefore, the ovum, which has the same electrical charge as the external spermatozoa, starts repelling them.

This means that the electrical charges of the two substances, forming independently and separately from each other, are also in accordance with each other.

Finally, the male's DNA in the sperm and the female's DNA in the ovum combine. Now, there is the first seed, the first cell of a new human being in the mother's womb: the zygote.

THE CLOT CLINGING TO THE UTERUS...

When the sperm of the male unites with the ovum of the female as described above, the essence of the baby to be born is formed. This single cell known in biology as the "zygote" will instantly start to grow by division and eventually become a "piece of flesh".

The zygote, however, does not spend its developmental period in a void. It clings to the uterus just like roots that are firmly fixed to the earth by their tendrils. Through this bond, the zygote can obtain the substances essential to its development from the mother's body.

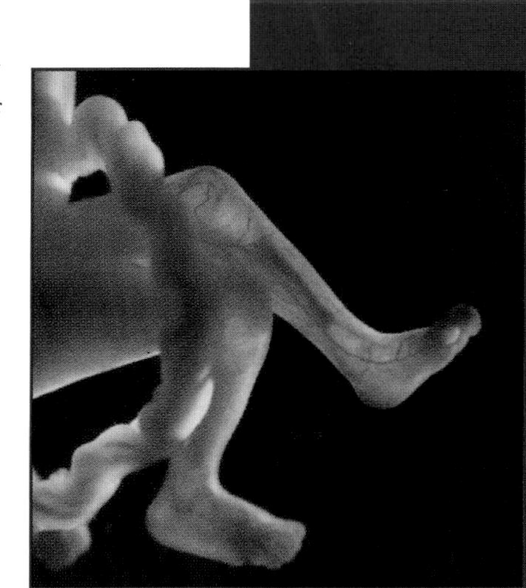

THE THREE DARK REGIONS

After fertilisation, the baby's development takes place in three distinct regions. These regions are:

1. The fallopian tube: this is the region where the egg and the sperm unite and the where the ovarium connects to the uterus.

2. Inside the uterus wall to which the zygote clings for development.

3. The region where the embryo starts growing in a sack full of a special liquid.

This is stated in the Qur'an as:

"He creates you stage by stage in your mothers' wombs in a threefold darkness. That is Allah, your Lord. Sovereignty is His. There is no god but Him. So what has made you deviate?..." (Surat az-Zumar: 6)

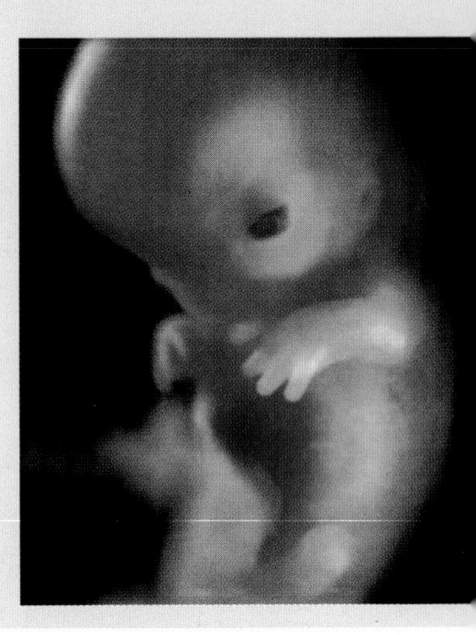

Such a detail could not be known without a sound knowledge of physiology. It is obvious that no one possessed such knowledge fourteen centuries ago. Interestingly enough, Allah always refers to the zygote developing in the mother's womb as "a clot of blood" in the Qur'an:

> **Recite: In the Name of your Lord Who created man from a blood clot. Recite: And your Lord is the Most Generous. (Surat al-'Alaq: 1-3)**
>
> **Does man reckon he will be left to go on unchecked? Was he not a drop of ejaculated sperm? Then a blood clot, which He created and shaped, making from it both sexes, male and female? (Surat al-Qiyamah: 36-39)**

The Arabic meaning of the word "blood-clot" is "a thing that clings to some place". The word is used literally to describe leeches that cling to a body to suck blood. It is obviously the best possible word to describe the zygote clinging to the wall of the uterus and absorbing its sustenance from it.

The Qur'an has more to disclose about the zygote. Perfectly clinging to the uterus, the zygote starts to develop. The uterus of the mother, meanwhile, is filled with a fluid called the "amnion liquid" that surrounds the zygote. The most important function of the amnion liquid in which the baby develops is to protect the baby against blows from outside. In the Qur'an, this fact is revealed as follows:

WHILE THE EYES FORM...

Being a dark spot at the first stage, the baby's eye takes its final form during the passing months.

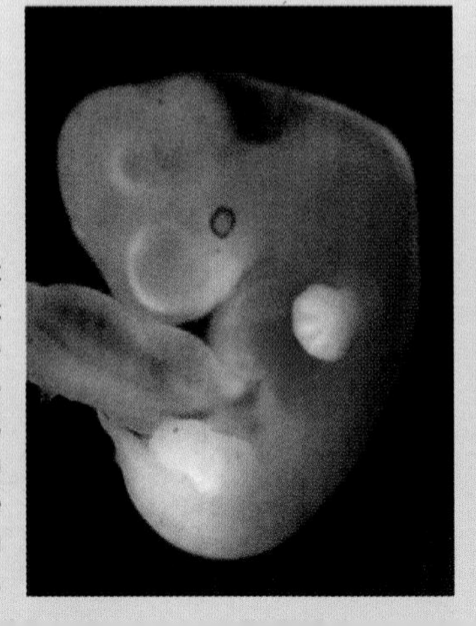

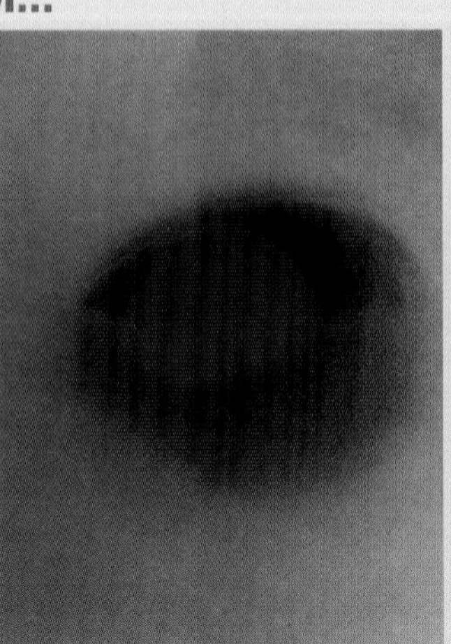

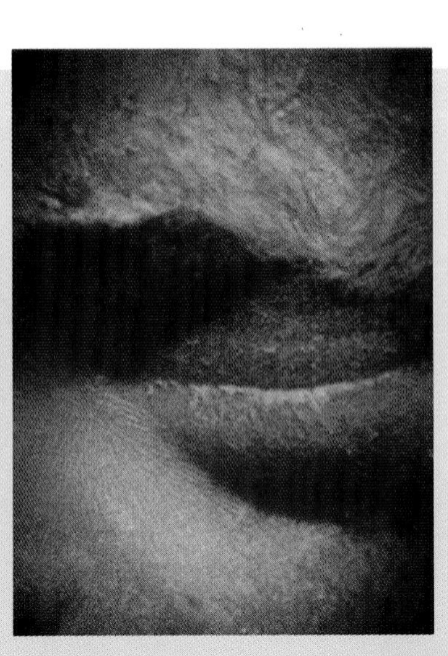

Did We not create you from a base fluid? Then place it in a secure repository? (Surat al-Mursalat: 20-21)

All of this information given in the Qur'an about the formation of man demonstrates that the Qur'an comes from a source that knows about this formation down to its slightest detail. This situation once more proves that the Qur'an is the word of Allah.

Meanwhile, the embryo that previously looked like a gel, with time transforms. In the initial soft structure, hard bones begin to form to provide the body the ability to stand upright. The cells, which were initially the same, become specialised: some form light-sensitive eye cells, some nerve cells sensitive to cold, heat and pain, and some cells sensitive to sound vibrations. Do the cells by themselves decide on this differentiation? Do they by themselves first decide to form a human heart or a human eye and then accomplish this incredible task? On the other hand, are they created appropriately for these purposes? Wisdom, intellect and soul will assent to the second alternative.

At the end of these processes, the baby completes its development inside the mother's womb, then is born into the world. Now it is 100 million times bigger and 6 billion times heavier than it was initially....

This is the story of our first step into life, not those of any other organism. What can be more important for a man than finding the purpose of such an amazing creation?

It is illogical to think that all of these complicated functions occur "of their own volition". No one has the power to create himself, or another person or any other object? Allah creates all the events hitherto described, each moment, each second and each stage.

Or were they created out of nothing, or are they the creators? Or did they creat the heavens and the earth? No, in truth they have no certainty. (Surat at-Tur: 35-36)

"Allah created you from dust and then from a drop of sperm and then made you into pairs. No female gets pregnant or gives birth except with His knowledge. And no living thing lives long or has its life cut short without that being in a Book. That is easy for Allah." (Surah Fatir: 11)

Our body, which from only a "drop of sperm", transforms itself into a human, has millions of delicate balances. Even though we are not aware of them, there are extremely complex and delicate systems in our body that help us survive. Allah, the only Owner, Creator and Lord of man built all these systems, in order for him to understand that "he is created".

Man is a being Allah created. Since he is created, he is not to be "left uncontrolled (without purpose)".

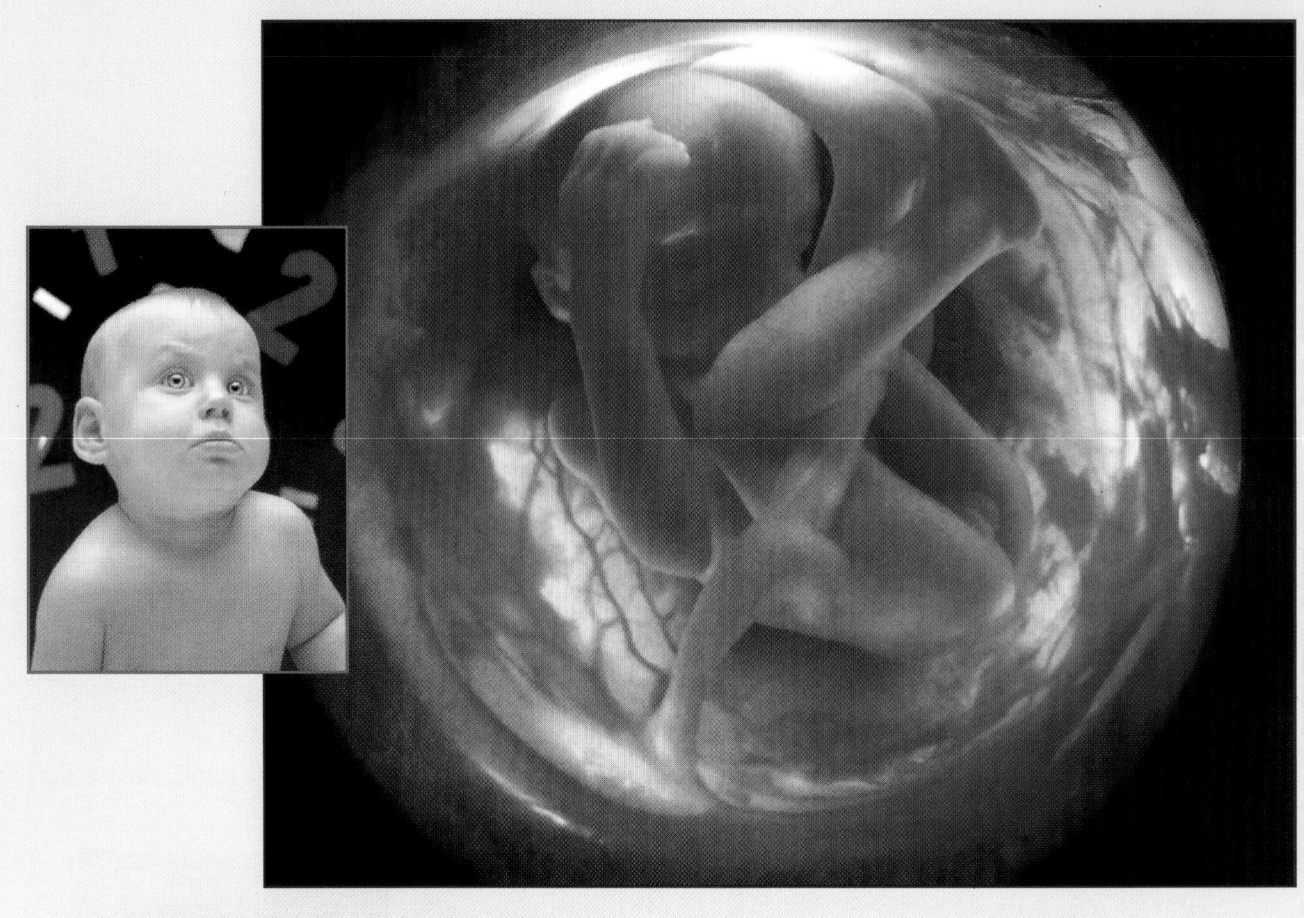

"O man! What has deluded you in respect of your Noble Lord? He Who created you and formed you and proportioned you and assembled you in whatever way He willed."

(Surat al-Infitar: 6-8)

The first days of a human being's face (left) and its final shape.

"It is Allah Who made the earth a stable home for you and the sky a dome, and formed you, giving you the best of forms"

(Surat Ghafir: 64)

MOTHER'S MILK...

The feeding of a new human being, which has grown from the transformation of a sperm to a baby, is a miracle on its own. Human milk is the best nutrition possible, and it is produced neither by the mother's help nor by anyone else's.

Thanks to the substances in its composition, mother's milk is both an excellent food-source for the newborn and a substance that increases the resistance of the mother as well as the baby to diseases. Doctors agree that artificial baby food should only be preferred if the milk of the mother is not adequate, and that babies should be fed with mother's milk, especially in the first months. Now, let us look at the features of this milk:

THE SUCKING REFLEX

Babies are born from their mother's womb with the reflex to suck. Their sucking exercises, which start with thumb sucking in the womb, have a vital importance in the feeding of the baby after birth, because there is no other way for the baby to get milk, which is its only food source.

* The most interesting aspect of mother's milk is that its concentration changes according to the developmental phases of the baby. The amount of calories and the food content change according to whether the baby's delivery was premature or on time. If the baby is premature, the fat and protein concentration is higher in the mother's milk than a baby would normally need, because the premature baby needs more calories.

* Immune system elements that the baby needs, such as antibodies or defence cells, are given to the baby ready-made in the mother's milk. Just like professional soldiers, they defend the body to which they do not belong and protect the baby from its enemies

* It is antibacterial. Although bacteria are produced in normal milk if it is left at room temperature for six hours, no bacteria are produced in mother's milk if left for the same period.

* It protects the baby against arteriosclerosis.

* The baby quickly digests it.

We know that none of the artificial baby food produced in modern laboratories by expert dieticians is as beneficial as the natural mother's milk. How can we answer the question, "Who produced this baby milk in a human body when the mother herself is even unaware of its production, and yet it is superior to those produced in laboratory conditions"? It is very clear that mother's milk is brought into being by the Creator of the baby who is in need of this milk....

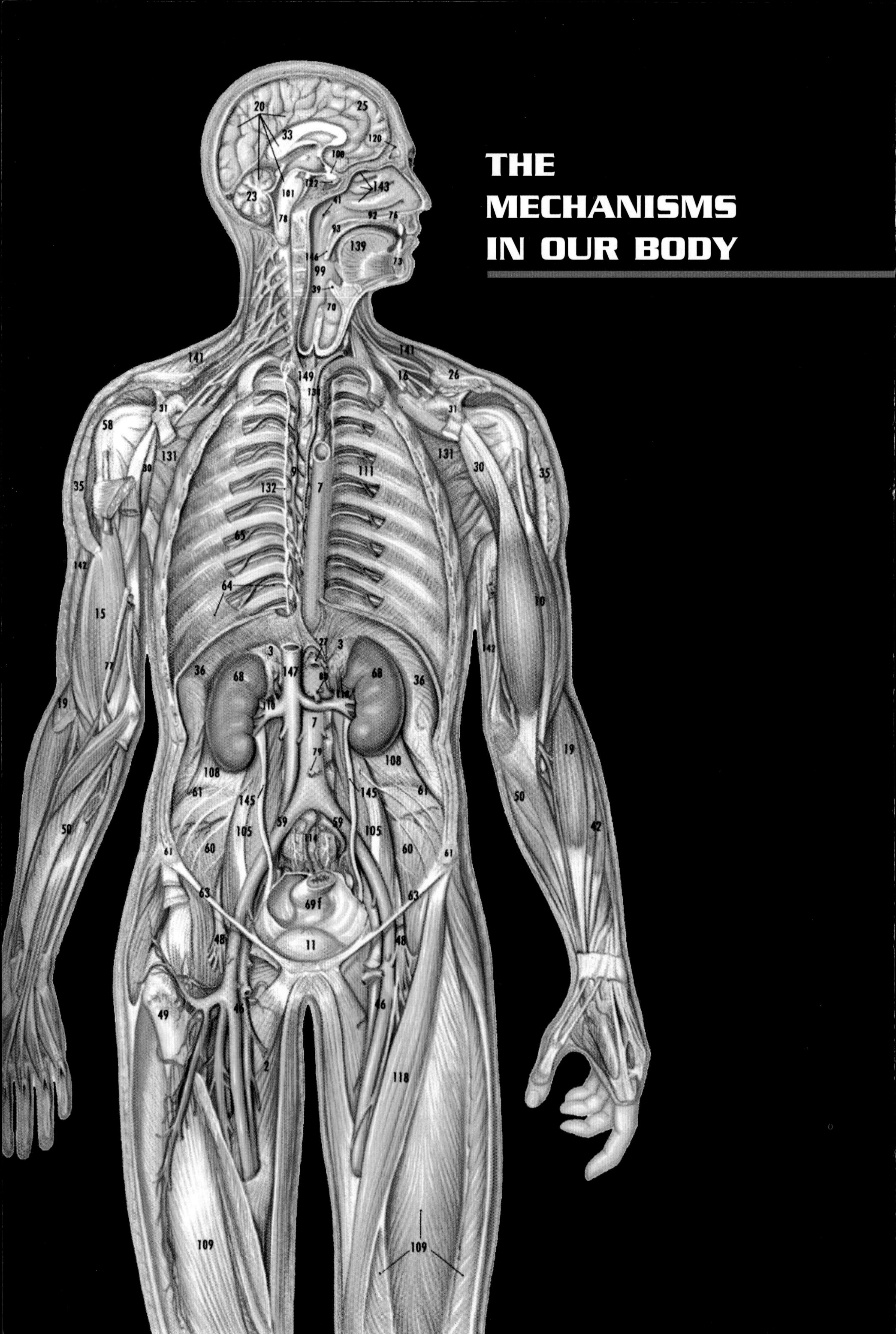
THE
MECHANISMS
IN OUR BODY
20
25
33
120
100
122
143
23
101
41
78
92
76
93
139
146
99
73
39
70
141
149
16
26
31
58
131
30
35
9
111
132
7
65
64
142
10
15
27
3
147
77
36
68
88
19
79
108
61
145
50
59
105
114
42
60
63
69 f
48
11
49
46
2
118
109

In many verses of the Qur'an, Allah calls our attention to the creation of man and invites people to ponder on this creation: **"O man! What has deluded you in respect of your Noble Lord? He Who created you and formed you and proportioned you and assembled you in whatever way He willed." (Surat al-Infitar: 6- 8)**

The human being is one of the living beings with the most excellent, sophisticated and amazing systems in nature, whom Allah fashioned in due proportion.

The human body is an amount of flesh and bone of approximately 60-70 kilograms. As is well known, flesh is one of the most fragile materials in nature. When left in the open, it decomposes within a couple of hours, becomes maggoty within a few days and starts to stink unbearably. This feeble substance constitutes a large part of the human body. However, it is maintained without being spoilt, and without decaying, for about 70-80 years by means of the blood circulation that feeds it, and by the skin that protects it from external bacteria.

On the other hand, the skills of the body are very impressive. Each one of the five senses is a miracle. Man gets to know the external world through these senses, and lead his life peacefully thanks to the wholeness of these senses. Details that we encounter as we survey the senses of sight, smell, touch, hearing and taste and their flawless designs are each pieces of evidence that prove the being of the Creator.

The miraculous structures of the human body are not limited to the five senses. Each of the organs facilitating our lives is a separate miracle. They all function just to meet our needs. Let's just imagine how hard life would be if we were created without hands. What would happen if we did not have legs, or if our bodies were covered with thorns, scales or a hard outer layer, instead of skin?

Moreover, the existence of complex systems in the human body, such as respiration, feeding, reproductive and defence mechanisms, and the aesthetics of the human body are each separate wonders.

As seen, there are many delicate balances in the human body. The perfect relation of the entirely interdependent systems to the other systems in the body enables man to carry on his vital functions without problem.

Moreover, he does all these without spending any extra effort, or facing any difficulties. Most of the time, the person does not even become aware of all that happens. Man is not aware of many things: the time when digestion starts or ends in his stomach, the rhythm of his heart, the blood's carrying exactly the required material to exactly the right places, and his seeing and hearing.

A flawless system has been established in the human body and it works perfectly. This is the creation of Allah, Who regulates all affairs from the heavens to the earth. Allah creates everything, every detail and every living being in the universe. The design we confront when we closely examine the human body is evidence of the uniqueness and flawlessness of Allah's art of creation.

Allah draws our attention to the perfection in the universe in Surat al-Mulk:

> **He Who created the seven heavens in layers. You will not find any flaw in the creation of the All-Merciful. Look again - do you see any gaps? Then look again and again. Your sight will return to you dazzled and exhausted! (Surat al-Mulk: 3-4)**

A few of the millions of delicate balances in the human body are as follows:

The five senses are arranged entirely according to the human's needs. For instance, the ear can only sense those sound vibrations that are within certain limits. At first glance, to hear within a larger range might seem more advantageous, yet these sensory limits - called the "hearing threshold" - are regulated for a purpose. If we had very sensitive ears, every moment we would have to bear the sound of many noises from the beating of our hearts to the rustling of microscopic mites on the floor. Then, life really would be very irritating for us.

The same "punctuated equilibrium" holds true also for the sense of touch. The nerves sensitive to touch lying under the human skin are made sensitive in the best possible way and are spread all over the body. The nerves are amassed mainly on our fingertips, lips and sexual organs. Comparatively, "less important" regions of the body such as our backs have fewer nerves. This provides great advantages for man. Let us imagine if the contrary was the case: that our fingertips were extremely insensitive, and that the majority of nerves were collected on our backs. Undoubtedly, this would be quite irritating, for while we would not be able to use our hands effectively, we would feel the tiniest substance - for instance, the creases of our shirt - on our backs.

Development of the organs is an example of this "delicate balance". For instance, think about hair and the eyelashes. Although both are ultimately "hair", they do not grow equally in the same period. Suppose that eyelashes grew as fast as our hair. They would impede our sight and go into our eyes, thus harming one of our most vital organs. Eyelashes have a certain length that stays constant. If by any means, such as burning or an accident, they shorten, they then elongate until they reach their "ideal" length and stop again.

Even the shape of the lashes is very important. Since they curl slightly upwards, they do not restrict sight and they give the eyes an aesthetic look. As the lashes grow, they are covered by an unusual oil secreted by specific glands located at the rim of the eyelids. This is why our lashes are not rough and straight like a brush. There is exactly just such a "subtle adjustment" in every spot of the human body.

This punctuated creation is strikingly revealed in the new-born baby as well as in adolescents. For instance, the new-born baby's skull bones are very soft and can, to a limited extent, move over one another. This flexibility facilitates the emergence of the baby's head from the womb without harm. If these skull bones were inflexible, during birth they could crack and cause serious damage to the baby's brain.

With the same flawlessness, all of the organs in a human being develop in harmony with each other in the course of development. For example, in the development of the head, the skull that encases the brain grows along with it. A skull developing comparatively slower than the brain would compress it, and cause death in a short time.

The same balance is true also for other organs such as the heart, lungs and thorax, the eye and eye socket.

For this reason, it is useful to examine the extraordinary structures of our body to see the art and might in the creation. Every part of our body, the structure of which is more perfect than the most advanced factories equipped with the latest technologies, displays the matchless creation of Allah and proves His sovereignty over our entire body.

If we briefly examine the systems and organs in the human body, we will witness intimately the evidence of a flawless and balanced creation.

DIGESTION

The saliva that is brought into play right at the beginning of the digestive process, moistens the food so that it can be easily chewed by the teeth and move down the oesophagus with facility. Saliva is also a specialised substance for turning, through its chemical properties, starch into sugar. Just think what would happen if saliva were not secreted in the mouth. We would not be able to swallow anything or even talk because of our dry mouths. We would not be able to eat anything solid, but have to feed on liquids or the like.

There is excellent balance in the system of the stomach. In the stomach, food is digested by the hydrochloric acid therein. This acid is so strong that it could even eat away the stomach walls as well as the food taken in. Yet, a solution is created for man: a substance called mucus, secreted during digestion, coats the stomach walls providing exceptional protection against the disintegrative effect of the acid. Thus, the stomach is prevented from destroying itself. An error in the composition of the mucus could destroy its protective function. There is a perfect match between the acid used for digestion and the mucus secreted to protect the stomach from it.

When the stomach is empty, the secretion that breaks up proteins, that is, foods derived from animals such as meat, is not produced in the stomach. In fact, it exists in the form of a harmless substance without any disintegrative properties. As soon as a protein-containing food enters the stomach, the HCI is secreted in the stomach and breaks this neutral substance down into proteins. Thus, when the stomach is empty, this acid does not injure the stomach that is itself made of proteins.

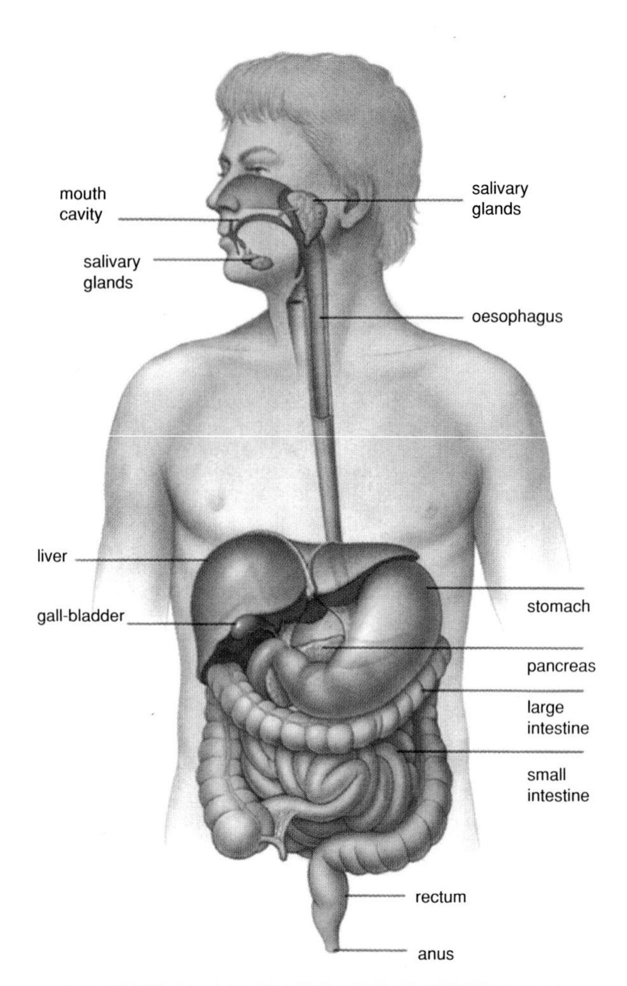

The digestive system is one in which mouth, saliva, stomach, pancreas, liver and intestines operate in harmony and discharge their own functions. If one or more of these complementary organs do not function fully, the whole system becomes locked in stasis.

It is noteworthy that 'evolution' can never explain the existence of such a complex system, for it defends the idea that complex structures around us gradually evolved from primitive organisms by the accumulation of small structural improvements. However, it is obvious that the system in the stomach could not have evolved gradually and step-by-step. Absence of even a single factor would bring an end to the organism. One example is sufficient to better understand the inconsistency of the theory of evolution. Think of an organism that wears down its own stomach by the acid it produces there - first its stomach would be destroyed painfully and then its other organs would be consumed by the same acid. The organism would die by eating itself alive.

The liquid in the stomach acquires the capacity to break down proteins after a series of chemical reactions. Think of an organism within the process of evolution, in the stomach of which such a chemical transformation cannot be realised. If the liquid in the stomach of an organism did not acquire the feature of decomposing proteins, that organism would not be able to digest food, and eventually would die with a lump of undigested food in its stomach.

Let us look at the subject from another point of view. The stomach cells produce the acid in the stomach. Both these cells and other cells in any other part of the body (for instance the cells of the eye) are twin cells originating from the division of the same original single cell in the mother's uterus. Moreover, both of them have the same genetic information. This means that the data bank of both cells includes genetic information about the proteins needed by the eye and the acid used in the stomach. Yet, submitting to an order coming from an unknown source, among millions of other pieces of information, the eye cell utilises the information belonging to the eye and the stomach cell utilises the information belonging to the stomach. What if the cells of the eye that produce the proteins necessary for the eye (for a reason unknown to us), began to produce the acid used in the stomach - about which they possess the necessary information? If something like that happened, a person would melt and digest his own eye.

Let us continue to examine the amazing balance inside our body:

The rest of the digestive process is equally well planned. The useful part of the food, which has been digested, is absorbed by the lining of the small intestine and diffuses through the blood. The lining of the small intestine is covered with lateral folds that look like a wrinkled cloth. On each fold are smaller folds called "villus". These folds increase immensely the absorptive surface of the intestine. On the upper surface of the cells over the villus are microscopic projections named "microvillus". These projections absorb the food and function as pumps. The interiors of these pumps are connected to the circulatory system through a conveyance system furnished with diverse conveyance routes. This is how the nutrition that has been absorbed reaches the whole body through the circulatory system. Each of the villi has nearly 3,000 microvillus. A 1 mm square area in the lining of the small intestine is covered by approximately 200 million microvillus. In an area of one square millimetre, 200 million pumps work, without breaking down or becoming exhausted, in order to sustain human life. So many pumps, which would normally cover a very large area, are squeezed into a very limited space. This system sustains our lives by ensuring that our body makes maximum use of the food we take in.

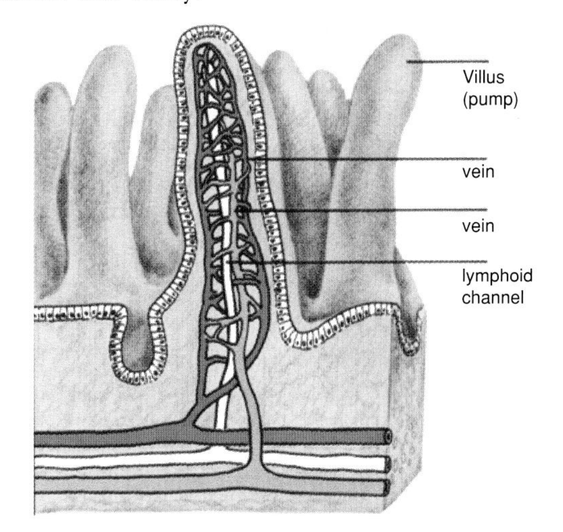

A pump (villi) situated in the small intestines that absorbs the necessary materials from the digested food. There are 200 million such pumps in a square millimetre, and each one of them functions every second for the maintenance of our life. In the figure are seen special channels (veins, capillaries, and lymphoid channels) found in the pumps and through which nutrients are absorbed.

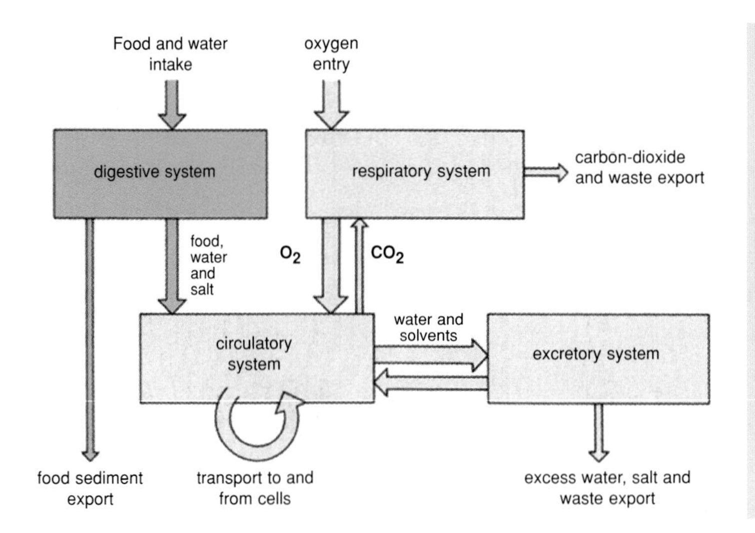

All the systems in the human body (digestive, circulatory, respiratory and excretory systems) work in co-operation and in harmony with each other. In the figure, you may see their interrelation with each other.

RESPIRATION

Respiration is based on delicate balances. Cold or polluted air we breathe may effect our health negatively. For this reason, air should be warmed and cleaned before inhalation. Our nose is created appropriately for this task. The hair and nasal mucus on the walls of the nostrils filter air by capturing dust particles within it. Meanwhile, the air is warmed while travelling through the nostrils. The nasal bones are especially structured so that the air inhaled can go to the lungs only after circulating several times in the nose and thus warming up. The structure that enables air to travel several times within a tiny bone, can only be the outcome of design. If human beings were to try to duplicate this effect, directing the movement of air would only be possible by specific complex calculations. The fact that this special structure exists to meet the needs of another system - namely, cleaning and warming the air travelling to the lungs - is evidence that both systems are specially created by the same Creator. After all these stages, the air arrives in the respiratory tube after being moistened and freed of dust.

SKELETON

The skeleton is an engineering marvel on its own. It is the structural support system of the body. It protects vital organs like brain, heart and lungs, and upholds the internal organs. It furnishes the human body with a superior capacity for movement that cannot be imitated by any artificial mechanism. Bone tissue is not inorganic as many people think. Bone tissue is the mineral bank of the body that includes many important minerals like calcium and phosphate. In accordance with the needs of the body, it either stores these minerals or delivers them to the body. Besides all these, bones also produce red blood cells.

In addition to the uniformly perfect functioning of the skeleton, the bones constituting it also have an exceptional structure. Having the tasks of bearing and protecting the body, bones are created with the capacity and strength to fulfil this function. The worst conditions possible are taken into consideration as well. For instance, the thighbone can carry a weight weighing a ton when perpendicular. Surprisingly, at each step we take, the bone carries a weight equivalent to three times our body weight. When an athlete pole-vaults and he lands on the ground, every square centimetre of his pelvis is exposed to a pressure of 1,400 kilograms. What makes this structure, which is formed by the division and replication of the single original cell, so strong? The answer to the question is hidden in the unequalled creation of bones.

An example from today's technology would be helpful to further clarify the subject. The scaffolding system is used in the construction of spacious and tall buildings. The support elements of the constructions made with this technique do not have a monolithic structure, but consist of many intersecting rods forming a scaffold. By the help of complex calculations that can only be made by computers, it could be possible to build stronger and more cost-effective bridges and industrial constructions.

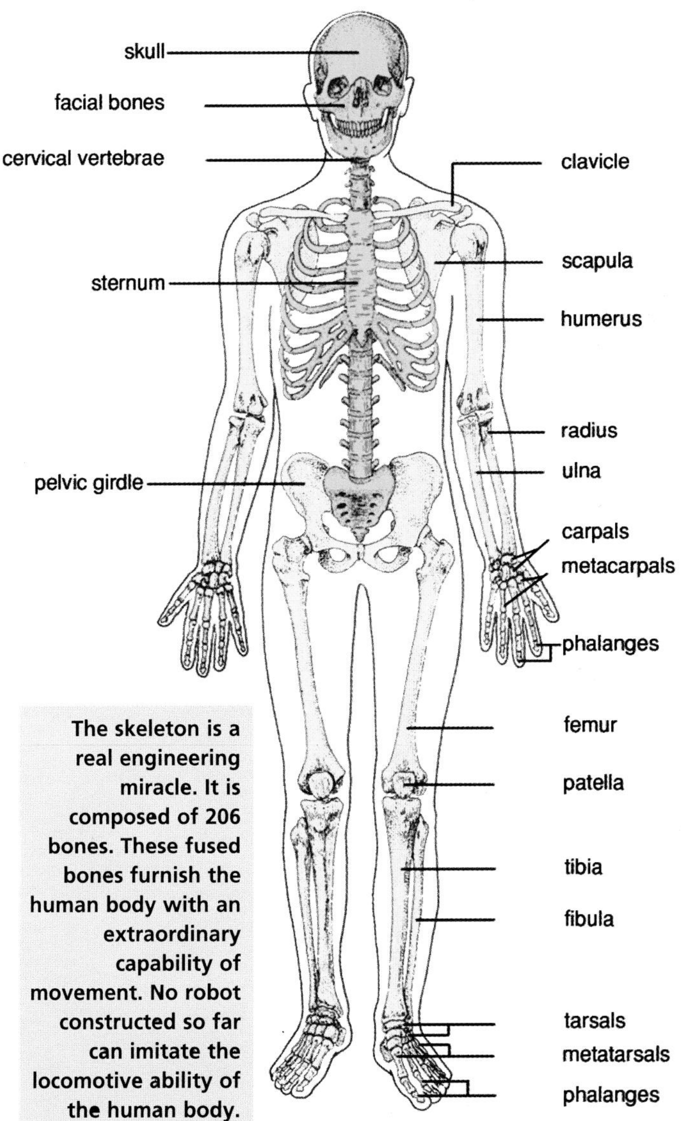

The skeleton is a real engineering miracle. It is composed of 206 bones. These fused bones furnish the human body with an extraordinary capability of movement. No robot constructed so far can imitate the locomotive ability of the human body.

The internal structure of bones is similar to that of the scaffold system used in the construction of those bridges and towers. The only important difference is that the system in bones is more complicated and superior to those designed by men. By means of this system, the bones are extremely strong and yet light enough for comfortable use by humans. If the opposite were the case, i.e., if the interior of the bones was hard and full like its exterior, it would be too heavy to be carried by a human and would easily break or crack at the slightest blow due to its rigid and hard structure.

The perfect design of our bones helps us lead our lives very simply, manage to perform even very difficult tasks easily without pain. Another feature of bone structure is its flexibility in certain parts of the body. Just as the rib-cage protects the vital organs of the body such as the heart and lungs, it also expands and contracts to let air move in and out of lungs.

The elasticity of bones may change over time. For instance, in women, the hipbones are extended towards the last months of pregnancy and move apart from each other. This is an extremely important detail, because during birth, this extension allows the baby's head to come out of the mother's womb without being crushed.

The miraculous aspects of the bones are not limited to these. Besides their flexibility, durability and lightness, the bones also have an ability to repair themselves. When a bone is broken, one only has to keep this bone firm to

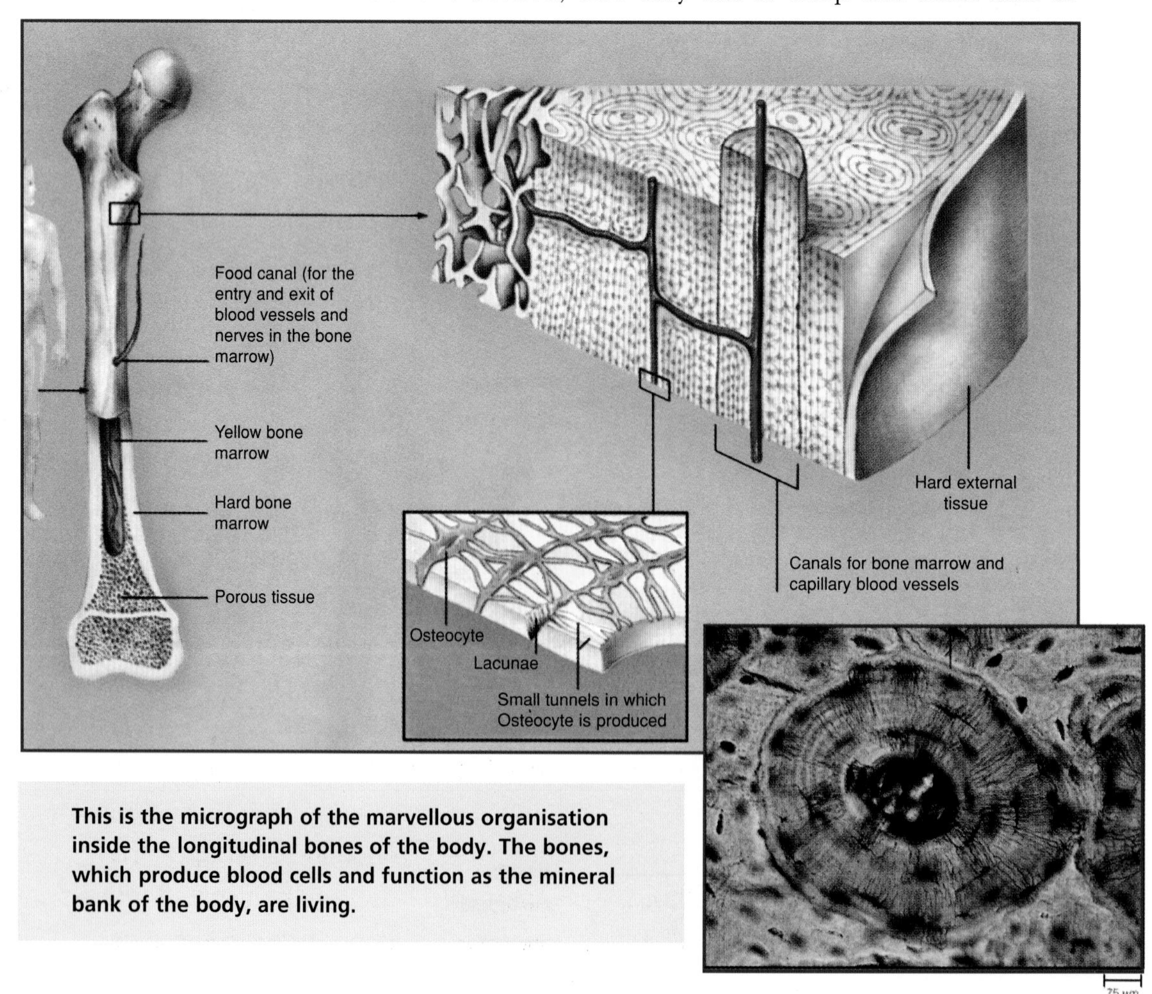

This is the micrograph of the marvellous organisation inside the longitudinal bones of the body. The bones, which produce blood cells and function as the mineral bank of the body, are living.

allow it to repair itself. As is obvious, this, like all other processes in the body, is an extremely complex process in which millions of cells collaborate.

The locomotive capability of the skeleton is another important detail to consider. With each step we take, the vertebrae making up our backbone move over each other. This continuous movement and friction might normally cause the vertebrae to wear out. In order to prevent this, between each vertebra, resistant cartilages, called 'disks', are placed. These disks function as shock absorbers. At each step, a force is exerted by the ground on the body as a reaction to the body's weight. This force does not do any harm to the body due to the shock absorbers of the backbone and its "force distributing" curved shape. If this flexibility and special structure that reduce the force of reaction did not exist, the released force would be transmitted directly to the skull and the top end of the spine would break into the brain by shattering the skull.

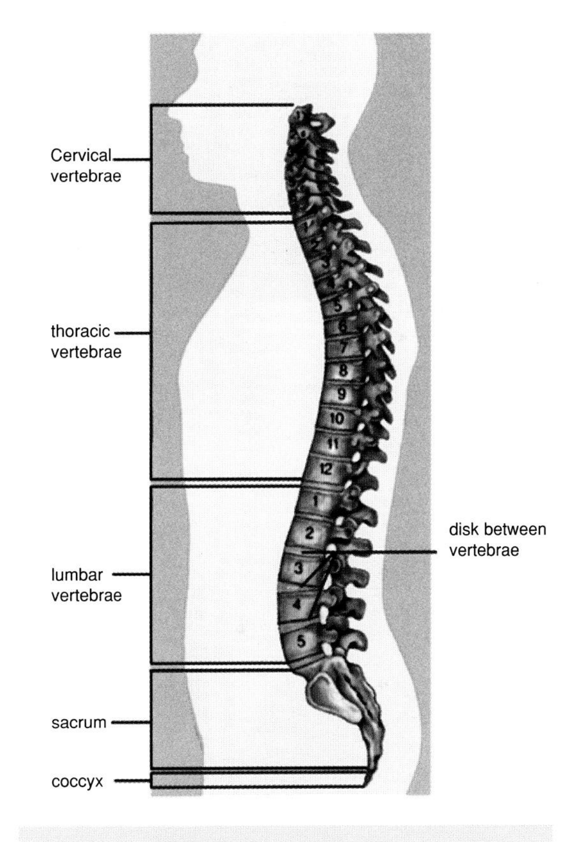

With each step, a force is exerted by the ground on the body as a reaction to the body's weight. If the shock absorbers between the vertebrae did not exist, and if the spine had a straight structure, this force would be transmitted directly to the skull. Consequently, the top of the spine would break into the brain and shatter the skull.

The traces of creation are also visible at the joint surfaces of the bones. The joints do not need to be lubricated although they move continuously for a lifetime. Biologists conducted research to find the reason: how is the friction in joints being eliminated?

Scientists saw that the event was solved by a system that can be regarded as an "absolute miracle of creation". Joint surfaces exposed to friction are covered with a thin, porous cartilage layer. Under this layer is a lubricant. Whenever the bone compresses the joint, this lubricant gushes out of the pores and makes the joint surface slide "as if on oil".

These all show that the human body is the outcome of perfect design, and it is a superior creation. This perfect design helps a human being to make very dissimilar movements with great swiftness and facility.

Just imagine if everything were not so perfect and the entire leg were formed of a single long bone. Then, walking would be a serious problem and we would have very clumsy and idle bodies. Even taking a seat would be dif-

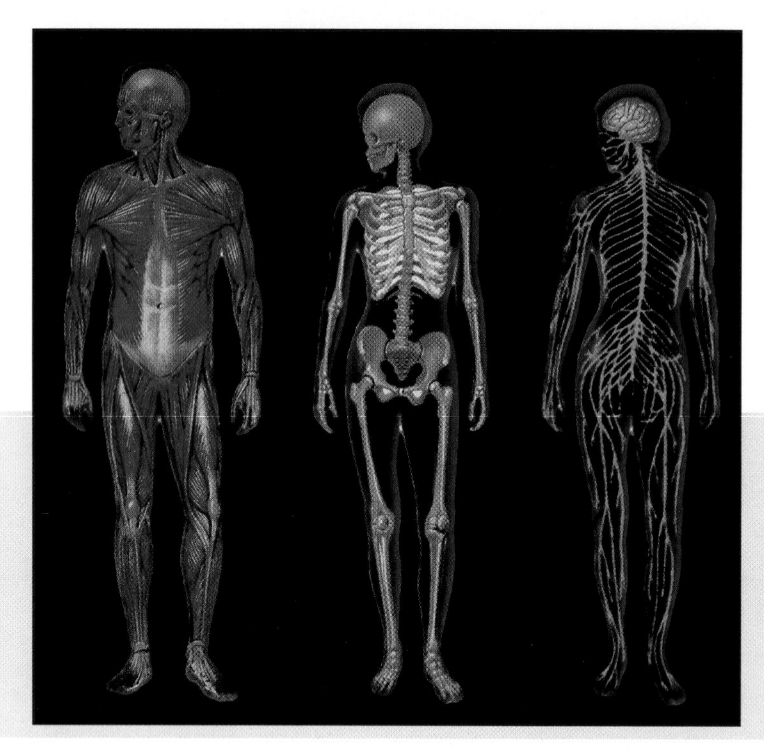

Even one of the systems seen in the picture cannot have been established by coincidence. In addition, it would have no meaning for these systems to form separately one by one. They have to come into existence concurrently in absolute harmony.

ficult, and the leg bone would easily break because of being forced during such acts. However, the human skeleton has a structure that permits all kinds of body motions.

Allah created, and still creates, all the features of the skeleton. Allah invites man, whom He has created, to ponder this:

> **...Look at the bones -Look further at the bones, how We bring them together and clothe them with flesh... (Surat al-Baqara: 259)**

Man must ponder this, appreciate the might of Allah, Who has created him, and be thankful to Him. If he does not do so, he will be in great loss. Allah, Who created the bones and clothed them with flesh, is able to do it again. This is stated in the verse:

> **Does not man see that We created him from a drop yet there he is an open antagonist! He makes likenesses of Us and forgets his own creation, saying, "Who will give life to the bones when they are decayed?" Say "He Who made them in the first place will bring them back to life. He has complete knowledge of every created thing." (Surah Yasin: 77-79)**

CO-ORDINATION

In the human body, all the systems simultaneously work in a co-ordinated way and in full harmony for a definite purpose, namely, to keep the body alive. Even the smallest movements we do everyday, such as breathing or smiling, are outcomes of perfect co-ordination in the human body.

Inside us is an incredibly complicated and comprehensively co-ordinated network that operates without stopping at all. The purpose is the continuance of living. This co-ordination is particularly visible in the locomotive system of the body, because, for even the smallest movement, skeletal system, muscles and nervous system must work in perfect collaboration.

The precondition of co-ordination in the body is correct information delivery. Only by delivering correct information can new assessments be made. For this purpose, a highly developed intelligence web functions in the human body.

In order to perform a co-ordinated act, first, the organs involved in this act and their inter-relations should be known. This information comes from the eyes, the balance mechanism in the internal ear, muscles, joints and skin. Every second, billions of pieces of information are processed, evaluated and new decisions are taken accordingly. Man is not even aware of the processes accomplished in his body at dizzying speed. He just moves, laughs, cries, runs, eats and thinks. He spends no effort in performing these acts. Even for a faint smile, seventeen muscles have to work together at the same time. Non-function or malfunction of even one of these muscles changes the expression on the face. In order to be able to walk, fifty-four different muscles in the feet, legs, hips and back must work in co-operation.

There are billions of microscopic receptors in the muscles and the joints, giving information about the present condition of the body. The messages coming from these receptors reach the central nervous system and new commands are sent to the muscles according to the assessments made.

The perfection of the co-ordination of the body will be better understood with the following example. In order just to lift the hand, the shoulder has to

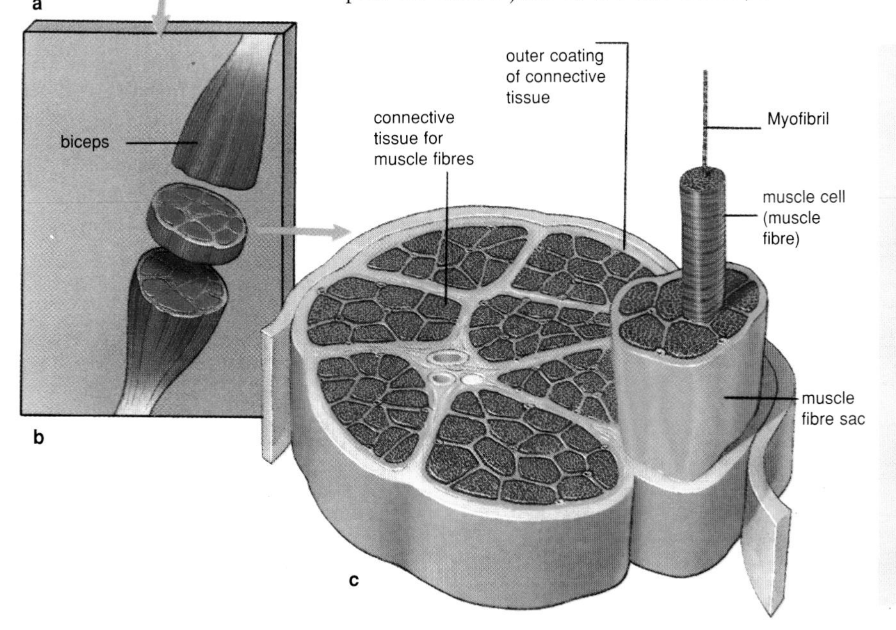

a) Biceps
b) Muscle sacs
c) Muscle fibres in muscle sacs.
The sensors between these fibres transmit information to the central nervous system about the present condition of the muscles. The central nervous system exercises absolute control over the muscles through the information it receives from billions of receptors.

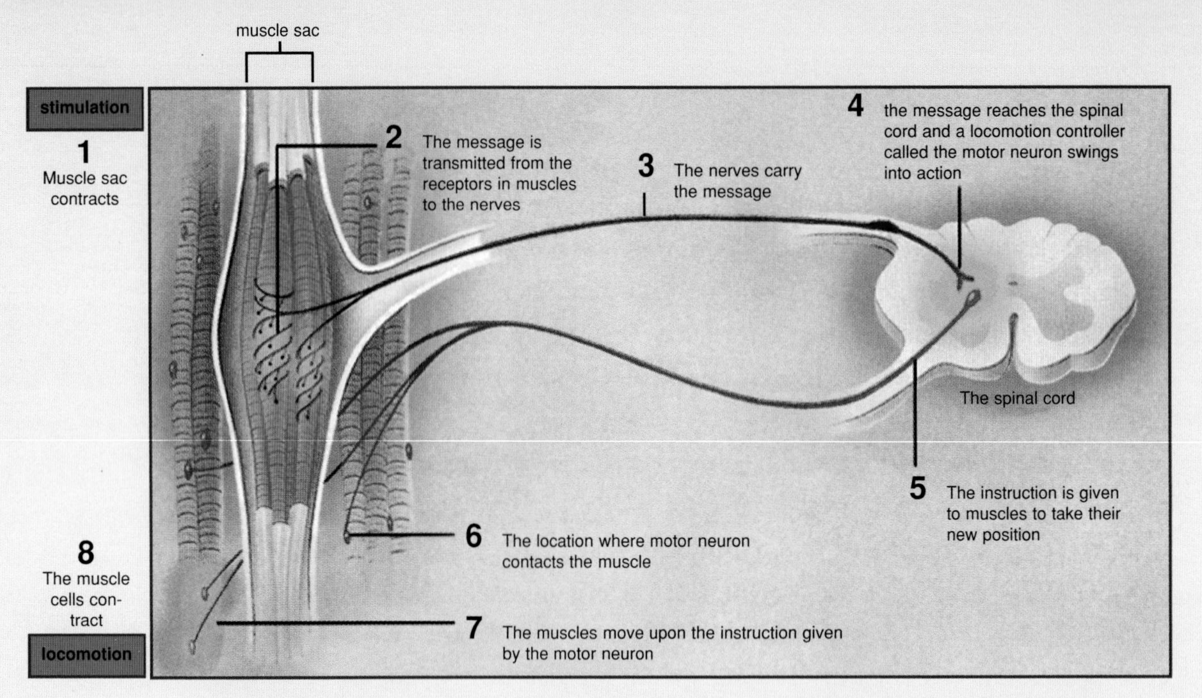
muscle sac
stimulation
1
Muscle sac contracts
2
The message is transmitted from the receptors in muscles to the nerves
3
The nerves carry the message
4
the message reaches the spinal cord and a locomotion controller called the motor neuron swings into action
The spinal cord
5
The instruction is given to muscles to take their new position
6
The location where motor neuron contacts the muscle
7
The muscles move upon the instruction given by the motor neuron
8
The muscle cells contract
locomotion

The scheme illustrates the transmission of information from sensors in the muscles to the spinal cord, which in turn gives the muscles new instructions. Each second while you read these lines, billions of pieces of information transmitted by billions of receptors are evaluated and the same number of instructions are given. Man finds himself born into this miraculous system. He, however, has no share either in its creation or even in its operation.

be bent, the front and rear arm muscles - called "triceps" and "biceps" - should be contracted and relaxed, and the muscles between elbow and wrist have to twist the wrist. In every part of the act, millions of receptors in the muscles pass on information immediately to the central nervous system about the position of the muscles. In return, the central nervous system tells the muscles what to do in the next step. Of course one is not aware of any of these processes, but just wishes to lift one's hand, and does it right away.

For instance, to keep your body straight, many pieces of information derived from billions of receptors in your leg muscles, feet, back, abdomen, chest and neck are evaluated and a similar number of commands are given to the muscles each second.

Nor do we spend extra effort to speak. Man never plans how far apart the vocal cords should be, how often they should vibrate, in which sequence, how often and which of the hundreds of muscles in mouth, tongue and throat should be contracted and relaxed. Nor does he calculate how many cubic centimetre of air should be inhaled into the lungs, and how fast and in which frequency this air should be exhaled. We could not do this even if we wanted to! Even a single word uttered from the mouth, is an outcome of the collective working of many systems stretching from man's respiratory system to the nervous system, from the muscles to the bones.

What happens in case of a problem in this co-ordination? Different expressions might appear on our faces when we want to smile, or we might not manage to talk or walk when we want to. However, we can smile, talk, walk anytime we want and no problems occur, because everything mentioned here is accomplished as a result of the fact of Creation which logically requires "infinite intelligence and power".

For this reason, man should always remember that he owes his being and life to his Creator, Allah. There is nothing for man to be arrogant or boastful about. His health, beauty or strength is not his own work, and it is not given to him eternally. He certainly will become old and lose his health and beauty. In the Qur'an, this is stated as:

> **Anything you have been given is only the enjoyment of the life of this world and its finery. What is with Allah is better and longer lasting. So will you not use your intellect?" (Surat al-Qasas: 60)**

If a person wants to attain attributes far superior to these, eternally in the hereafter, he must be grateful to Allah for the favours He has bestowed upon him, and live his life according to His commands.

As seen in these examples, all the organs and systems in the human body bear "miraculous" characteristics. When these characteristics are examined, man will see on what delicate balances his existence depends and the miracles in his creation, and will come to grasp once more the great art of Allah as exemplified in man.

THE LIVER

The liver, which lies on the upper right side of the abdominal cavity, functions as an excellent filter within the blood's circulatory system. While the kidney filters simple water-soluble, surplus human materials, the liver cleans complex surpluses, like medicine and hormones.

Supports the defence system logistically: The liver does not only function as a filter for food and surpluses of metabolism, but also produces globulins, which are immune substances, and enzymes, which are vein-repairing groups.

Cleans bacteria: Kupffer cells found in the liver engulf bacteria in the blood passing through the liver, especially when coming from the intestines. When the number of particles or other side products in the blood increases, Kupffer cells, too, increase in number to filtrate these materials from the blood.

Produces the energy resources of the body: One of the most significant features of the liver is its production of glucose, which is the main energy source of metabolism.

Glucose taken in from the everyday diet is converted into glycogen and stored in the liver. The liver continually controls the glucose level of the blood.

When nothing is eaten between meals and the glucose level of the blood starts to fall, the liver turns the stored glycogen back into glucose and releases it into the blood. Therefore, the level of glucose is not permitted to fall critically. The liver can produce glucose also from fatty acids and amino acids as well, just as it can convert other carbohydrates, which are not likely to be used in energy production, into glucose.

Stores blood: The liver has a structure that can expand or shrink. Given this feature, it can both store blood and release it into the veins.

In a healthy body, the liver can hold 10% of the total blood of the human body, which makes 450 ml of blood. In some conditions, e.g., when there is a heart defect in a person, the amount of blood usually circulating in the body will be too much for the working pace of the heart. In this circumstance, the liver doubles its blood-retaining capacity and stores 1 litre of blood. Thus, it allows the heart to work at a tolerable pace.

When need for blood increases, (e.g., while exercising) the liver releases the blood it has stored into the circulatory system and meets the need for blood.

Works economically: When glucose is consumed in the muscles, lactic acid, a surplus of metabolism, is released. As long as lactic acid stays in the muscle, it gives pain and prevents its operation. The liver collects this acid from the muscles and can convert it back into glucose.

Produces new red blood cells instead of the dead ones: The spleen and liver are the locations where new red blood cells are produced replacing dead ones, and a major part of the proteins are broken down and put to re-use as amino acids for different purposes. The liver is the organ where iron, which has important functions in the body, is stored.

The liver is the most developed reserve of the body. All minerals, proteins, a small amount of fat and vitamins are stored in the liver. Whenever needed, it delivers the stored substance to the necessary area in the shortest way possible. It scrupulously controls whether the body has enough energy or not by a specialised intelligence system. All organs in the body are related to the liver.

Is able to repair itself: The liver has the capability to repair itself. If a certain part of it is damaged, the remaining cells make up for the defective part by increasing in number instantly. Even if two-thirds of the organ is amputated, the remaining part can re-compose the liver entirely.

While repairing itself, the organ removes the ruined or dead cells from the milieu and replaces them with new ones. A liver cell is specialised enough to perform more than 500 operations at a time. It usually makes these not successively but concurrently.

SKIN

Think of a tissue metres in length yet integral; let it be a tissue bearing features that provide simultaneously both heating and cooling; firm yet very aesthetic, that can offer a very effective protection against all external effects.

The skin tissue that covers the human body and the bodies of all living beings, with some differences according to species, bears all of these characteristics.

Skin tissue, like many other structures, is an organ important enough that its absence puts human life at risk. The injury of even a section of the skin, leading to a considerable water loss in the body, would cause death. Given this feature, the skin is an organ that refutes the theory of evolution on its own. It is impossible for a living being to survive, which has all of its organs fully formed but its skin not yet evolved or partly formed. This shows us that all the bodily parts of human beings as well as animals have been formed intact and flawless at the same time, that is, they were created.

Beneath the skin, which is made up of totally different structures, lies a layer made up of lipids. This lipid layer has the function of insulation against heat. Above this layer is a section most of which is made up of proteins and which gives the skin its quality of elasticity.

The view we would come across when we look at a centimetre below the skin is a picture formed by these lipids and proteins, with various vessels therein. It is not aesthetic at all, and even terrifying. Covering all these structures, the skin both makes a very aesthetic contribution to our body and it protects

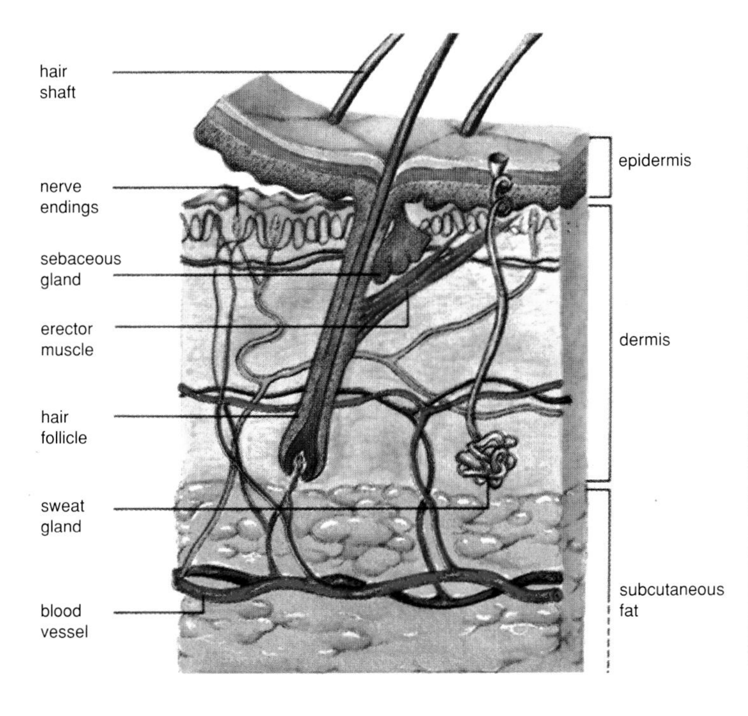

Although the skin is assumed to have a simple structure, it truly is a highly complex organ composed of various layers, in which are receptor nerves, circulatory channels, ventilation systems, temperature and humidity regulators, and it can even produce a shield against sun-light when necessary.

us from all external effects, which alone is enough to show how important the existence of our skin is to us.

All of the functions of the skin are vital. Some of these are:

It prevents disturbance of the body's water balance: Both sides of the epidermis, the outer layer of skin, are waterproof. Water concentration in the body is controlled by means of this feature of the skin. The skin is a more important organ than the ear, nose and even the eye. We can live without our other sense organs, but it is impossible for man to survive without skin. It is impossible for "water", the most vital fluid of human body, to be retained in the body without the skin.

It is strong and flexible: Most of the cells of the epidermis are dead. Dermis, on the other hand, is made up of living cells. Later, epidermal cells start to lose their cellular characteristics and are converted into a hard substance called "keratin". Keratin holds these dead cells together and forms a protective shield for the body. It may be thought that its protective quality would increase if it were thicker and harder, but this is deceptive. If we had a skin as hard and thick as that of the rhinoceros', our highly mobile body would lose this mobility and be clumsy.

Regardless of the species in question, the skin is never thicker than required. There is a very well balanced and controlled plan in the structure of the skin. Let us suppose that epidermal cells constantly died and this process did not stop at a certain point. In this condition, our skin would continue to thicken, and become thick like an alligator's skin. Yet, this is never the case, the skin is always just thick enough. How does this happen? How do skin cells know where to stop?

It would be very illogical and ridiculous to claim that the cells constituting skin tissue determine where to stop on their own, or that this system came about in a coincidental way. There is a manifest design in the structure of the skin. No doubt, it is Allah, the Sustainer of all the worlds, the One and Only, Who has brought about this design.

It has mechanisms to cool down the body in hot weather: The dermis is surrounded by very thin capillaries which not only feed the skin, but also check the blood level within it. When body temperature rises, the veins expand and help the excessively warm blood to travel through the outer layer of the skin, which is relatively cooler, and the heat is released. Another mechanism that cools the body down is sweating: the human skin is full of many tiny holes called "pores". These pores reach as deep as the lowest layer of the skin where sweat glands lie. These glands pass the water they take from the blood through the pores and throw it out of the body. The water thrown out uses the body heat to vaporise and this causes coolness.

It retains body heat in cold weathers: In cold weathers, the activity of sweat glands slows and the veins narrow. This decreases the blood circulation under the skin therefore preventing body heat from escaping.

What all of this shows is that human skin is a perfect organ specially designed to facilitate our lives. Skin protects us, functions as an "air-conditioner", and facilitates easy locomotion thanks to its flexibility. Moreover, it is aesthetic.

Instead of this type of skin, we could well have a thick and coarse skin. We could have an inflexible skin that would crack and split in the event we put on even a few kilograms. We could have skin that would cause us to faint from heat in summer and freeze in winter. However, Allah, Who created us, has covered our body in the most comfortable, serviceable and aesthetic way. For He is **"the Creator, the Maker, the Giver of Form."** (Surat al-Hashr: 24).

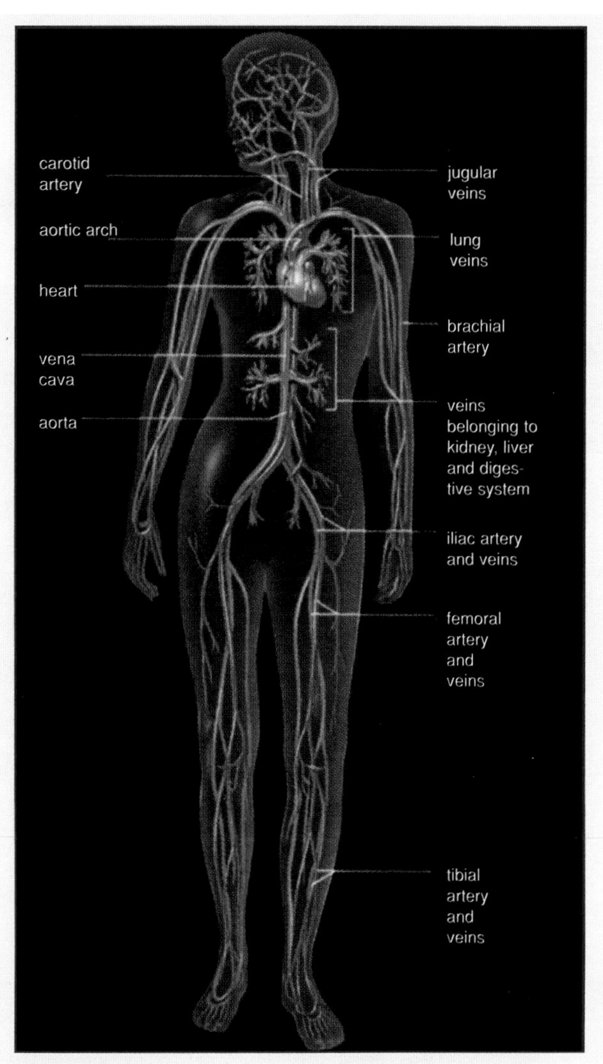

The circulatory system connects each one of the 100 trillion cells in the human body. In the picture, the red capillaries represent blood with high oxygen content and the blue ones represent blood with low oxygen content.

THE HEART

The most important component of the circulatory system that connects the 100 trillions cells in the human body one by one, is, without doubt, the heart. With its four different chambers that pump deoxygenated and oxygenated blood to different parts of the body without mixing them with one another, and with its valves that function as safety valves, the heart's design depends on highly delicate balances.

Our heart, which constantly beats throughout our lives at a certain pace although we do not intervene at all, is one of the clearest pieces of evidence of the Creation.

Starting to beat in the mother's womb, the heart works, without stopping at all during our entire lifetime, with a rhythm of 70-100 beats per

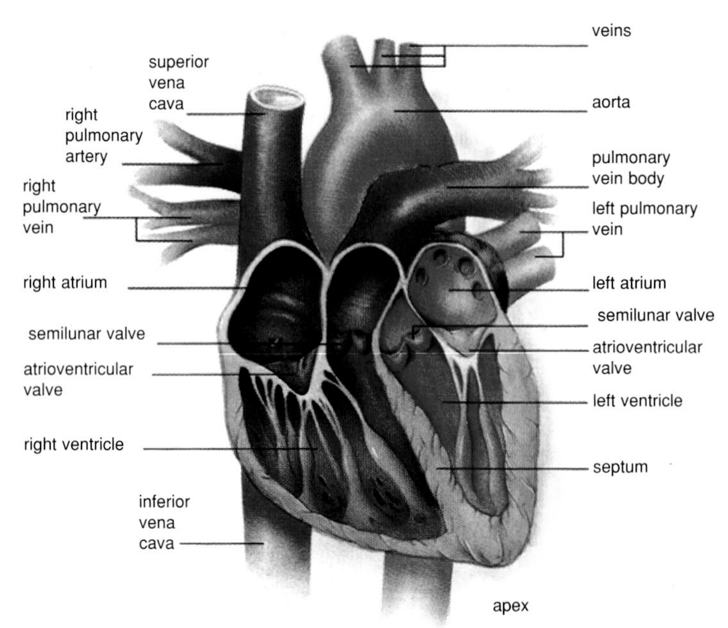

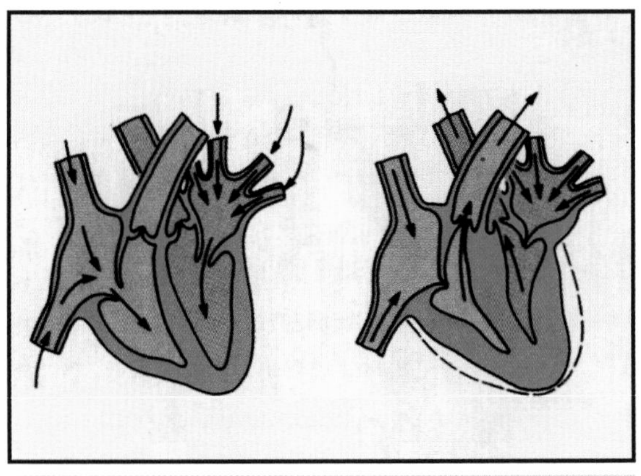

The heart has an excellent design based on delicate balances, with its four chambers pumping blood to different parts of the body without mixing two different kinds of bloods one with another, and its openings functioning as safety valves.

minute. It rests only for half a second between each beat and it beats approximately 100,000 times a day. When a human's life span is considered, we would come across a figure quite hard to calculate.

All the structures in the heart, which has an extremely delicate order in its operation, are specially designed. In the heart, every detail has been considered: the deoxygenated and oxygenated blood's not mixing with one another, the regulation of body pressure, the operations required for the delivery of nutrients to the whole body, and the systems that pump blood only as much as needed. The heart is accordingly designed for all of the above.

In the heart, which is a wonder of design, exists a system so complex that it could not by any means have been formed by coincidence. All of these features present us their designer, that is, Allah, the Sustainer of all the worlds, Who creates flawlessly and without an example.

A few features of the heart can be listed:

The heart is placed in one of the most protected places in the body: By being placed in the rib-cage with a special design, the heart, one of the most important organs, is very well protected against external blows.

Deoxygenated and oxygenated bloods never mix: In the heart, deoxygenated and oxygenated bloods are in constant motion. A special tissue divides the heart into four chambers with different features. The upper part comprises the right and the left atria, which are filling chambers. They pass the blood to the ventricles below. Thanks to the delicate order here, the bloods never mix with each other.

It regulates the blood pressure in such a way that it does no harm to the organs: The heart works not like a single pump, but like two adjacent pumps, each of which has its own ventricle and atrium. This separation also divides our circulatory system into two. The right side of the heart sends blood with a relatively lower pressure to the lungs and the left side pumps blood with a higher pressure to the whole body. This pressure regulation is very important, because if the blood sent to the lungs were pumped with the same pressure as the blood sent out around the body, the lungs would be crushed, being unable to stand this pressure. The perfect balance in the heart does not permit such a problem to occur in the lungs, because the heart is flawlessly designed.

It provides for the transportation of many needed materials to the organs: Clean blood coming from the heart is transmitted to the tissues by the aorta and oxygen is carried to the tissues by the vessels that reach all the cells. During its circulation in the capillaries, blood distributes substances other than oxygen such as hormones, food and other kind of nutrients to the tissues.

It has valves arranging the direction of bloodstream and working in perfect harmony: In the heart, there are valves in the mouth of each chamber that prevent the blood from flowing in the reverse direction. These valves between the atria and ventricles are made of fibrous tissues and held by very thin muscles. Since excess blood would leak towards the atriums if one of these muscles stopped functioning, then serious heart disease would occur that would cause even death. We come across with such a condition only in cases of disease. A contrary condition never occurs.

It pumps the required amount of blood depending on changing conditions: The amount of blood pumped by the heart changes according to the needs of the body. Under normal conditions, the heart beats 70 times a minute. While doing strenuous exercise, during which the muscles need more oxygen, the heart increases the amount of blood it pumps and raises its pace to 180 times per minute. What would happen if this were not so? If the heart were to work at a normal pace when the body needed more energy, the balance would be harmed and the body would be injured. However, no such thing occurs because of the perfect structure of the heart. Without making us obliged to engage in its regulation, the heart regulates the amount of blood to be pumped.

It functions away from our control, yet, exactly as it should: The amount of blood to be pumped by the heart is controlled by a special nervous system. Whether we are asleep or awake, our nervous system by itself regulates the amount of blood to be pumped and the speed of pumping. The structure of the heart - that regulates without any intervention as to where, when and how blood is needed - is flawless. Since the heart could not have formed this system on its own, or this perfect system could not have formed by coincidence, the heart is created. Allah, Who has infinite knowledge, designed it in the most flawless manner possible.

It operates with a special electrical system: The muscle which makes the heart beat and which is called the heart muscle, is different from all other muscles in the body. Ordinary muscle cells in the body contract whenever stimulated by the nervous system. However, heart muscle cells contract by themselves. Those cells have the capability of initiating and spreading their own electrical current. Although each cell possesses this capability, none of them contracts independently from the others because then they would function against the instructions of the electrical system controlling them. In other words, they do not cause a chaos that would disturb the regular pace of the heart, in which one part contracts while the other relaxes. These cells, which are found in the form of a chain, act together as per the instruction given by the electrical system. Again, a flawless harmony is at work.

As seen in all of its features, the structure of the heart shows us its flawless design, that is, its "being created", and it thus presents us its Designer. It presents us Allah, the Sustainer of all the worlds, Who is not seen, yet presents Himself to us in everything He has created:

That is Allah, your Lord. There is no god but Him, the Creator of everything. So worship Him. He is Responsible for everything. (Surat al-An'am: 102)

THE HAND

Our hands, which enable us to perform some very ordinary acts such as stirring a cup of tea, turning the pages of a newspaper, or writing, are incredible engineering wonders.

The most important feature of the hand is its ability to operate with high efficiency in very distinct activities, despite having a standard structure. Being furnished with a great number of muscles and nerves, our arms help our hands grip objects strongly or softly according to different circumstances. For instance, the human hand, although when not formed into a fist, can strike a blow strike against an object with a weight of 45 kilograms. However, our hand can also feel, between its thumb and forefinger, a sheet of paper one tenth of a millimetre in thickness.

Obviously, these two acts are of a totally different character. As one requires sensitivity, the other requires great force. We, however, never even think for a second what we have to do when we take a sheet of paper between our fingers or hit with a fist. Nor do we think how to adjust the strength for these two acts. We never say, "Now I will pick up some paper. Let me apply a force of 500 g. Now I will lift this bucketful of water. Let me apply a force of 40 kg."

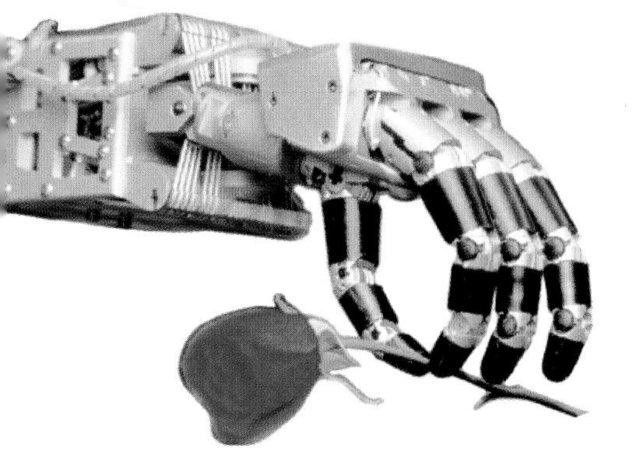

A robot, no matter how advanced, can never possess the features of a real hand.

We even do not bother to think about these.

The reason is that the human hand is designed to perform all these acts simultaneously. The hand is created together with all its functions and all its related structures concurrently.

All the fingers in the hand are the appropriate length and position, and proportionate to each other. For instance, the strength of a fist formed with a hand having a normal thumb is greater than that formed with a hand having a shorter thumb, because with its pre-determined appropriate length, the thumb covers other fingers and helps augment their power by supporting them.

There are many small details in the structure of the hand: for instance, it has smaller structures besides the muscles and nerves. The nails at the tip of the fingers are by no means trivial accessories. When we try to pick a needle from the floor, we use our nails as well as our fingers. The rough surface comprising our fingertips and nails helps us in picking up small objects. Last but not least, nails play a big role in the regulation of the minute pressure fingers have to exert on the object they hold.

Another distinctive feature of the hand is that it does not get tired.

The worlds of medicine and science spend a considerable effort on making an artificial copy of the hand. The robotic hands so far manufactured have the same performance as human hands in terms of power, yet it is hard to say the same thing for sensitivity of touch, perfect manoeuvrability, and the ability to do diverse jobs.

Many scientists agree that no robot hand can be made having the complete functions of the hand. Engineer Hans J. Schneebeli, who has designed the robotic hand known as "The Karlsruhe Hand", stated that the more he worked on robotic hands, the more he admired the human hand. He added that they still need a lot of time to make possible even a certain number of the jobs accomplished by a human hand.

The hand usually functions in co-ordination with the eye. The signals reaching the eye are transmitted to the brain, and the hand moves according to the command given by the brain. These, of course, are completed in a very short time and without making us spend a special effort to do them. Robotic hands, on the other hand, can only rely either on sight or touch. Different commands are needed for every move they make. In addition, robotic hands cannot accomplish diverse functions. For instance, a robotic hand playing the piano cannot hold a hammer, and a robotic hand holding a hammer cannot hold an egg without breaking it. Some robotic hands that have only lately been produced are able to perform 2-3 actions together, but this is still very primitive when compared to the abilities of the hand.

In addition, when you consider that the two hands co-operate with each other in perfect harmony, the flawlessness of the design of the hand becomes more explicit.

Allah designed the hand as an organ especially for human beings. With all these aspects, it shows us the perfection and uniqueness in Allah's art of creation.

CONCLUSION

These excellent mechanisms in the human body generally work without our knowledge or awareness of them. The beating of the heart, the functions of the liver, the rejuvenation of the skin are all away from our direct knowledge. The same is true for hundreds of other organs not mentioned here. We are not even aware that our kidneys filter blood, our stomachs digest the food we eat, the movement of our intestines, or the perfect operation of our lungs that help us breathe.

The human being realises the worth of his body only when he is sick and his organs become dysfunctional.

How, then, has this perfect mechanism come into being? It is unquestionably not so difficult for a conscientious person with wisdom to comprehend and feel that this body is "created".

The claim of evolutionists that this body has come into being because of coincidences is ridiculous, because they assert that accumulation of coincidences bring an organism into being. The human body, however, can only function with all its organs intact. A human without a kidney, heart or intestine cannot live. Even if these organs exist, a human cannot survive if they do not function properly.

Therefore, the human body must have come into being as a whole in order to survive and carry on his generation. That the human body has "come into being instantaneously and completely" means that it is "created".

We created you so why do you not confirm the truth? Have you thought about the sperm that you ejaculate? Is it you who create it or are We the Creator? We have decreed death for you and We will not be forestalled from replacing you with others the same as you and re-forming you in a way you do not know. (Surat al-Waqi'ah: 57-61)

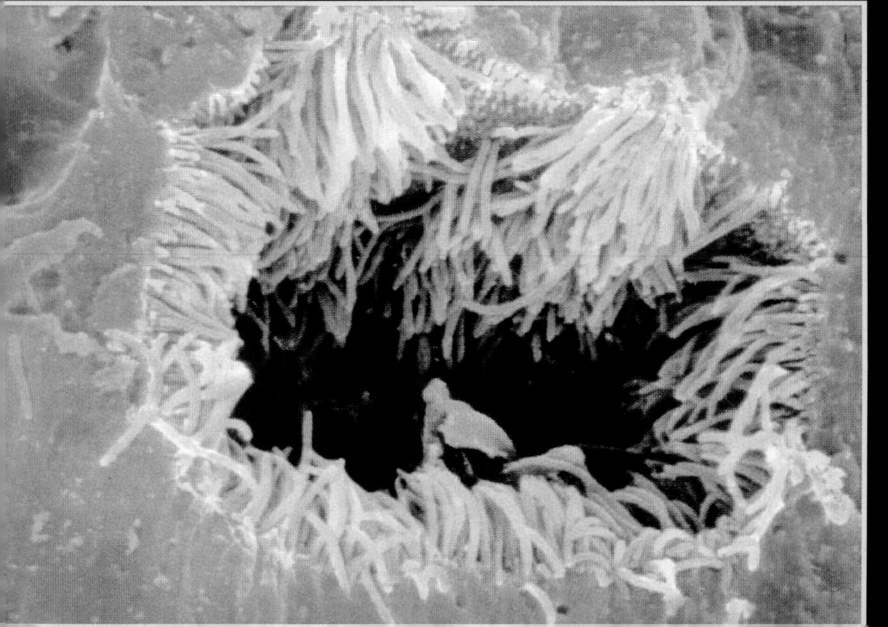

BONE FORMATION

The tissues seen above are building blocks of a developing bone. Resembling unordered timbers at the first look, these tissues will increasingly strengthen and become an extremely hard and strong bone.

TRACHEA

Green extensions function like an air filter. Their job is to clean the air we inhale. The extensions are covered with a viscous substance called "mucus". Thus, foreign materials are prevented from reaching the lung.

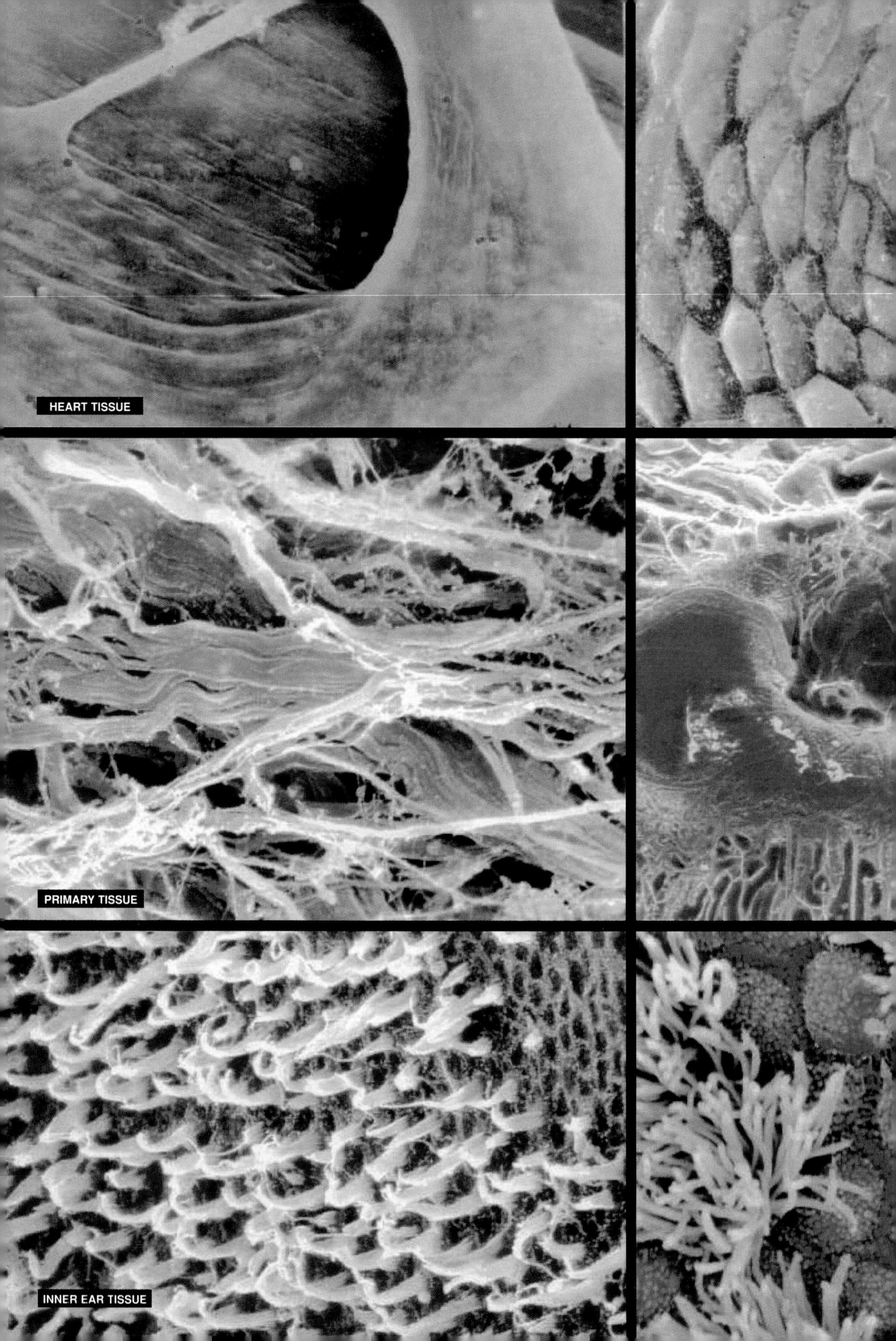
HEART TISSUE
PRIMARY TISSUE
INNER EAR TISSUE

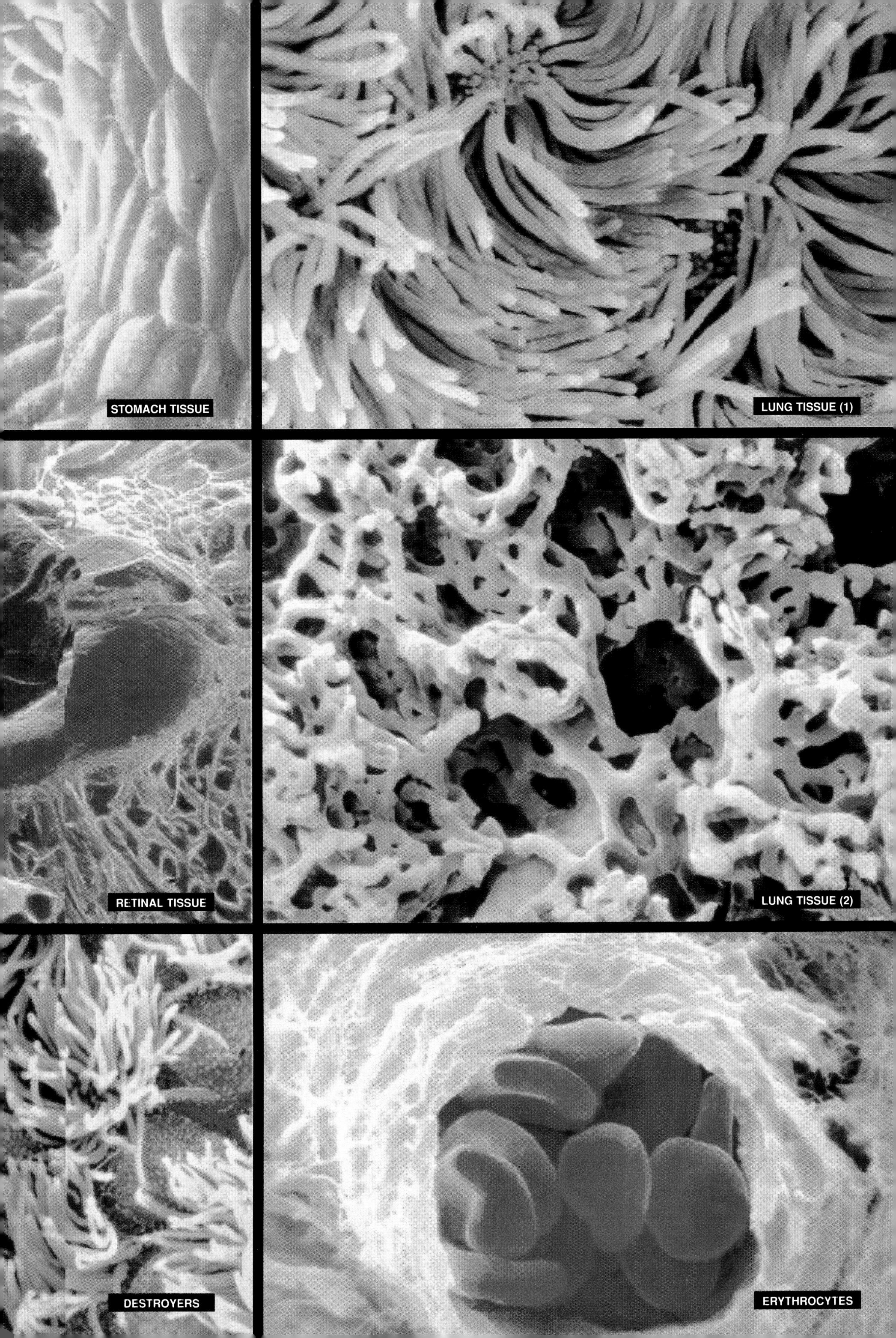
STOMACH TISSUE
LUNG TISSUE (1)
RETINAL TISSUE
LUNG TISSUE (2)
DESTROYERS
ERYTHROCYTES

THE DEFENCE SYSTEM

As acknowledged, defence is an issue that has to be given top priority by a country for the continuance of its existence. Nations have always to watch out for all kinds of internal and external threats, assaults, risks of wars and terrorist actions. This is why they allocate a great part of their official budgets to defence. Armies are provided with the most advanced aircraft, ships, and arms, and the forces of defence are always kept at the highest level of preparedness.

The human body is surrounded by a great number of enemies and threats. These enemies are bacteria, viruses, and similar microscopic organisms. They exist everywhere; in the air we inhale, the water we drink, the food we eat, and the environment in which we live.

What most people are not aware of is that the human body has an excellent army, the immune system, which fights against enemies. This is a real army made up of many "soldiers" and "officials" with different assignments, who are specially trained, employ high technology and fight with conventional and chemical weapons.

Every day, even every minute, a permanent war is fought between this army and the enemy forces, but away from our knowledge. This war can also be in the form of minor, local skirmishes as well as battles in which the whole body is involved and alarmed. We call these battles "diseases".

The general conduct of this war almost never changes. The enemy attempts to fool the other side by camouflaging itself when intruding into the body. The trained investigative forces are assigned by the defence to identify the enemies. The enemies are identified and appropriate weapons are produced to exterminate them. Then there is close contact, the defeat of the enemy, cease-fire, and clearance of the battleground. Last, there is storage of every type of information about the enemy as a precaution against the possibility of a later attack....

Now let us examine this interesting war closer.

THE BESIEGED CASTLE: THE HUMAN BODY

We can liken the human body to a castle besieged by enemies. The enemies look for various ways to invade this castle. The human skin is the wall of this castle.

The front defence line of the body is the skin. When a cut or wound is inflicted on the skin, it means that the body is in danger. Viruses and bacteria can easily make their way through. When such a wound is inflicted, "virus- and bacteria-hostile" cells called "phagocytes", rush to the afflicted spot and try to swallow the micro-organisms that intrude into the body. On the other hand, the wound on the skin has long since started to receive treatment to prevent further foreign materials from entering the body.

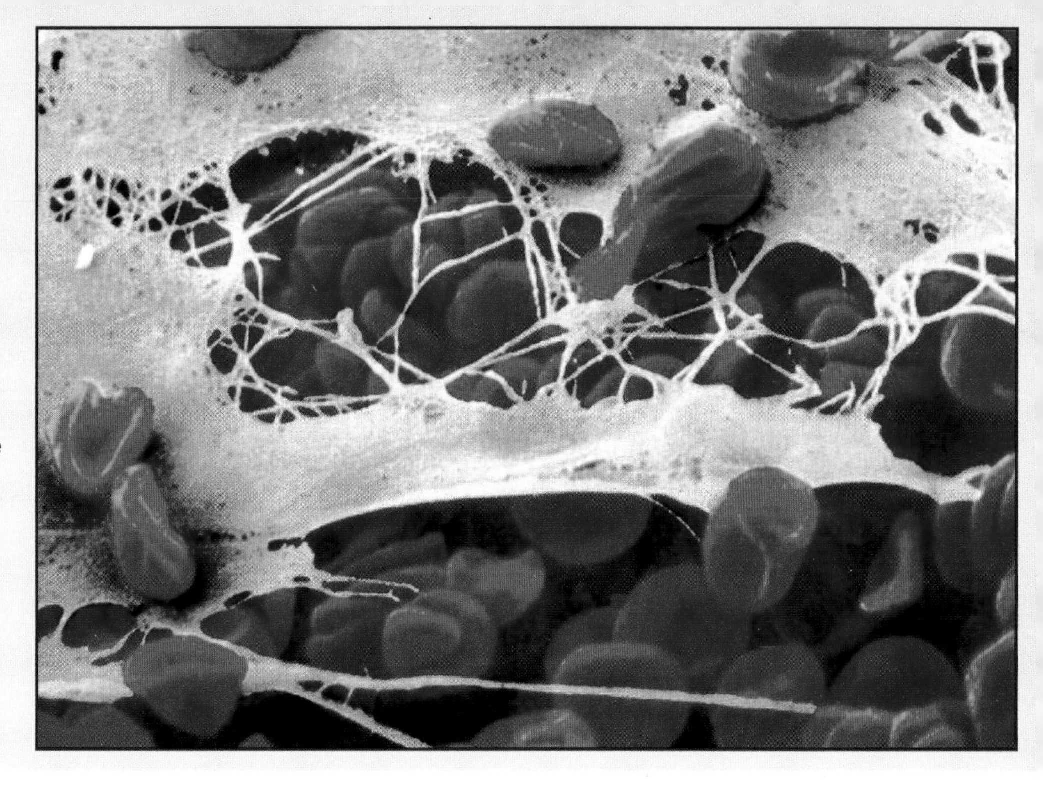

The substance of keratin in the cells of the skin is an impassable barrier for bacteria and fungi. Foreign substances that reach the skin cannot pass through this wall. Moreover, although the outer layer of skin that contains keratin is continuously rubbed off, it is renewed by skin growing from beneath. Thus, all unwanted guests that have squeezed between the skin are ejected from the body together with dead skin, during renewal of the skin from inwards to outwards. The enemy can only make its way in through a wound that is inflicted on the skin.

THE FRONT LINE

One of the ways through which viruses enter the body is air. The enemy pushes its way to the body through the air inhaled. However, a special secretion in the nasal mucous membrane and cell-swallowing defence elements in the lungs (phagocytes) meet these enemies and take control of the situation before the danger grows. Digestive enzymes in the stomach acid and small intestine eliminate a great number of the microbes that seek to enter the body through food.

THE CLASH OF THE ENEMIES

There are some microbes that have settled in various parts of the human body (such as skin, skin folds, mouth, nose, eye, upper respiratory canals, digestive canal, the genitals) yet do not cause illness.

When a foreign microbe enters the body, these domestic microbes - thinking that their habitation would be invaded- and not wishing to give way to the foreigners who invade their habitation - fight strenuously. We can define them

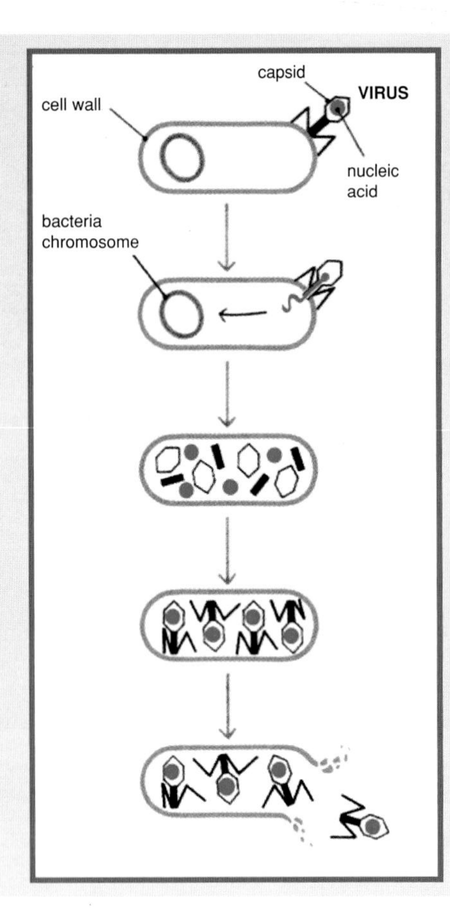

"THE CELL INVASION"
OPERATION OF THE VIRUS

1. **Virus contacts the cell it approaches and adheres to its surface. (It is seen on a bacteria cell in the scheme).**

2. **The virus discharges a special enzyme at the point of contact that will help melt the membrane of the cell it approaches. Because of this action, a hole forms in the cell wall. The virus pulls back its tail and, by shrinking, it injects the nucleic acid in its body (DNA or RNA) into the cell.**

3. **The nucleic acid of the virus that enters in the cell takes it under control. The vital functions of the cell stop. The nucleic acid of the virus self-replicates by using the resources of the cell.**

4. **The newly formed parts of the virus come together and form new viruses.**

5. **When sufficient viruses are formed, the cell bursts and developed viruses swing into action to find new host cells. The time from the virus' intrusion into a cell to the end of its reproduction is around 20-25 minutes. At the end of each replication, 200-300 new viruses are formed in a host cell.**

as professional soldiers. They try to protect their territory for their own ends. Thus, the complex army in our body is reinforced by these micro supports.

STEP BY STEP TO HOT WAR

If a microscopic intruder entering the body can overcome defence elements on guard and bacteria serving as soldiers, it causes war to begin with. After that, the body, with its ordered army, fights a perfect offence-defence war against this foreign army.

The war fought by the defence system is comprised of four parts:

1. Identification of the enemy.

2. The fortification of defences and the preparation of offensive weapons.

3. Attack and battle.

4. Retreat to normal state.

The cells that first meet the enemy units are macrophage cells that make "phagocytosis", i.e., that engulf the enemy. These cells are involved in close contact with the enemy, and fight a hand-to-hand war. They are just like infantrymen who fight a bayonet war against enemy units and struggle at the distant front line of the army.

Moreover, macrophages function as intelligence units, or as the secret service of an army. They hold one portion of the enemy they destroy. This portion is used to identify the enemy's identity and to determine its features. Macrophages pass this portion to another intelligence unit, messenger-T cells.

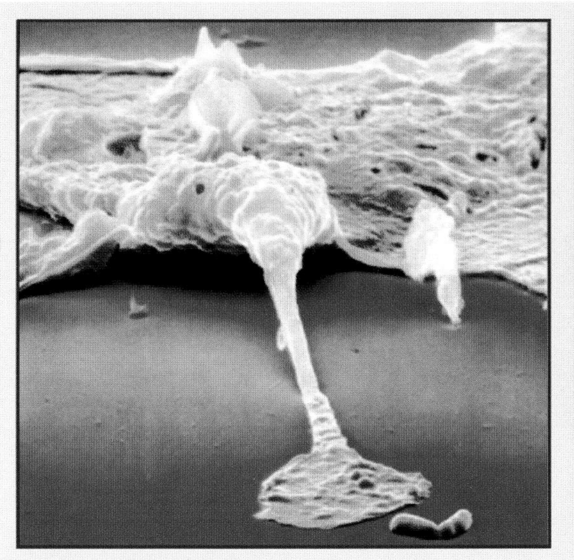

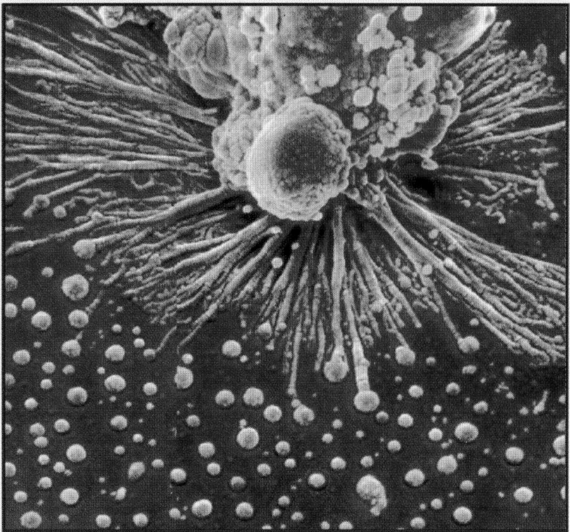

Macrophages are those elements of the immune system that fight at the front. They engulf and digest all kinds of foreign substances in the blood. Their other task is to call the T cells for help wherever they meet the enemy. In the photograph on the left, a macrophage is seen trying to catch a bacterium with its extensions. On the right, the macrophage is trying to engulf a lipid molecule that has entered the body.

GENERAL ALARM

When a country is involved in war, a general mobilisation is declared. Most of the natural resources and the budget are spent on war expenses. The economy is re-arranged according to this extraordinary situation and the country is involved in total action. In a war, which the defensive army of the body will fight as a whole, mobilisation is also declared. Do you wonder how?

If the enemy is more than they can handle, the cavalcades (macrophages) that launch an attack secrete a special substance. The name of this substance is "pyrogen" and it is a kind of alarm call. After travelling a long way, "pyrogen" reaches the brain and stimulates the fever-increasing centre of the brain. Following this stimulation, the brain sets off alarms in the body and the person develops a high fever. The patient with a high fever naturally feels a need to rest. Thus, the energy needed by the defence army is not spent elsewhere. As seen, there exists an extremely complex plan and design at work.

THE ORDERED ARMY SWINGS INTO ACTION

The war between the microscopic intruder and the immune system becomes more complicated after mobilisation, that is, your falling ill in bed. At this stage, infantrymen (phagocytes) and cavalrymen (macrophages) have proved insufficient, the whole body is alarmed, and the war becomes heated. At this stage, lymphocytes - (T and B cells) - intervene.

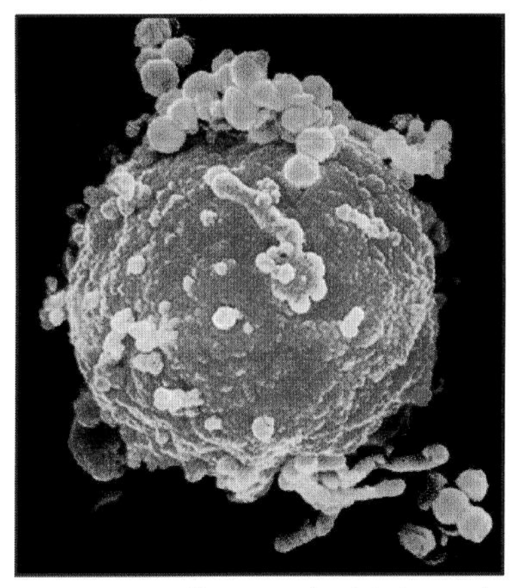

A B Cell covered with bacteria

Cavalrymen (macrophages) pass the information they have on the enemy to T helper cells. These cells summon

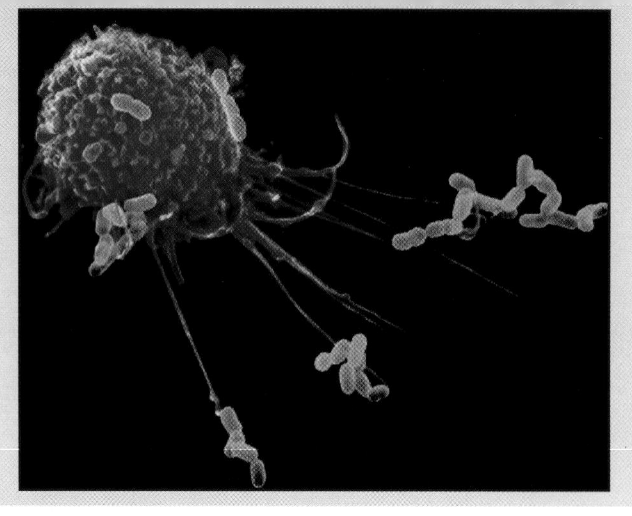

In this incident called "phagocytosis", a macrophage stretches out to engulf a great number of bacteria. Bacteria are surrounded by one of the extensions of a macrophage. Then a cell engulfs them. Afterwards, strong chemical materials in the macrophage decompose the enemy and destroy it. In other words, the macrophage engulfs the enemy, digests it and uses the released materials.

T cytotoxic and B cells to the battleground. These are the most effective fighters of the immune system.

WEAPONRY PRODUCTION

As soon as B cells receive information about the enemy, they start producing weapons. These weapons, just like ballistic missiles, are only produced to hit the enemy on whom information is available. This production is so perfect that the three dimensional structure of the microscopic intruder and the three dimensional structure of the weapon fully match each other. This accord is like that between a key and its lock.

Antibodies advance towards the enemy and clamp tightly on it. After this stage, the enemy is neutralised like a tank that has its treads, cannon and gun destroyed. Afterwards, other members of the immune system come and eliminate the neutralised enemy.

Here, there is a very important point to consider: there are millions of types of enemy that the immune system will confront. B cells can produce an appropriate weapon for all types of enemy no matter what they are. This means that the immune system innately has the knowledge and capability to produce the keys appropriate to millions of different types of locks. These unconscious cells have the ability to make millions of types of antibodies, and their using it in the best way proves the existence of a creation by the Owner of an exalted power.

Furthermore, the system is more sophisticated. As B cells destroy the enemy with ballistic weapons, T cytotoxic cells also fight a tough war against the enemy. When some viruses enter a cell, they can hide from the weapons produced by the B cells. The T cytotoxic cells find the diseased cells in which this camouflaged enemy hides and destroy them.

AFTER THE VICTORY

After the enemy is defeated, the T suppressor cells swing into action. These cells give the army of defence the command to cease fire, and cause the T cytotoxic and B cells to stop their activities. Thus, the body does not carry on in a state of mobilisation in vain. After the war is over, most of the T and B cells produced specifically for the war complete their lifecycle and die. This tough war, however, is not to be forgotten. Before the war, a short time passed while the enemy was identified and the necessary preparations made. If the enemy ever comes back, the body will be much better prepared. A group of memory cells, which have come to know the features of the enemy, will constantly serve in the immune system in future. In a possible second attack, the immune system, with the information in the memory cells, will have the means to react before the enemy gains force. The reason why we do not catch mumps or measles again, after we have once caught them, is because of the memory of our immune system.

WHO IS HE WHO CREATES THE SYSTEM?

After all the information we have examined, we have to take our time and think about how this perfect immune system to which we owe our lives has come to exist. There is a flawless plan at work. Everything needed for the operation of this plan is intact: macrophages, the pyrogen substance, the fever raising centre of the brain, the body's fever raising mechanisms, B cells, T cells, weapons... How, then, has this perfect system come into being?

Not surprisingly, the theory of evolution, which proposes that living beings have come into being by coincidence, cannot explain how this complex system came about. The claim of the theory of evolution is that living beings and living systems have originated step-by-step by the accumulation of little coincidences. However, the immune system cannot by any means have originated "step-by-step". The reason is that in the case of the absence or malfunction of even one of the factors that make up the system, the system cannot work and the person could not survive. The system must have come into being completely and flawlessly with all its components intact. This reality renders the notion of "coincidence" meaningless.

> ***O mankind! You are the poor in need of Allah whereas Allah is the Rich beyond need, the Praiseworthy. (Surah Fatir: 15)***

Who, then, makes this plan? Who knows that the body's fever must rise, and that only that way the energy needed by the army of defence will not be spent elsewhere? Is it the macrophages? Macrophages are merely tiny cells. They do not have the capacity to think. They are living organisms that obey an established superior order and that fulfil their duties.

Is it man? Certainly not. People are not even aware that such a perfect system is at work in their own bodies. However, this system, of which we are unaware, protects us from certain death.

It is obvious that the one who created the immune system, and who created the whole human body, should be a Creator Who has exalted knowledge and might. This Creator is Allah, Who has created the human body from a "drop of fluid".

THE IMMUNE SYSTEM

The leucocytes, around a trillion in number, form a highly specialised army of defence. The most important agents of this army and the duties they perform during a war with the enemy are described below.

THE VIRUS
The virus, a genetic data package, is dependent on the environment to be activated. It has to use the mechanisms of a host cell in order to reproduce.

THE MACROPHAGE
It is a watchman and the defence cell in the front line. It engulfs and digests all kinds of foreign materials in the blood. When it runs into a microscopic intruder, it summons up T helper cells to the site of action.

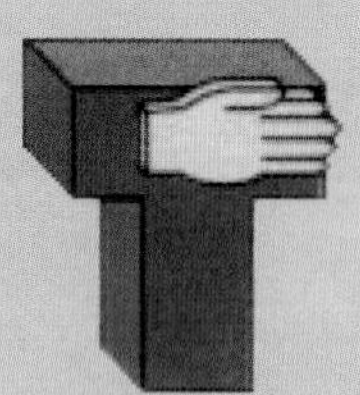

THE T HELPER CELL
It is the administrator of the immune system. After identifying the enemy, it goes to the spleen and lymphatic glands and warns other cells to fight against the agent of disease.

T CYTOTOXIC CELLS
Warned by the T helper cell, these cells destroy the cells that are occupied by foreign materials and cancer cells.

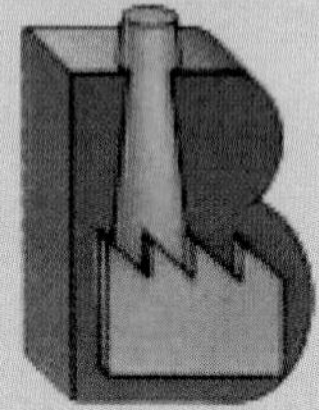

THE B CELL
These cells, considered as biological weapon factories, are found in the spleen and the lymphatic glands. When warned by T helper cells, they produce strong chemical weapons named antibodies.

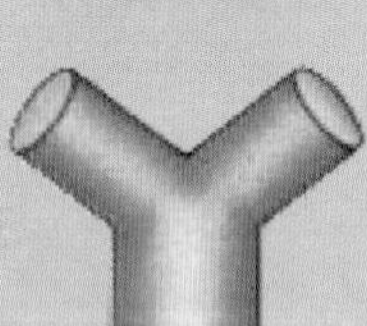

ANTIBODIES
This protein in the shape of a "Y" sticks onto the disease agent, renders it ineffective and turns it into a target for killer cells.

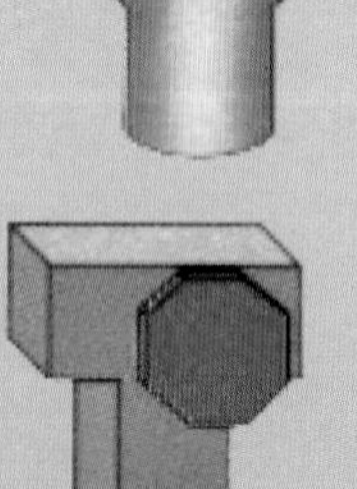

THE T SUPPRESSOR CELLS
This third type of the T cells slows the activities of the T and B cells or stops them. It ends the assault after the illness has been overcome.

THE MEMORY CELL
This defence cell is formed after the first disease is over. By remaining in the body for years, it ensures that the immunity mechanism is activated very rapidly and effectively when the body meets an agent of the same disease again.

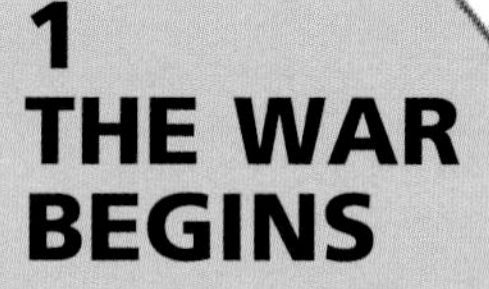

1 THE WAR BEGINS

When viruses are disseminated in the body, some of them are engulfed by the macrophages. Macrophages split the antibodies off the virus and stick them onto their own surface. Very few out of millions of T helper cells travelling in the circulatory system have the ability to "read" this specific antibody. These particular T cells which stick on the macrophage become active.

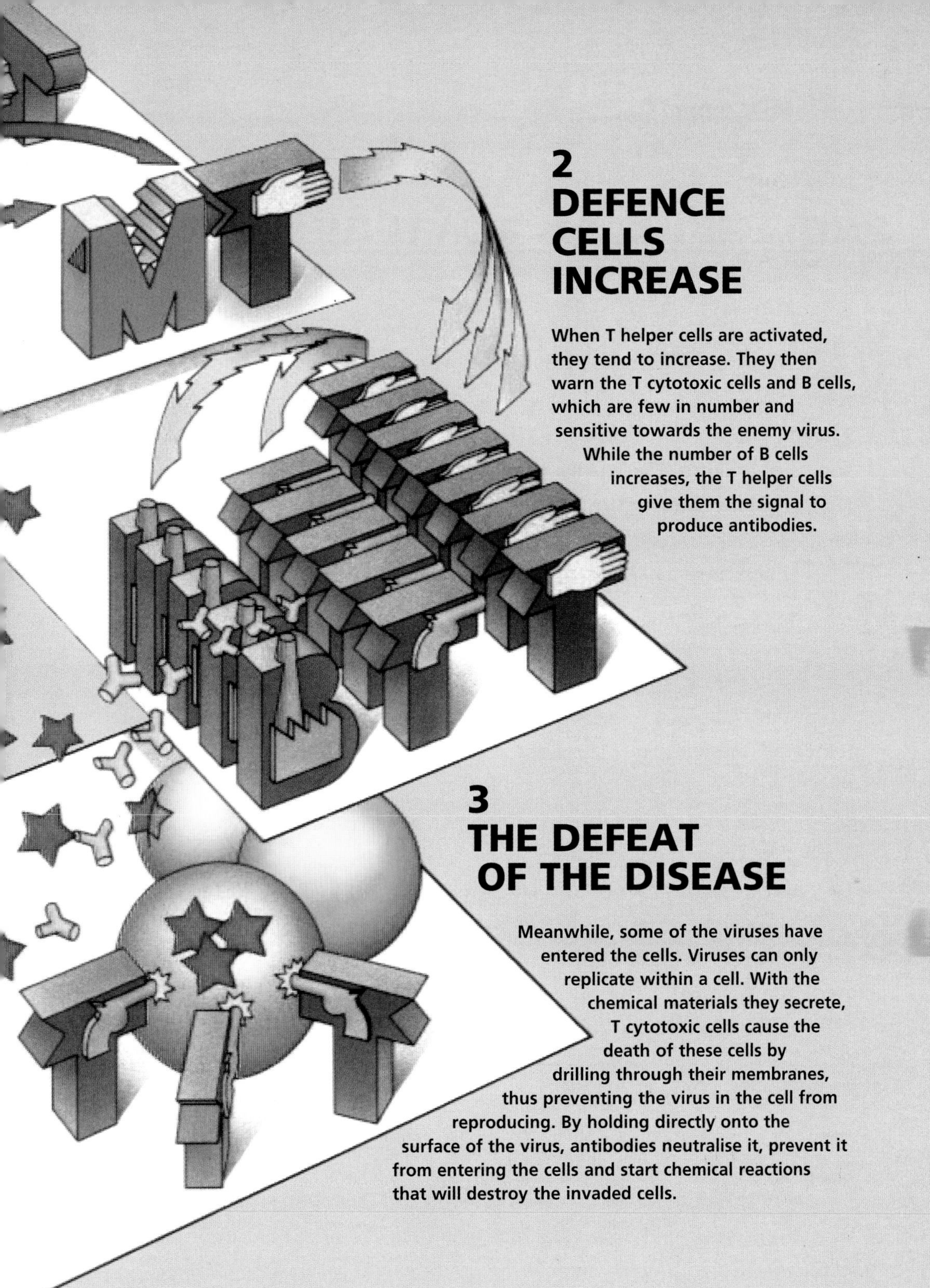

2
DEFENCE CELLS INCREASE

When T helper cells are activated, they tend to increase. They then warn the T cytotoxic cells and B cells, which are few in number and sensitive towards the enemy virus. While the number of B cells increases, the T helper cells give them the signal to produce antibodies.

3
THE DEFEAT OF THE DISEASE

Meanwhile, some of the viruses have entered the cells. Viruses can only replicate within a cell. With the chemical materials they secrete, T cytotoxic cells cause the death of these cells by drilling through their membranes, thus preventing the virus in the cell from reproducing. By holding directly onto the surface of the virus, antibodies neutralise it, prevent it from entering the cells and start chemical reactions that will destroy the invaded cells.

4
AFTER THE WAR

After the disease is won, T suppressor cells stop the whole offensive system. Memory-T and B cells remain in the blood and lymphatic system in order to become immediately activated in case a virus of the same type is met.

PROFESSIONAL HUNTERS

In the sixth ayah of Surah Hud, Allah states that Allah gives the "sustenance" of all living things, that is, Allah creates all the provisions that provide for their subsistence:

There is no creature on the earth which is not dependent upon Allah for its provision. He knows where it lives and where it dies. They are all in a Clear Book. (Surah Hud: 6)

One can easily recognise how Allah "gives sustenance" to all living things once one looks around oneself conscientiously and with wisdom. All our food and drink are things that are "made" and "created". The water we drink, the bread, fruits and vegetables we eat are all the results of a special creation. Take a fruit, an orange for instance.... This fruit is originally formed on the branch of a tree, which is, in fact, a mass of wood. The tree absorbs minerals and water from the soil and combines them with the energy it obtains from the sun. The result it yields is extremely useful for the human body, extremely tasty and fragrant when consumed by humans. Moreover, it is in a very healthy and aesthetically pleasing wrapping.

How does a tree bring about such a yield? Why is it so useful to the human body? Why do all fruits contain essential vitamins appropriate to the seasons in which they grow? Why are they so tasty and not bitter? Why are they so fragrant and do not stink?

Certainly a tree is just a bulk of wood and it is out of the question for it to produce a fruit on its own and equip it with features essential for human use. Just as Allah sustains human beings, so does He sustain the animals. In the following pages, we will review the hunting techniques some living beings use to reach their sustenance.

It is by no means difficult for one to understand the might and omnipotence of Allah if one conscientiously examines, within the boundaries of wisdom and logic, the systems with which animals are endowed to get their food. Every animal that we cover in this chapter is one of the great examples Allah has spread out on the earth.

For instance, the "hunting technique" of the fish you see on the next page is amazing. This fish neither chases its enemy nor does it lurk secretly to dash upon them. The fish is no different from others at first glance. Yet, as soon as it lifts its fin, a "fake fish" appears on its back. When other fish approach this

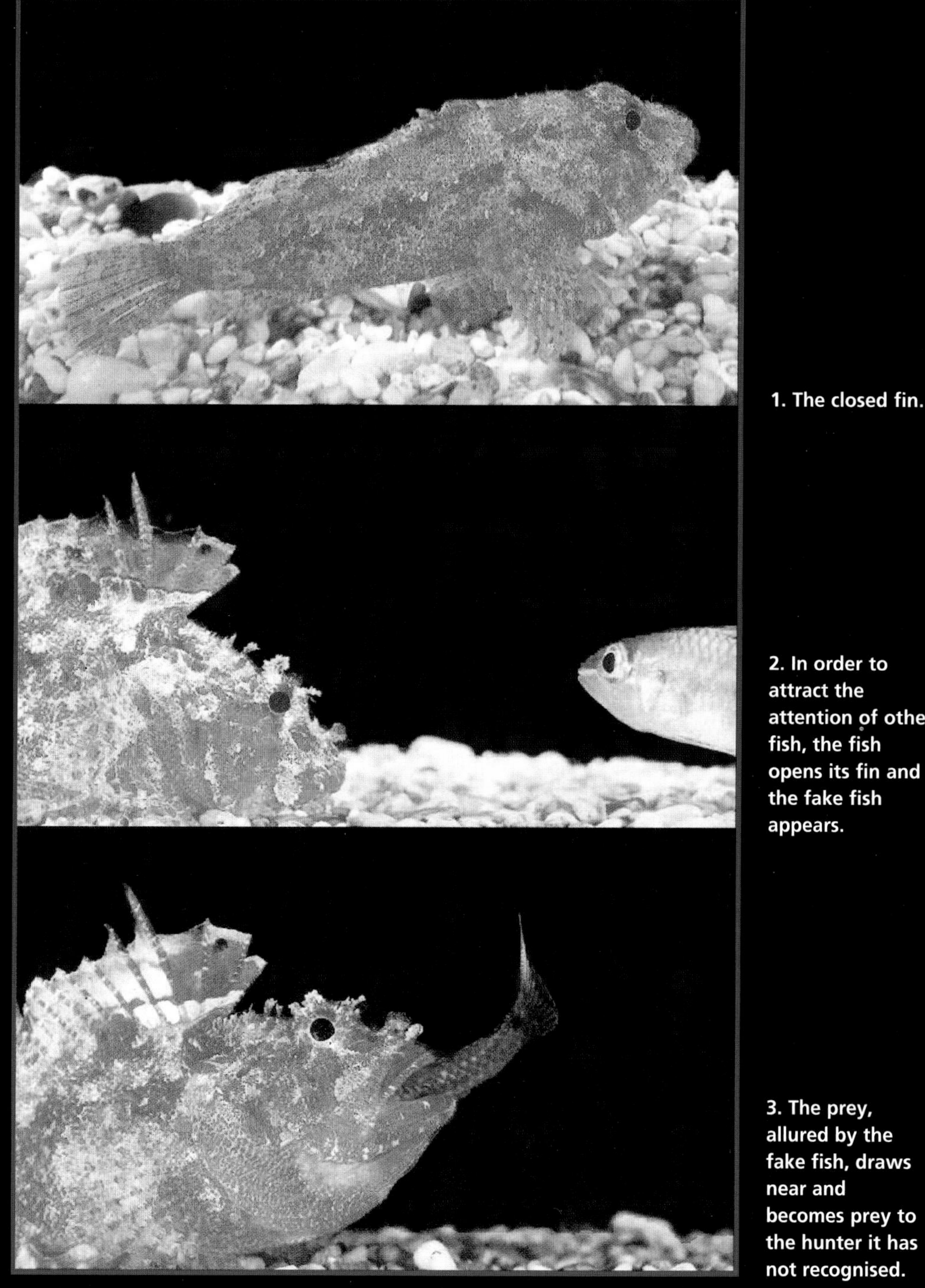

1. The closed fin.

2. In order to attract the attention of other fish, the fish opens its fin and the fake fish appears.

3. The prey, allured by the fake fish, draws near and becomes prey to the hunter it has not recognised.

small fake fish, not realising who the real owner of the fins is, they become easy prey to the hunter fish.

Has this fish by itself given its fin a fish image? Or rather, have coincidences accumulated and given the fish such a feature? It is unquestionably impossible to claim that a fish could conceive of such a conscious plan, and act and carry it out. No doubt, all the features the living things possess bring us face to face with a single reality: the existence of the owner of the superior wisdom and design prevailing in nature, the existence of Allah....

THE JUMPING SPIDER

As is widely known, spiders construct a web and wait for insects to become trapped. The jumping spider, contrary to others, prefers to go after its prey itself. It makes a nimble leap to reach its prey. It may capture a fly that passes half a metre away from itself in the air by leaping upon it.

The spider makes this amazing leap by its eight feet that work on hydraulic pressure principles, and all of a sudden it descends on its prey and inserts it powerful jaws in it. This leap usually takes place in a convoluted environment of plants. The spider must calculate the most appropriate angle for a successful leap, and consider the speed and direction of its prey.

More interesting is how it saves its own life after catching its prey. The insect could possibly die, because when jumping to catch its prey, it launches itself into the air and so it could easily crash down to the ground from the heights (the spider is usually at the top of a tree).

The spider, however, does not face such an end. The spider thread, which it had secreted just before jumping and which it sticks on the branch it is on, saves it from falling to the ground and keeps him dangling in the air. This thread is so strong that it can hold both the spider and its prey.

Another interesting feature of this spider is that the poison it injects into its prey liquefies its tissues. The food of the spider is nothing else than the liquefied tissues of its prey.

Certainly, the features of this spider are not gifts (!) of coincidence. It is necessary that it should have gained the skill of both jumping and, at the same time, making a thread that will prevent it from falling. If it could not jump, it would starve and die. If it could not make a thread or if its thread were not strong enough, it would crash to the ground. Then the spider must both have a body structure suitable for jumping and a system to secrete a thread strong enough to lift its prey.

Besides that, the spider is not only a mechanism that produces thread and jumps but a complex living organism and must exist with all its features intact at the same time. The development of none of these features can be deferred. For instance, can you think of a spider with an incomplete digestive system?

IT SEES 360 DEGREES AROUND

Another extremely interesting feature of the jumping spider is its skill in seeing. Many living organisms, including human beings, can only see a limited space with their two eyes and are unable to see behind them. However, the jumping spider can see everything around itself including its back with its four pairs of eyes located on top of its head. Two of these eyes are extended forward from the middle of the head like test-tubes. These two big eyes (called A.M. eyes) can move from right to left, and up and down in their sockets. The other four eyes on the sides of the head cannot perceive the image completely, yet can detect every movement around them. In this way, the animal can easily identify a prey behind it.

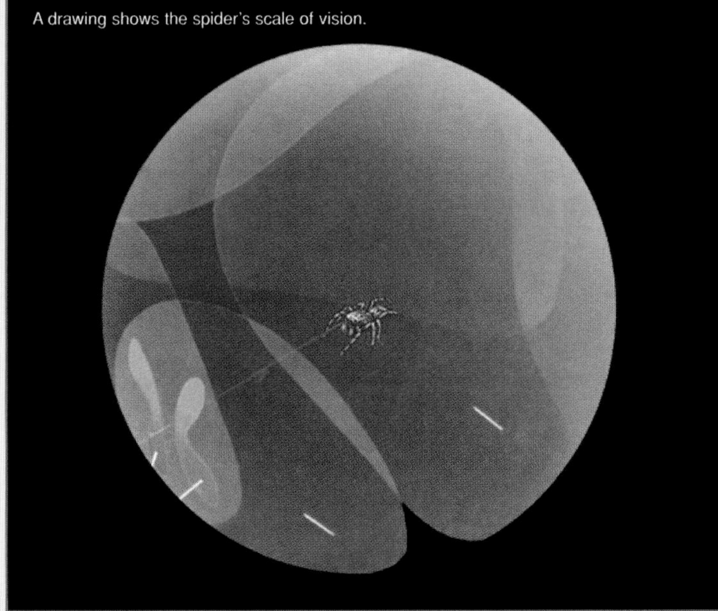

A drawing shows the spider's scale of vision.

The ability of the jumping spider's eyes to see independently from each other helps the animal perceive objects more rapidly. In the pictures, the dark eye looks at the camera, and the light eye looks elsewhere. It is a wonder that the jumping spider has eight eyes and an angle of vision of 360 degrees whereas other creatures have only two eyes. Certainly, the animal has not, by itself, "thought" that this would be more useful and thus produced additional eyes, or - to be accurate - these eyes did not originate coincidentally. The animal has been created with all these features.

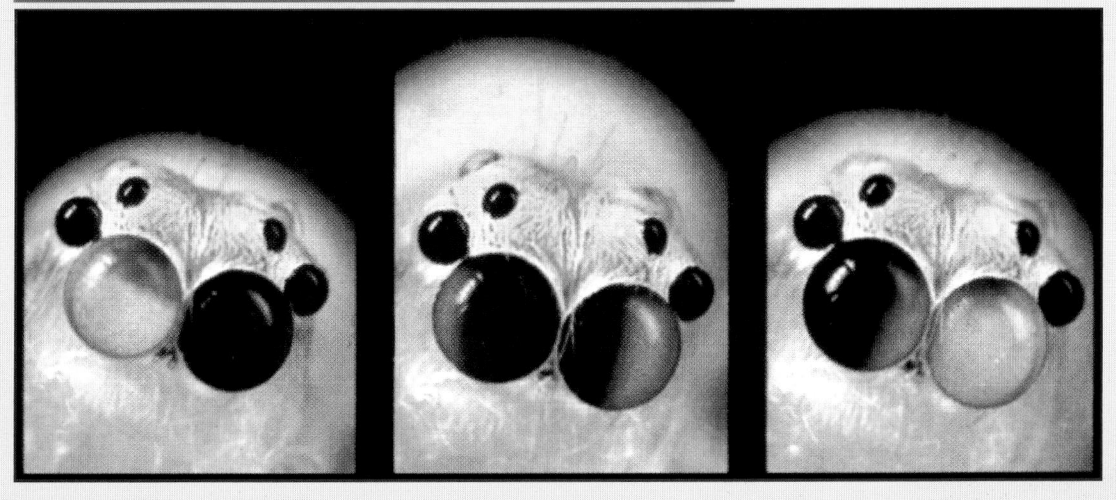

CAMOUFLAGE TECHNIQUE

If you were asked what you see in the above picture, you would definitely say, "there are some ants above and below the leaf".

However, what you see under the leaf is a jumping spider lurking to hunt living ants. This species of the jumping spider looks so similar to the ants that even the ants think it is one of them.

The only difference between the ant and the spider is the number of legs. The spider has eight legs whereas the ant has six.

In order to do away with this "handicap", which will make him readily recognised, the jumping spider stretches its two forelegs forward and lifts them up. Thus, its two legs look exactly like the antennae of ants.

Yet, the camouflage does not consist solely of this. The animal needs also an eye pattern that will make it seem like an ant. Its own eyes are not big and in the shape of a dark spot like those of the ants. One feature it possesses by birth helps it solve this problem. The spider has two big spots at the two sides of its head. These two spots resemble the ant's eyes (notice the spots at the sides of the spider's head in the above picture).

On the left are two ants and a jumping spider. You have no other way but to count the legs to find out which one is the ant and which one is the spider.

THE WATER GUN OF THE FISH

This fish shoots the water it has filled in its mouth on inse sitting on branches overhanging the water. The insect falls due to the pressurised water and becomes an easy prey to fish. It is worth noting that while launching the attack, the fish does not lift its head out of the water at all, and spots location of its prey accurately. As is widely known, when viewed from under water, objects outside the water seem due to the refraction of light, at a different location from where they really are. Therefore, to be able to "hit" a targ outside the water from under the water, one needs to kno the refractive angle of the light and make the "shot" accordingly. However, this fish innately copes with this difficulty and hits the mark every time.

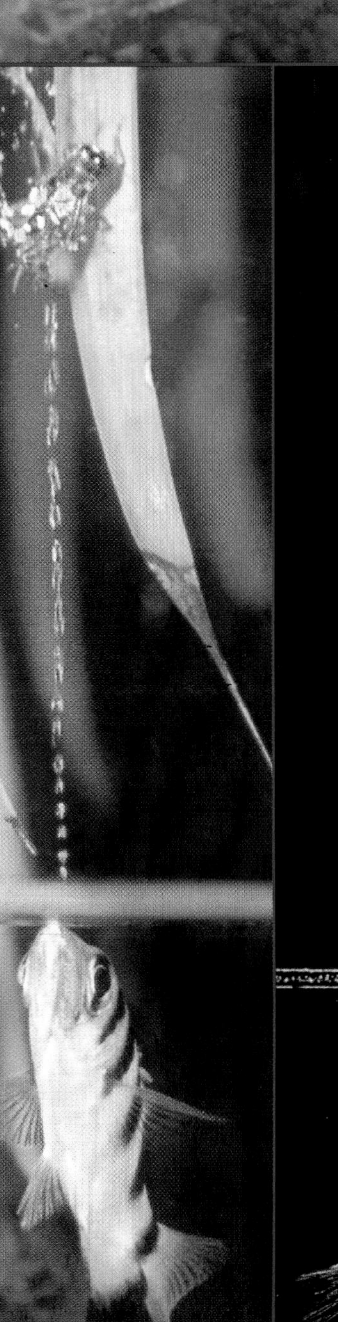

He is Allah - the Creator, the Maker, the Giver of Form. To Him belong the Most Beautiful Names. Everything in the heavens and earth glorifies Him. He is the Almighty, the All-Wise.

(Surat al-Hashr: 24)

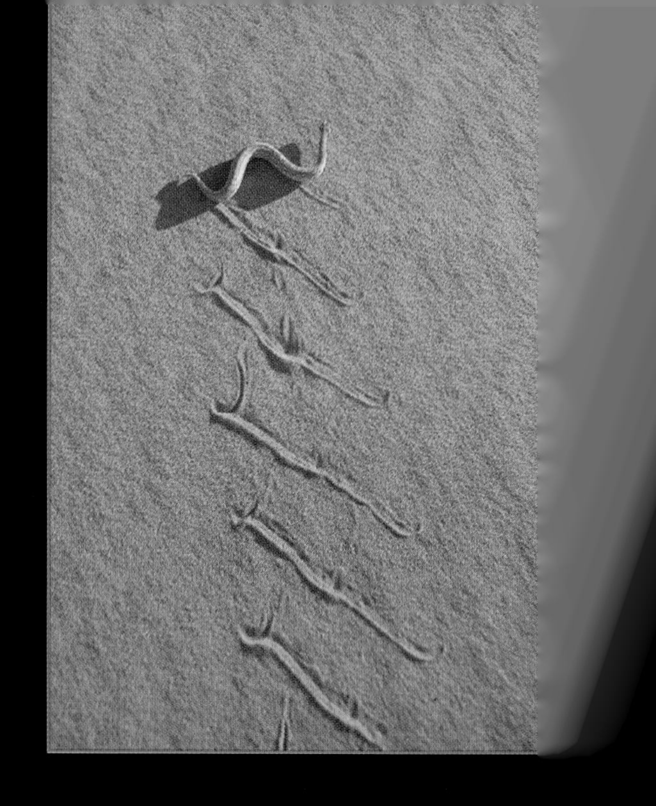

HOW DOES IT MOVE ON THE SA

This desert-dwelling snake can move swiftly on the sand. contracting its chest muscles by degrees, it moves its body S-form.

At the beginning of the movement, it twists its body, lifts head and keeps it poised in the air. As the contraction, w drives the movement, proceeds to the tail, the head move forward and touches the earth. In the meantime, the mot contraction has reached the tail. A fresh wave lifts the tai from the sand and brings it up to the level of the head. Thus, the snake moves forward by leaving parallel traces slope of 45 degrees on average.

Throughout this movement, only two parts of the snake the sand. With this form of movement, the snake's body protected from being scorched by making minimal contac the extremely hot, burning sand.

S
d
ja
c
m
a
O
y
h
c
a
is
th
p
s
w
d

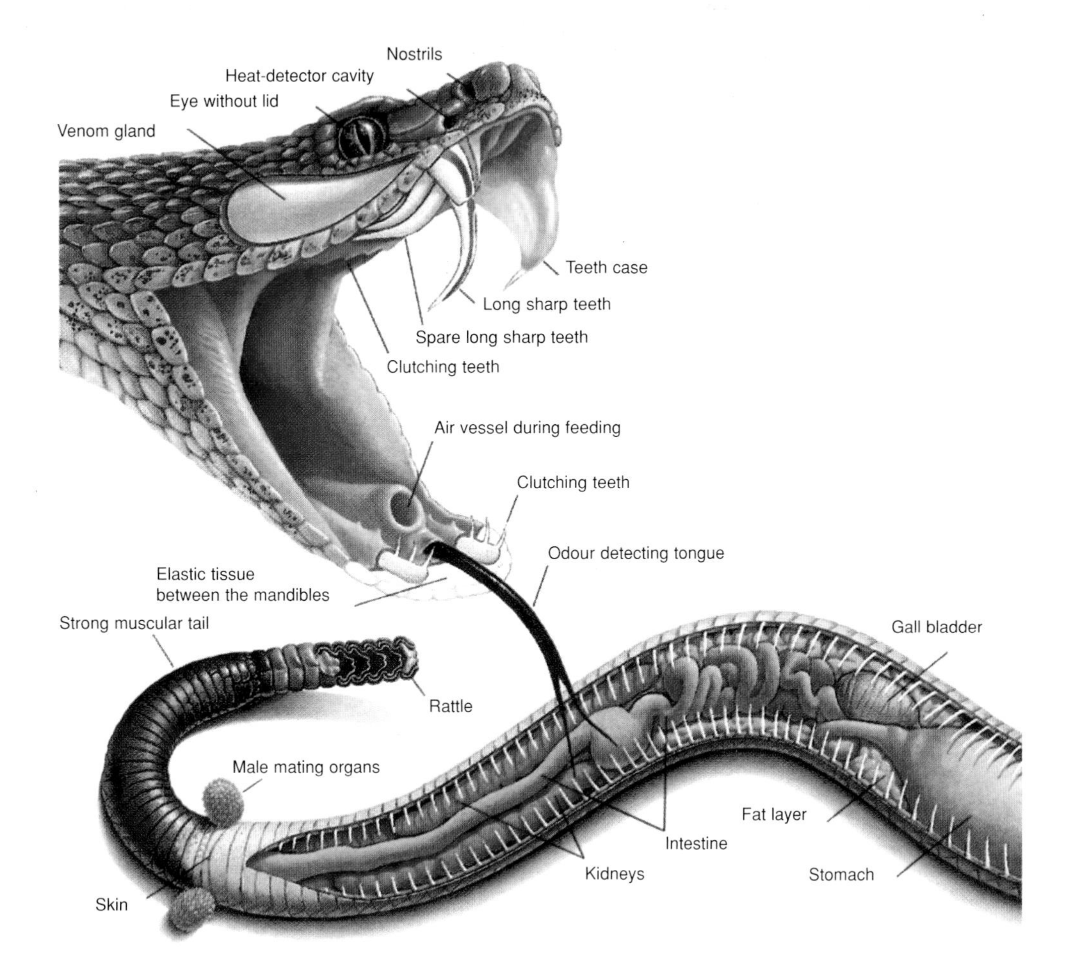

THE RATTLESNAKE

The heat-detectors located in the facial cavities at the anterior of the rattlesnake's head detect the infrared light caused by the body heat of its prey. This detection is so sensitive as to perceive a temperature increase of 1/300 in the heat of the setting. The snake, with the help of its forked-tongue, which is its organ of smell, can sense a motionless red squirrel sitting half a metre away in deep darkness. Fixing the location of its prey faultlessly, the snake first silently sneaks towards it, then comes close enough to attack, arches and stretches its neck and closes upon its target at great speed. By then, it has already inserted the teeth on its strong jaw, which can open to 180 degrees. All of this takes place at a speed equivalent to an automobile's accelerating from 0 km/h up to 90 km/h in half a second. The length of the snake's "venomous teeth", its greatest weapon in rendering its victim ineffective, is about 4 cm. The insides of its teeth are hollow and connected to the glands of venom. As soon as the snake bites, the gland's muscles contract and with great power shoot the poison first into the teeth canal and then under the prey's skin. The snake venom either paralyses the central nervous system of the prey or causes its death by coagulating the blood. Only 0.028 g of some snakes' venom is strong enough to kill 125,000 rats. The poison shows its effects so quickly that the prey does not have time to do any harm to the snake. From now on, all that is left to the snake is to engulf its paralysed prey with its highly flexible mouth.

Though everyone knows the poisonous feature of snakes, almost no one thinks about how this takes place. In fact, an animal's possessing a technology to kill another animal by poison is quite astonishing and extraordinary. Those who insist on denying the existence of Allah are certainly incapable of explaining how snakes possess such an extraordinary skill. The venomous system in the mouth of the snake is a very complex and sophisticated one. In order for this system to function, the snake has to have special "venomous teeth", which are hollow inside, and venomous glands connected to these teeth. A very powerful venom that will paralyse its enemies has to have been formed, and this reflex has to work as soon as the animal bites its prey. This multi-component system would not work with one of its components missing. That would result in the snake's falling prey to the animals it has chosen to hunt. The extraordinary skills of the animal in sensing temperature change and odour show the detailed nature of the design we are facing.

Here, there is an extraordinary and unusual occurrence that we can only term a "miracle". It is, however, out of the question that nature could create a miracle which is "supernatural". Nature is a name given to the entire order we see around us. The founder of this order can surely not be the order itself. The laws of nature are those laws Allah fixed, which set the relationships among those that He created. Defining concepts properly reveals the truth. Confusing concepts, on the other hand, is a characteristic of the unbelievers. They do it to conceal the facts and deny the crystal-clear creation.

LION FISH

After trapping smaller fish in cave-like or rocky shelters, this dazzlingly coloured fish closes their exits by using its fins as a net. Those fish that try to flee face the poisonous spines of the lion fish. The powerful venom of the lion fish takes instant effect and causes the deaths of its victims.

WAR MACHINE: THE SCORPION

Brain

The brain's structure extends from head to tail and consists of fifteen nerve lobes. This structure of the brain provides a great advantage for the animal, allowing it to make quick decisions and to transmit reflexes and all necessary orders to the organs.

Feet

The detectors on its feet help the animal perceive every kind of movement, noise and vibration. These detectors are so sensitive that the scorpion can sense the vibrations caused by a nearby living organism in 1/1000th of a second.

Poisonous sting

The potent poison of scorpions, which is capable of killing a human being, is injected into enemies via the stings located at the back of their body.

Pincers

The function of the scorpion's pincers is to render its victims ineffective before stinging them. Moreover, it can use its pincers to dig the sand and hide under ground.

A robust armour

Its outer covering that wraps it like an armour is sturdy enough to protect it not only from its enemies but also from radiation. The human body has resistance to approximately 600 rads of radiation, whereas the tolerance of scorpions rises as high as 40-150 thousand rads.

Lungs

It has eight air vessels in its abdomen. It continues to breathe easily even if only one of them is open. It can stay under water for two days owing to its strong lungs.

Abdomen

On its underside , the female scorpion bears a pair of unique sense organs called "pectines". With these, it identifies the surface texture and selects the most appropriate place for laying its eggs.

HOOK FISH

When this fish needs to hunt, it sets free the appendage coming out from its head like a hook and begins to wait. The other fish that approach this extension, thinking that it is a small fish, cannot escape falling a prey to the sudden attack of the hunter fish. We all know that a fish has no means to create a hook in its own body, and that such an issue cannot be side-stepped by a senseless explanation such as "it just happened to be so by coincidence".

It brings bait for the fish.

The hunting method of this bird, which feeds on fish, is also very astonishing.
First, the bird finds bait for the fish. It then brings the food to the waterside, leaves it on the water and waits. When small fish cluster around the bait and start to feed on it unaware of what's going on, the bird catches the fish with a sudden move.

It leaves the bait on the water and waits.

The fish cluster around the bait.

And it catches the fish.

With their outward appearance being quite suitable for camouflage, some animals have a great advantage in hunting. For instance, it is impossible to notice the snake above when hidden under the sand. For this snake waiting in ambush, it is quite easy to hunt its prey, which comes right under its nose without realising it.

Another animal endowed with the ability of camouflage is a fish named "the stargazer". This fish hides itself under the sand on the seafloor. Over the mouth of the fish is a tooth-like fringed structure. It comfortably breathes under the sand via this organ, which looks like a tooth and can hardly be distinguished from sand. It waits in ambush for its prey and once it comes close, it rushes out from under the sand and catches it.

A MASTER HUNTER: CHAMELEON

Tongue

The chameleon's tongue is kept collapsed within its mouth like an accordion. In the middle of its tongue is a sharp-ended cartilage. When the circular muscles at the tip of its tongue contract, the tongue shoots out. The animal's tongue is covered with a mucous-like viscous liquid. When it approaches close enough to its prey, it opens its mouth and rapidly hurls its tongue towards its victim. The viscous tongue, owing to the intertwining muscles, reaches as far as 1.5 times the length of the chameleon. The time for the tongue to retrieve the prey and retract is only 0.1 seconds.

Camouflage

The chameleon is certainly the first animal that comes to the mind when camouflage is raised. The chameleon changes its colour according to the ground on which it stands. To the left can be seen the mark made on the coat of the chameleon by the fern left on its back. Light and temperature changes are considered to have a role in the reactions that cause this mark. Yet, the animal is not even aware of its advantageous skill in changing colours. Its body is originally created to automatically match the colours of its surroundings.

This tiger which is perfectly camouflaged, with its agility, powerful jaw, claws, speed and strength, is the perfect hunter. Another characteristic of the tiger is that it never allows the wind to be at its back while tracing its prey, since the wind blowing from behind it would carry its odour to its prey and hence cause it to be noticed.

A few hairs inside the petals of the plant activate the trapping mechanism of the flower.

AN UNCONVENTIONAL HUNTER: THE VENUS PLANT

Besides the predators we have mentioned so far, there are also some plants which "hunt" by using amazing methods. One of these is the "Venus" plant, which catches and feeds on insects that visit it.

The hunting system of this plant works as follows: a fly looking for food among the plants suddenly comes across one which is very attractive: the Venus plant. What makes this plant, which resembles a pair of hands holding a bowl, attractive, is its charming red colour and, more importantly, the sweet scent secreted by the glands surrounding its petals. The fly is charmed by this irresistible smell and lands on the plant without hesitation. While moving towards the origin of the food, it inevitably touches the seemingly harmless hair over the plant. After a short while, the plant suddenly snaps its petals shut. The fly is left tightly compressed between two petals. The Venus plant starts to secrete a "flesh dissolving" liquid, which causes the fly to turn into a jelly-like substance, and then the plant consumes the fly by absorbing it.

The swiftness of the plant in catching the fly is remarkable. The speed of the plant in closing is faster than the fastest closing speed of the hands of a human (if you try to catch a fly sitting on your palm, you most probably would not succeed, but the plant does). How, then, can this plant, which has no muscles or bones, make such an abrupt move?

Research has shown that there exists an electrical system inside the Venus plant. The system works as follows: the strokes of the fly on the hairs of the plant are transmitted to the receptors under the hairs. If this mechanical push is strong enough, these receptors will send electrical signals along the petal, just like waves in a pool. These signals are carried to the motor cells that cause the petals to make sudden moves, and finally the mechanism is activated to swallow the fly.

In addition to the stimulus system of the plant, the mechanical system by which the trap is closed also is created perfectly. As soon as the cells inside the plant receive electrical stimulation, they change the concentration of water within themselves. The cells inside the trap release water from their bodies. This event is like the dying of a deflated balloon. The cells outside the trap, on the other hand, take in excess water and swell. Thus, the trap

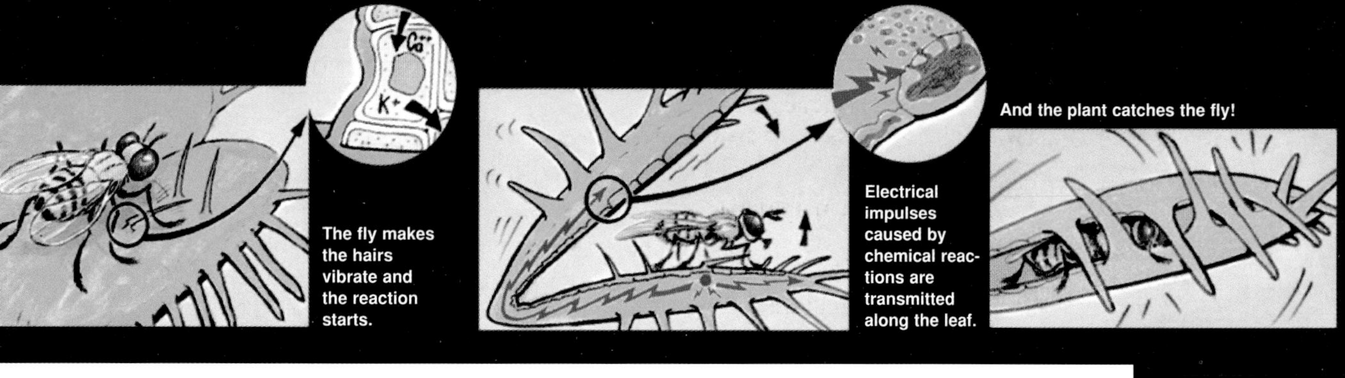

is closed in the same way as when a person, in order to move his arm, needs to have one muscle contract and one relax. The fly trapped inside the plant actually touches the hairy strands repeatedly, causing the propulsive electrical force to discharge again, and making the trap more tightly closed. Meanwhile, the digestive glands in the trap are also activated. As a result of stimulation, these glands kill the insect and start slowly dissolving it. Thus, the plant feeds on digestive fluids that have turned into a bowl of soup enriched by plant proteins. At the end of the digestion, the mechanism that makes the trap close works conversely to open it.

The fly makes the hairs vibrate and the reaction starts.
Electrical impulses caused by chemical reactions are transmitted along the leaf.
And the plant catches the fly!

This system has yet another interesting feature: in order to activate the trap, the hairs have to be touched twice in succession. The first touch generates a static electric charge but the trap is not closed. The trap is only closed with a second touch after the static charge reaches a certain point and discharges. Due to this dual action mechanism, the flytrap is never closed without purpose. For instance, the trap does not become activated as soon as a raindrop falls on it.

Now, let us contemplate this striking system. The whole system has to exist at the same time for the plant to catch its prey and digest it properly. The absence of only one element would mean death for the plant. For instance, if there were no hairs inside the leaf, the plant would not close, as the reaction would never start although the insect would walk all over and inside the plant. If the closing system were there, but if the plant were devoid of secretions to digest the insect, the whole system would be useless. In brief, any element lacking in the system would mean the death of the plant.

This plant, since the moment it was created, must have always possessed the features we refer to here. The plant, no doubt, did not suddenly transform into a hunter. It is certainly not the "magical spell of coincidences" that has made the plant such a professional hunter.

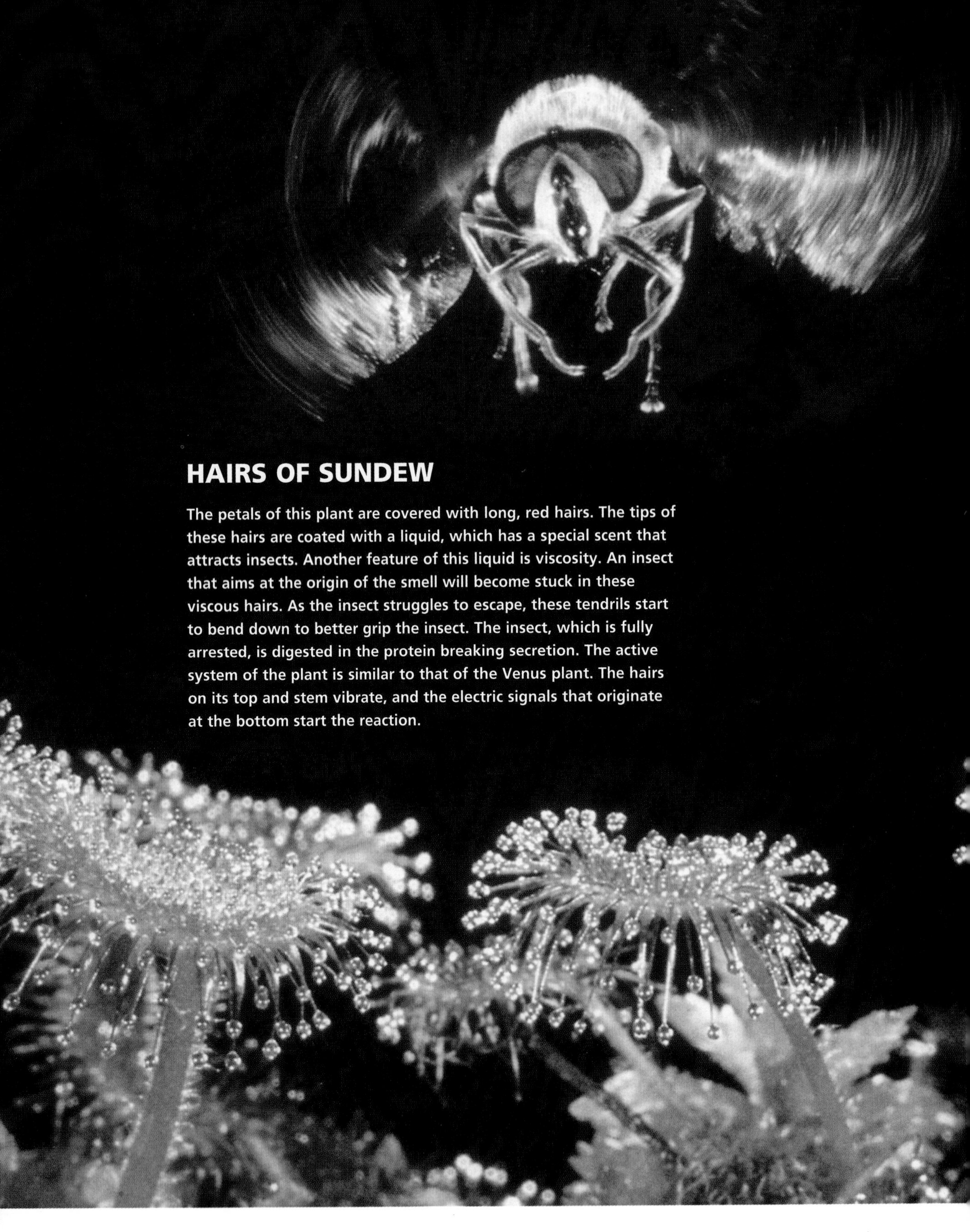

HAIRS OF SUNDEW

The petals of this plant are covered with long, red hairs. The tips of these hairs are coated with a liquid, which has a special scent that attracts insects. Another feature of this liquid is viscosity. An insect that aims at the origin of the smell will become stuck in these viscous hairs. As the insect struggles to escape, these tendrils start to bend down to better grip the insect. The insect, which is fully arrested, is digested in the protein breaking secretion. The active system of the plant is similar to that of the Venus plant. The hairs on its top and stem vibrate, and the electric signals that originate at the bottom start the reaction.

The most important point is that this proficient hunter does not have the capacity to think. If this living being were not a plant but an animal, then the advocates of evolution would possibly claim that the animal had progressed by itself with the estimable contributions (!) of "nature". What we are talking abo-

ut here is that this system is found in a plant, a being with no brain or similar structure, and which is certainly unconscious. The plant is not even aware that it is hunting. It, too, is already created with a system by which it can feed itself without any effort just like all other plants.

DEFENCE TECHNIQUES

The animal on the right page is not a snake but a tiny caterpillar, simply a tiny "caterpillar". This animal protects itself from its enemies by its similarity to a snake. When attacked by an enemy, this tiny creature calmly turns its tail towards its enemy and puffs it up. At that moment, a dreadful snake shows up right in the face of the enemy, which has no other choice than to run away and save itself.

The caterpillar's tail looks so much like a snake that even the sparkle of the eye, within the dark spots that stand for the snake's eyes, is not left out. As an extremely slow-mover and thus a very easy prey for its enemies, the caterpillar successfully escapes from many dangers owing to this extraordinary feature of its body.

How did the caterpillar acquire such a trait? Such a striking "design" must unquestionably have a satisfactory explanation. Now, let us examine the scenarios that could be fabricated as an answer to this question:

Scenario 1: Many years ago, a caterpillar looking for ways to protect itself from enemy attacks, started carefully observing its surroundings. It one day realised that all its enemies are afraid of snakes. At that moment, it looked at its body and decided to make it "look like" a snake. (We cannot provide an explanation as to how it would manage to make its body look like a snake's, how it would set up its outward appearance, the colour of its skin and the shape of its body to look like a snake! Let us say that it would "do its best, force itself and, in the end, do something". It, however, had a very limited time to "change". For it would spend a very short time of its life as a caterpillar, and then it would become a butterfly and fly.

It is very important that nothing was left out as it "changed" its body, because it had only one chance to test its new tail. If the first trial was not successful and if it could not deceive its enemy, all its efforts would be wasted, and on top of that it would lose its life. Certainly, it had to survive during this self-re-construction process. However, chance was on its side and it did not fall prey to its enemies. Finally, it achieved the difficult task and "made" its tail look like a snake.

Scenario 2: trees, flowers, insects, the sky, water, rain, sun and, in brief, all

This animal, which looks like a dreadful snake, is in fact nothing but a caterpillar that is only a few centimetres long.

powers prevalent on earth united to establish a system for themselves and simply added a tail to the caterpillar within this system!

Scenario 3: The great power called 'coincidence' (!) has added a snake-like tail to the caterpillar just as it gave various things to all living beings.

One does not have to be very intelligent to see the inconsistency in these scenarios, all based on the Theory of Evolution. Neither is the caterpillar an attentive and observant designer, nor has the earth itself a system that has the ability to design and create. In other words, neither can a living thing interfere in its own body to acquire advanced features or change itself into another species, nor is there a mechanism outside of it to do this. (This subject is described in detail in the chapter on the Theory of Evolution.)

Those who regard nature as a highly skilled machine and believe such things as "nature discovered", "wonder of nature", "mother nature", etc., know very well that what they mean by "nature" is the air, water, earth, trees, flowers and insects. In short, they mean the whole world and the solar system in which our world is located. If people were told that all living things were "made by the world" or "produced by the earth", they would most probably laugh. However, propaganda using the words "nature-cosmos" makes people regard nature almost like a conscious being. One must not forget that nature is the name of the extraordinarily orderly and perfect system we view, not the name of its establisher and eternal life-bestower. Allah created all living beings on earth and they continue to live, along with whatever features Allah has endowed them.

In this chapter of the book, we are going to review the defence systems of some animals in nature. While doing this, we have to keep in mind a very important point: much of nature is based on a continuous relationship between living things that hunt and that are hunted. This relationship rests on such a delicate bal-

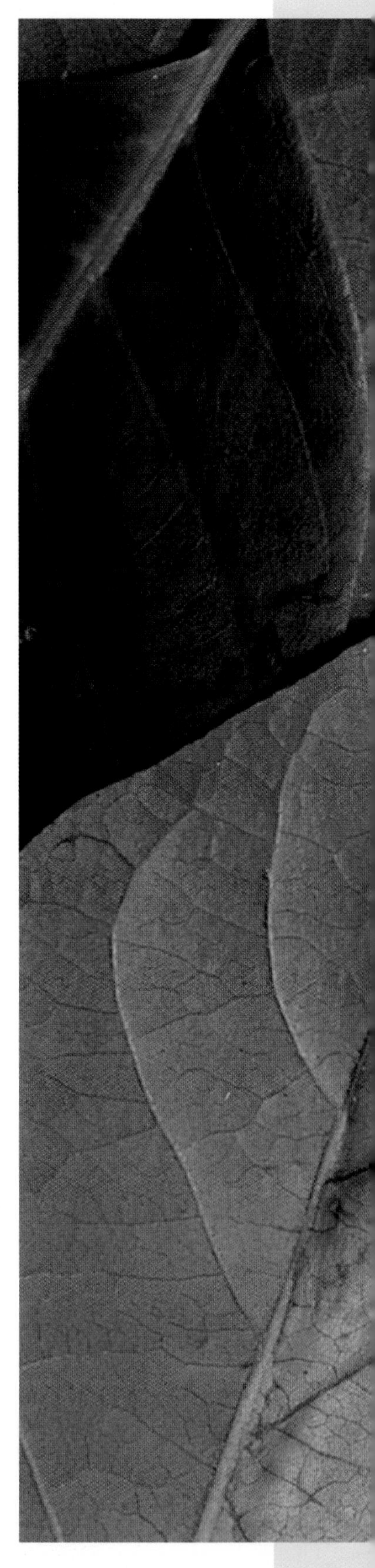

Allah is the Creator of everything and He is Guardian over everything. (Surat az-Zumar: 62)

ance that for millions of years, millions of species have been feeding on other species, yet none of them have disappeared. If one of the important species within the hunting chain became extinct, a great discord would be aroused. For instance, if the anteater species became extinct, then ants would invade vast areas in a very short time.

This predator-prey relationship between living things is carried out in great harmony unless human beings intervene. The most important elements in the system that maintains the perpetuity of this balance are the hunting and defence mechanisms of these animals. In previous chapters, we saw that some animals are created with very extraordinary hunting skills and thus are "provided". If nature were full of living beings equipped with such aggressive systems, then they would excessively devour those animals on which they prey and cause them to be extinct. When those animals were exterminated, those who feed on them would starve and nature would end in total destruction.

However, this problem is already settled within the system Allah established. As "hunter" animals are equipped with perfect attack systems, prospective preys are also equipped with perfect defence systems. The skills of both sides balance each other. In addition, these extraordinary skills give man the opportunity to come to know the infinite might, wisdom and knowledge of Allah, the Creator of all these skills.

Every living being is brought into being with distinct skills to defend itself. Some are very swift; they can save themselves by running away. Some cannot move but are covered with strong armour. Some have amazing "fear-creating" skills like the caterpillar described earlier. Some pour poisonous, burning or stinking gasses on their enemies. Still others are endowed with the ability to pretend they are dead. There are yet others created with bodies that are extraordinarily suitable for camouflage.

In the following pages, we will examine some of the most amazing and striking examples of these defence systems. Needless to say, however, that these are only specific examples and other living beings are endowed with thousands of interesting systems that we cannot possibly mention here, some of which even are not yet discovered by mankind. All of these systems reveal that there is no "want of proportion" in the universe Allah created and that His power, wisdom and knowledge are boundless, as Allah mentions in Surat al-Mulk:

> **He Who created the seven heavens in layers. You will not find any flaw in the creation of the All-Merciful. Look again - do you see any gaps? Then look again and again. Your sight will return to you dazzled and exhausted! (Surat al-Mulk: 3-4)**

COUNTERFEITING DEATH OR INJURY

Other than a few exceptions, most predators prefer live animals as bait. Carcass flesh is not preferred. This tendency forms the basis of the defence of some living species.

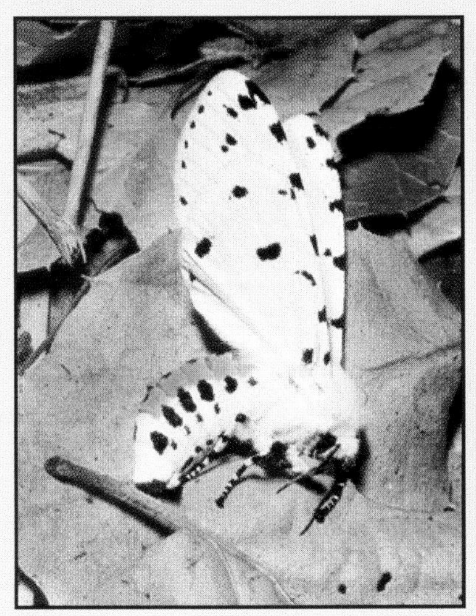

▲ The Tiger moth fakes its death, too. It, however, has yet another tactic. When it falls on one side, its orange body is seen. This bright colour is a warning to the hunter, which implies that the moth tastes bad. The moth unquestionably has neither the wisdom to devise this "tactic", nor the skill to turn the colour of its body into a colour suggesting to the enemy that it tastes bitter. It is just created with this interesting skill.

▲ In order to drive away animals heading for its offspring, the Rain Bird lowers one of its wings as if it was broken, and attracts the enemy towards itself by dragging its wing on the ground as if injured. It allows the enemy to follow it until the nest is fully secure. When it is fully convinced that the enemy is far enough from the nest, it stops play-acting and rushes back to its offspring.

The Hognose snake protects itself by mimicking its death. It turns face upwards, opens its mouth and stays in this position without moving at all, like a dead snake. ▼

◀ The animal called Opossum is created in such a way as to protect itself by counterfeiting its death. Thinking it is just a carcass, its enemy disregards it. It acts out its role so well that its heartbeat slows down to the point of stopping. Its ability to slow its heartbeats is unquestionably not a skill the animal subsequently acquired, but one that was given to it during its creation.

CHEMICAL WEAPONS

Some living beings can produce within their organisms quite complex chemical compounds, which if humans tried to make them would require very high technology and laboratory precision; the animals make them quite easily. Here are some of them:

Bombardier Beetle

The name of the animal you see in the picture is the "Bombardier Beetle". The defence method of this beetle is not like that of other animals. In moments of danger, a mixture of two chemicals (hydrogen peroxide and hydroquinone) that is previously stored in a storage chamber is transferred to an explosion chamber. With the accelerative effect of a special catalyst (peroxidase) secreted from the walls of the "explosion chamber", the mixture turns into a horrible chemical weapon at 100°C. Scalded by the boiling chemical substance squirted with pressure, the enemy panics and gives up the hunt.

If we look for an answer to the question "how did this extremely complex defence mechanism come into existence?", we see that it is impossible for this insect to have developed this mechanism "by itself".

How could an insect make the formulae for two different chemicals that explode on contact? Let us assume it did, how could it secrete and store these in its body? Let us assume it did, how could it form a storage chamber and an explosion chamber in its body for these chemicals? Even if it "achieved" all of these, how could it devise the formula of a catalyst that would speed up the reaction of these two chemicals? It must also, after all, insulate the walls of the "explosion room" and the walls of the channel through which it squirts the mixture with a flame-resistant alloy so as not to burn itself.

The operations "performed" by the beetle cannot even be performed by human beings, with the exception of chemists. Unquestionably, chemists can perform such an operation not within their bodies, but only in laboratories!

It is certainly unreasonable to think that the beetle is such a specialised chemist and a miraculous designer as to be able to organise its body according to the reaction it will trigger. It is obvious that the beetle performs these operations only as a reflex, unaware of the outcome. No creature with such a superior power and wisdom exists in nature. Humans cannot make such a creature. Creating such a complex creature aside, scientists have not even been able to make a protein - one of the simplest foundational chemicals of life - although they have samples of it in their hand.

It is obvious that a being that has exalted knowledge and power - Allah - created the animal. The "Bombardier Beetle", just as billions of other things that are created, is only one example of His boundless power and matchless creation.

THE ACIDIC DEFENCE OF THE RED-FACED CATERPILLAR

The red-faced caterpillar, which has a similar defence system to that of the bombardier beetle, squirts an acid it produces in its own body at its attackers. It, too, just as the bombardier beetle, is not an extraordinary chemist, a magical biologist or a miraculous designer, but a "sign" created as an example of the existence and power of Allah.

THE SMELL BOMBS OF THE SKUNK AND MARROW BUG

The sole feature of the chemical substance that skunks (on the left) squirt on their enemies is its awful smell. This disgusting and permanent smell is enough to protect them from their enemies. The marrow bug you see above is another animal with the same defence mechanism.

THE ADVANTAGES OF RESEMBLANCE

The picture on the top belongs to a bee, and the one below belongs to a fly. Owing to this resemblance, enemies of the fly stay away from it thinking that it is a bee. In addition to the resemblance of the fly to the bee, it has also a buzzing feature just like bees. Moreover, when attacked by an enemy, this fly takes the aggressive position of bees by lifting its wings upwards and bending its body forward.

The Viceroy butterfly on the left tastes good to birds. Yet, its similarity to the Monarch butterfly (above) largely protects it from the threats of birds.

The savage Aspidontus fish benefits from its resemblance to the Cleaner fish (in the picture below both are seen one on top of one another). It comes near to the fish that hope to be cleaned up and tears pieces from their tails and fins.

ARMOURS AND SPIKES

Some animals move extremely slowly and do not have the chance to run away and hide from their enemies. There is yet another defence mechanism given to them: their armours and spikes.

At an instant of danger, this reptile takes its tail in its mouth and forms a circular shape. Meanwhile, the armour covering its whole body protects it from all kinds of external dangers.

The hedgehog is the most famous of all the animals that protect themselves with their spikes. The animal, which moves very slowly, would surely have disappeared millions of years ago were it not protected by such a system. The protection method that enables its survival is assuredly neither "thought up" nor "produced" by it, nor brought into existence by coincidence. The animal is simply created like that and that is all.

The pill bug rolls inside, takes the shape of a ball at a moment of danger, and is protected, thanks to its strong shell.

The pangolin's hard armour looks like a cone. When it curls up, the armour on it pricks up. Almost no animal can open this sharp-edged armour.

CAMOUFLAGE

Some animals are protected by their body structures and appearances, which are extremely adaptable to their habitat. Camouflage features Allah bestowed upon those animals are so harmonious with their habitat that when you look at their pictures, you cannot tell whether they are plants or animals. Sometimes you cannot distinguish the animal from its surroundings. The camouflage is so effective and deft that it is obvious that this is a specially designed and "created" defence mechanism.

IS IT A DRY LEAF OR A BUTTERFLY?

At first glance, perceived as dry leaves, these pictures (above and below) actually are of butterflies. The leaf-like wings, which have many details on them - vessels to rotten parts and intonations of colour - provide an excellent protection for the butterflies.
It is indeed impossible to overlook this incredible resemblance between the butterfly and the leaf (even the vessels and dried parts of the leaf are not omitted) and call it "chance". Is it not equally nonsense to accept that the butterfly made itself "leaf-like"?

Three butterflies camouflaged on tree trunks.

THE MANTIS

is one of those insects that are created in harmony with their habitat. They conceal themselves sometimes on leaves, and sometimes on branches. The only weapon they have is the shape and colour of their bodies. In this way, they hide from their enemies.

It is quite difficult to distinguish the mantis from the orchid on which it perches.

This mantis looks so similar to the leaf it lies on that the butterfly, which has come to take nectar from the flower, has not even noticed it. It certainly has had to pay for this with its life.

This branch, which seems as if full with flowers, has only scores of caterpillars on it.

It is not so easy to distinguish the yellow spider, which has concealed itself in order to hunt flies, from the flower on which it lies.

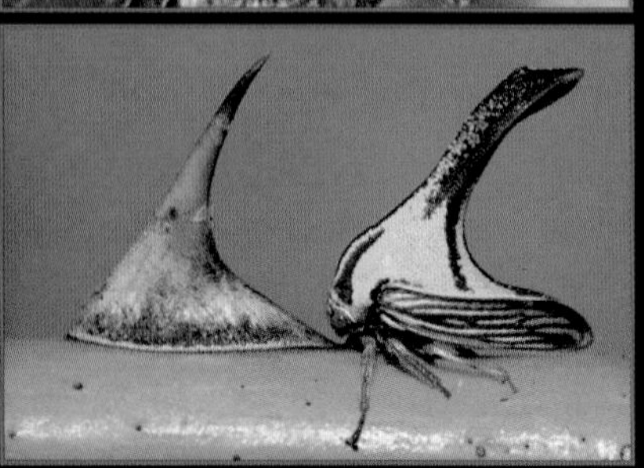

A leaf louse resembling a spike.

The lives of grasshoppers that feed on leaves pass naturally among the leaves. Because the colour of their bodies resembles that of leaves, it is generally not possible for their greatest enemies, lizards and birds, to notice them. Thus, grasshoppers live and feed in safety.
No one can claim that grasshoppers were transformed to "become like leaves" because they spent time besides leaves, or that they somehow turned themselves into leaves.
It is clear that the leaf-eating grasshoppers were created along with such a camouflage so that they could survive.

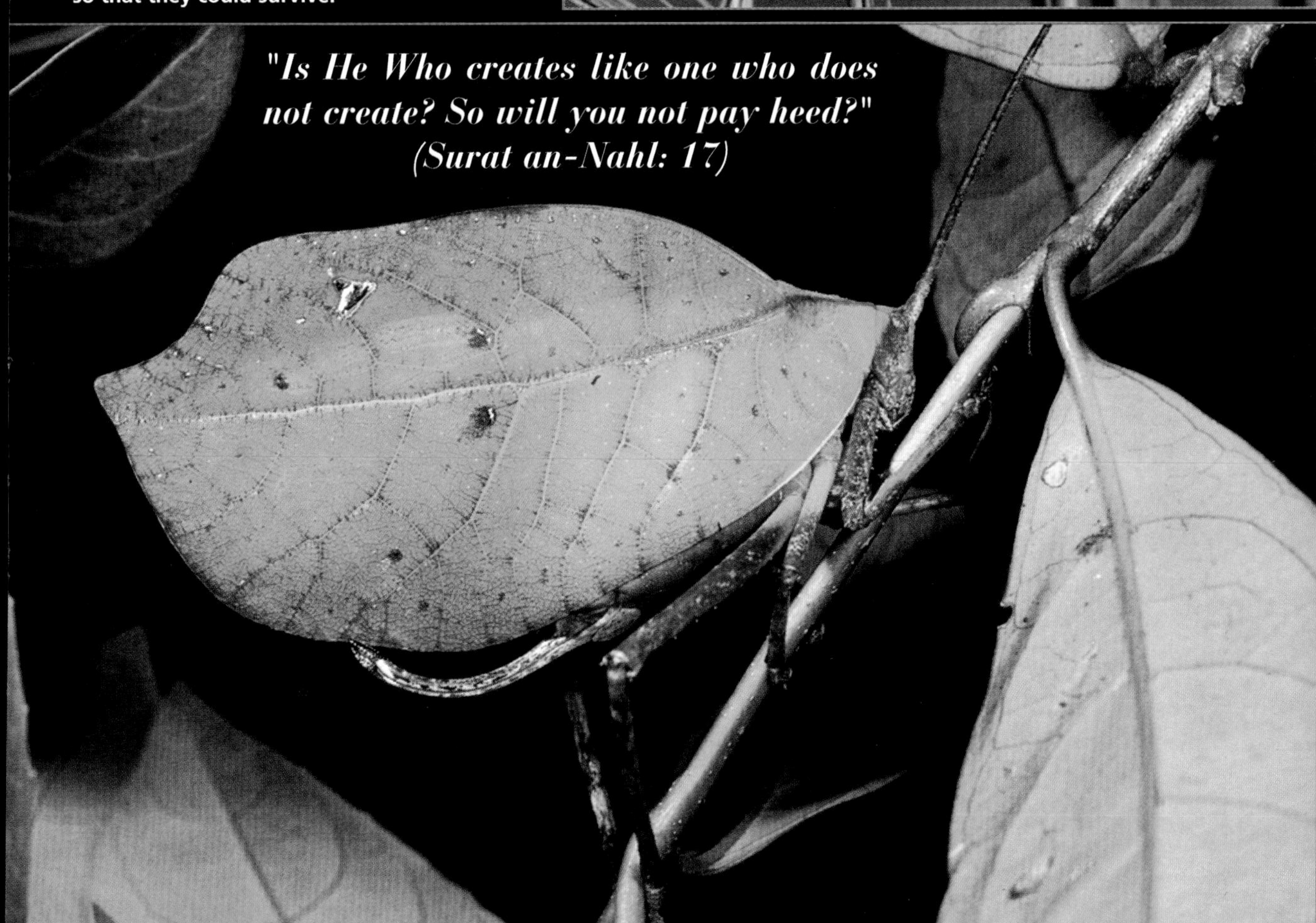

"Is He Who creates like one who does not create? So will you not pay heed?"
(Surat an-Nahl: 17)

Another example of a creature vith camouflage: a frog having exactly he same skin colour as the pattern on he tree trunk.

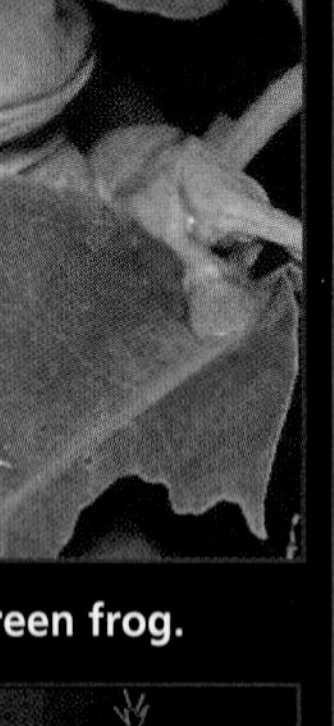

Green leaves and a green frog.

There is a caterpillar among the leaves!

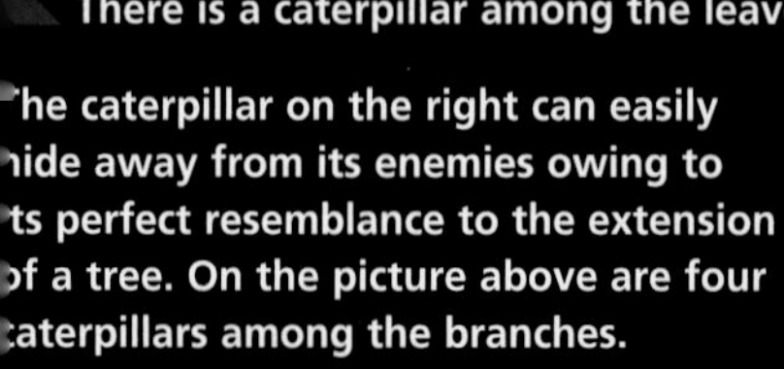

he caterpillar on the right can easily nide away from its enemies owing to ts perfect resemblance to the extension of a tree. On the picture above are four aterpillars among the branches.

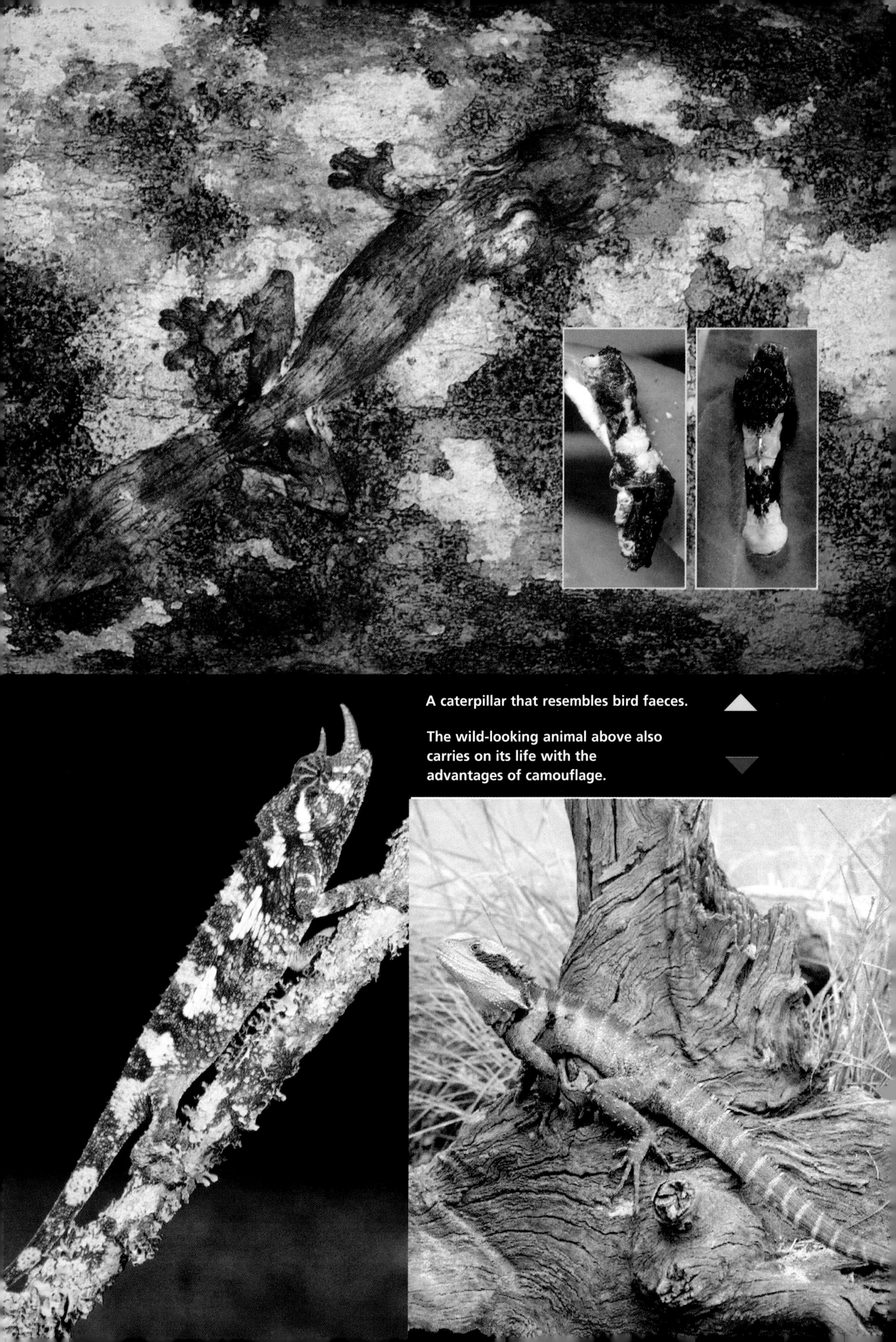

A caterpillar that resembles bird faeces.

The wild-looking animal above also carries on its life with the advantages of camouflage.

Gobies appear no different from rocks covered with moss and plankton.

It is hard to distinguish the Minnow fish among the pebbles even in a shallow pool.

Among the stones are exactly thirteen horned lizards.

The snake on the left can camouflage itself perfectly on the forest floor covered with leaves. The colour of its skin provides it a great advantage during hunting as well as defence.

It is quite difficult to distinguish snakes among the leaves.

ALTERNATING FUR COLOUR ACCORDING TO THE SEASON AND GROUND

The characteristic common to the bird at the top and the rabbit at the bottom is that the colours of their feathers change according to the season. These animals put on pure white clothes in winter months whereas they take on a new look in the spring in accordance with the colour of the soil and vegetation.
Changing colours according to habitat is realised through very complex mechanisms in the animals' bodies. These mechanisms, which can be said to resemble the tanning of human skin under the sun, cause colour changes in the coat and fur of the animals. Just as we cannot prevent our body from tanning or burning under the sun (except by utilising special methods of protection), the animals too have no control over the changes in their bodies. The important thing is that this feather change provides a great protection for the animal. Turning white on snowy winter days and ochre in other seasons, its feathers provide great camouflage for the animal.

It could well have been the reverse; the animal could have been ochre in winter and pure white in summer, or it could never have changed colour. In short, there is an obvious wisdom and calculation in the alternation of the colours according to the seasons. The animal cannot estimate and control this. Certainly the One Who created the animal endowed it with such a protection.

The colour of the gazelle, which is the same as the pasture, is a great advantage for the animal.

The colours and patterns of the birds' feathers, birds that nest on the ground, provide them a perfect disguise among the leaves. The eggs of these birds have also the same kind of colours and pattern so that they too can go unnoticed.

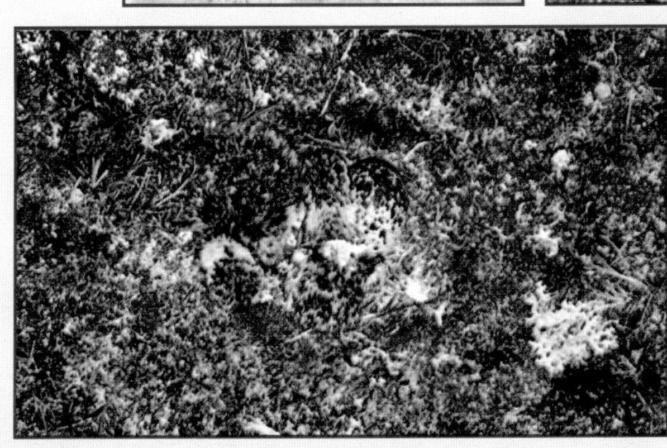

THE PRIVILEGE OF RED

The protection of some animals depends on the discouraging effect of red. For instance, in a moment of danger, the tree grasshopper shows the red on its back to its enemy, while crabs disclose the red colour in their pincers. The interesting thing is that the red part in the animal's body is located in such a place that it is normally not seen yet can easily be disclosed in a moment of danger. This helps it create an "effect which is "shocking" to the attacker.

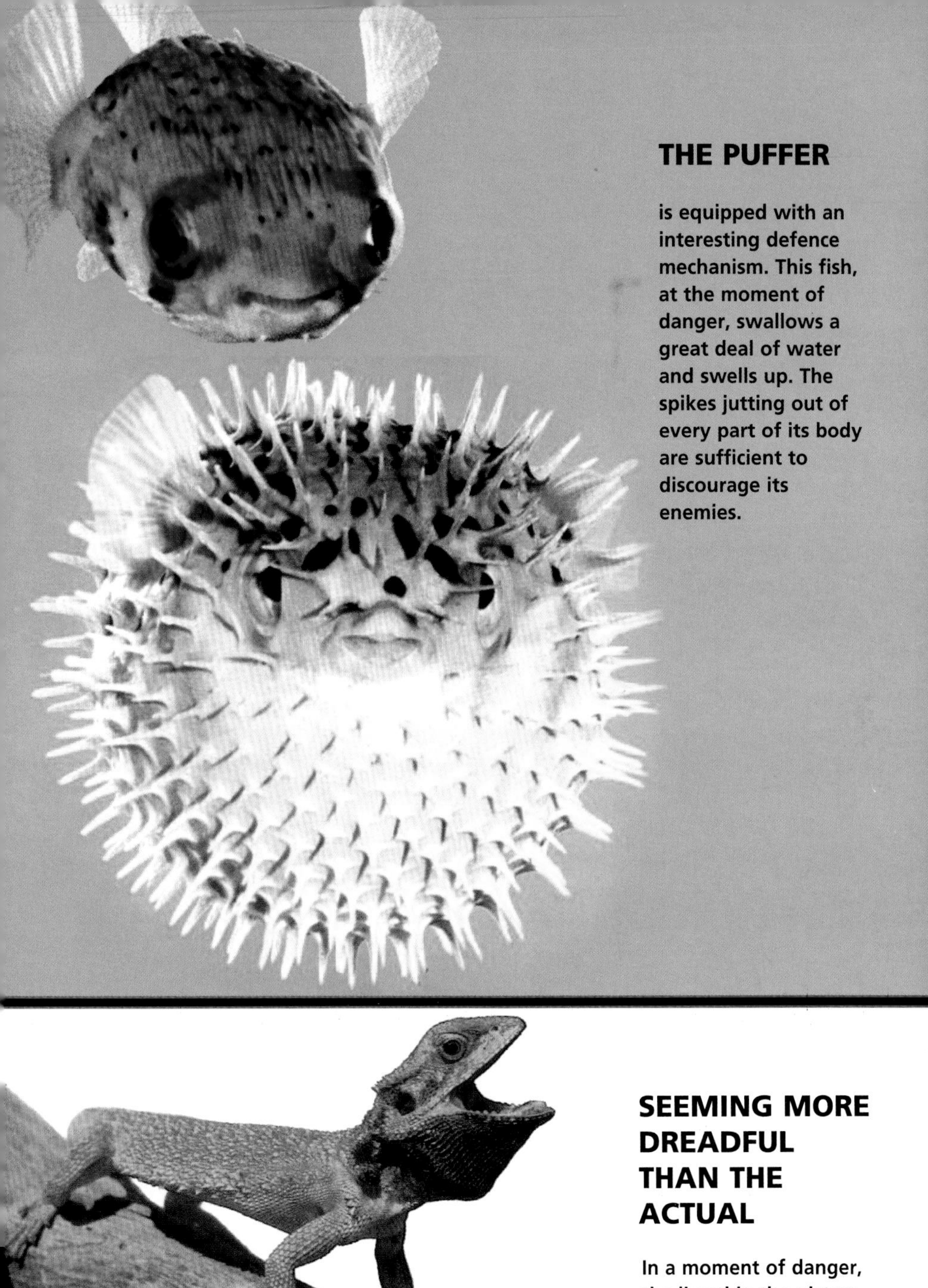

THE PUFFER

is equipped with an interesting defence mechanism. This fish, at the moment of danger, swallows a great deal of water and swells up. The spikes jutting out of every part of its body are sufficient to discourage its enemies.

SEEMING MORE DREADFUL THAN THE ACTUAL

In a moment of danger, the lizard in the picture swells itself and makes its body seem far greater than it really is. When it swells up, a mane emerging around its head makes it look even more terrifying.

FALSE EYES

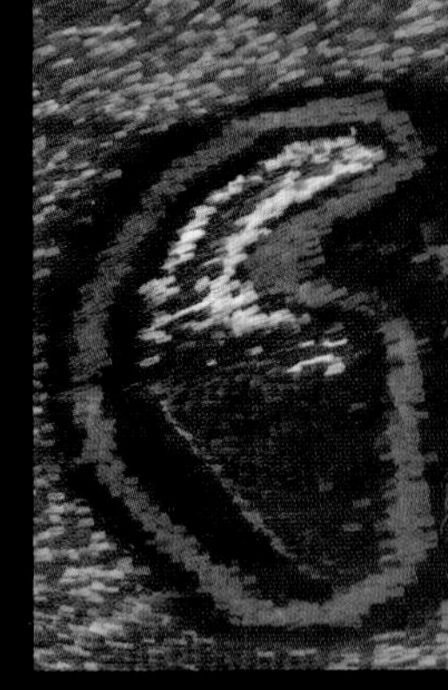

Another admirable and amazing method of defence is "false eyes". There are figures on the bodies of some animals that can be called "false eyes". The "false eyes" are so convincing that other animals that wish to hunt these animals cannot escape thinking that they face a much bigger animal. On the other hand, the animals possessing these "false eyes" enjoy the comfort of this trait of which they are not even aware.

When some butterflies open their wings, we encounter a pair of eyes, with all their symmetry and detail. These eyes alone are more than sufficient to convince their enemies that what they face is not a butterfly. Particularly, the false faces of some butterfly species such as the Shonling butterfly, seen below, are so perfect with their shiny eyes, facial features, frowning eyebrows, mouth and nose that the overall picture is quite discouraging to most of its enemies.
It is impossible to claim that this extraordinary picture emerged as the result of "an interesting coincidence". When the below picture is examined in detail, we understand that these facial features cannot have been formed by chance. Can coincidence make symmetry? Can coincidence form the same colours and designs in two different places? Certainly not. This claim is quite meaningless and unscientific.
Could the butterfly possibly make this system on its own, thinking that it would be useful? The answer to that question is certainly "no".
It is out of the question that a caterpillar with a life span of a few weeks could play on its own colours, designs, and make a drawing surpassing even that of artists, and use this for defence purposes. Like all other living things, Allah also created these beings with "false eyes". The owner of their flawless design is certainly Allah, the Sustainer of all the Worlds.

This bird, which lives in tropical forests, suddenly opens its wings when an enemy attacks its offspring, its eggs or itself. The sudden appearance of two brightly-coloured shapes on the wings proves dissuasive to its enemies.

Above are the real head and eyes of the thornback ray fish.

False organs work not only for frightening but also for escape. The tail part of the moth in the below picture has the look of a head with antennae. This shape causes attackers to head towards the tail of the moth, taking it for the head. The moth also misleads the attacker by turning its back. This target-confusing operation helps the moth gain time to escape. The same "false head" look is also seen in the butterfly below.

The thornback ray fish swims into its nest and leaves its tail outside. On the tail is a pair of "eyes". Other fish around it do not dare to approach it as the false eyes in the tail make them think that it is awake.

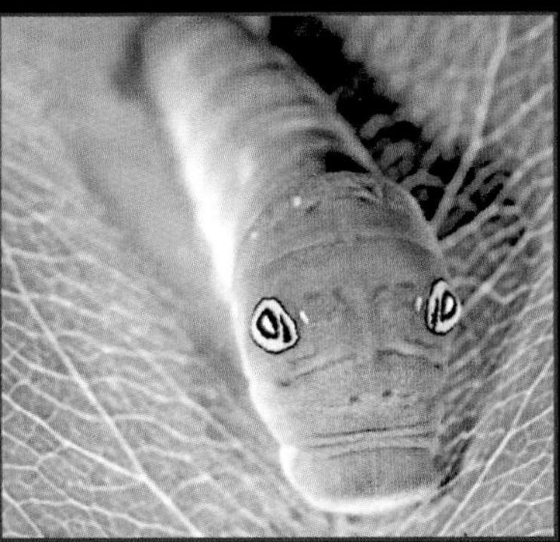

This green caterpillar can protect itself from its enemy thanks to the false eyes on its tail.

AMAZING ARCHITECTS

In the previous pages, we reviewed the wondrous features of the honeybee. We saw how the bee colony constructs the great architectural wonder of the hive, the intricate and subtle plans they employ while constructing it, and the jobs they automatically perform, which are quite hard even for men.

As mentioned previously, bees are able to do this extraordinarily hard work not because they are cleverer than men, but because they are "inspired" so. Otherwise, it would not be possible for thousands of unconscious animals to accomplish such a hard and complicated operation, which needs control and supervision from one centre.

However, bees are not the only excellent architects in nature. In the following pages, we will look at other animals, which very skilfully overcome very complicated and difficult "construction" works, as difficult as that of the bees. These animals, just like the bees, use the knowledge "inspired" in them and construct architectural wonders by the help of some interesting qualities given to them at their creation.

Beavers are the first among the excellent architects in nature that come to mind. These animals build their lodges in stationary ponds, but these ponds are special in being artificially formed by dams beavers build over the stream.

Beavers set about building a dam in order to block the stream and form a stationary pond in which they can build a lodge for themselves. For this purpose, they first push thick branches down into the stream-bed. Then they heap up relatively thinner ones over those heavier ones. They are yet faced with the problem that the running water might take this mass of branches away. Unless the dam is clamped tight to the streambed, the running water would soon damage the dam. The best thing to do to prevent the dam from being ruined by the water is to drive stakes into the streambed and to build the dam on these stakes. For this reason, beavers use large stakes as main buttresses when they build their dam. They, however, do not bother to drive these stakes into the streambed, but fix these stakes in the water by weighing them down with stones. Lastly, they fasten the branches they have piled up with a special mortar they make from clay and dead leaves. This mortar is water-resistant and is very firm against the corrosive effect of water.

The dam built by beavers blocks the water at an angle of exactly 45°. This means that the animal does not build its dam by throwing branches in the water at random, but in a carefully planned manner. What deserves attention here is that all modern hydro-electrical power stations are built at the same angle today. In addition, beavers do not make the mistake of completely blocking the water. They build the dam in such a way that it keeps the water at the desired level and leaves special canals for excess water to run through.

The beaver is full of special design characteristics for the construction work it performs.
The most important tools of the animal are its teeth. It constructs dams with branches that it has nibbled and cut down. Naturally, its teeth frequently wear away, erode and break. Had it not been especially equipped with a special system for this work, it would shortly lose its teeth and die from starvation.
However, as we have mentioned, the problem of the animal has been settled from the very start. Its four front teeth, which it uses for nibbling trees, continue to grow throughout its life. How have the teeth gained such a feature? Did the beaver decide to grow them after seeing its teeth break? Did the teeth of the beaver that constructed the first dam suddenly begin to grow? Apparently, the animal has been created possessing such a feature. That this is a special creation can be sensed from the fact that the size of the back teeth stays constant. If all the teeth of the animal had kept growing, the back teeth that are not worn away would grow excessively, force the jaw of the animal and make its mouth unusable. However, only the four teeth at the front grow, i.e., the ones it uses for nibbling trees.

In addition to its teeth, many other organs of the beaver are especially created in compliance with the work it does. It has transparent curtains that prevent the eye from being damaged while working under water, special valves to prevent water from entering its nose and ears, broad back feet enabling it to move like a fish under water, and a flat, wide and hard tail. These are some distinctive features the animal possesses from its creation.

Dam
Ventilation opening
Sleeping, eating area
Grooming area (for drying and cleaning fur)
Emergency exit
Bottom of pond

TERMITES TOWERS

The role of termites among the architects of nature is indisputable. Termites, which look very much like ants, live in imposing nests they make out of soil. The height of these nests reach up to 6 m, and their width up to 12 m. The most interesting thing is that these animals are blind.

The construction material of the nest is a hard resistant mortar which workers make by blending their saliva with soil. The most extraordinary aspect of the construction art of termites is that they provide continuous air to the colony and keep the heat and moisture amazingly constant. The hard and thick walls of the towers they make from soil seclude the inner part of the nest from the heat outside. For air circulation, they make special corridors along the inner walls of the nest. On the other hand, pores continuously filter the air.

For the oxygen needed by the inhabitants of a middle-sized nest, 1,500 litres of air are required every day. If this air were taken directly into the nest, the temperature of the nest would rise to a level that would be extremely risky for termites. However, they have taken precautions against this as if they knew what would later befall them.

They make damp cellars under the nest as a protection against excessive heat. Species living in the Sahara dig an irrigation canal 40 m underground and provide that water reaches the nest by evaporation. The thick walls of the tower help maintain interior humidity.

Temperature control, just like humidity control, is done in a very sensible and sensitive manner. The air outside passes through thin corridors lying on the surface of the nest, enters moist cellars and reaches a hall at the top of the nest; there, air warms by contacting the bodies of insects and rises. Thus, an air circulation system, which is continuously inspected by colony workers, is provided by way of simple physical principles.

Outside the nest, a roof - which is sloped as a protection against floods - and gutters strike the eye.

How do these living beings, with brains smaller than a cubic millimetre and devoid of the sense of sight, accomplish such a complex construction?

The work of termites certainly is the outcome of collective work among those creatures. Saying that "the insects dig independent tunnels and these happen to be in accord with each other" would be sheer nonsense. At this point, however, we face a question: how do these animals work in harmony while performing this complex job? We all know that when such a construction is made by men, beforehand the construction is drawn by an architect, then the plans are distributed to the workers, and all the construction is organised in a work site. How could termites, which have no such communication among

Being no taller than a few centimetres, termites can erect towers many meters high without using any tools. This admirable nest perfectly protects the inhabitant termite colony with a population of over a million from their enemies and unfavourable external life conditions.

them, and which are, after all, blind, manage to make this giant construction in harmony?

An experiment on the issue helps us find the answer to this question.

In the experiment, as a first step, a termite nest that was already in construction was split into two. Throughout the construction, the two termite groups were prevented from contacting one another. The result was surprising. What finally came to sight were not two separate nests, but two pieces of one nest. When the pieces were brought together, it was observed that all the corridors and canals fitted one another.

How can this be explained? First, it is obvious that not all the termites possess the necessary information on the construction of the termite nest as a whole. A termite can have knowledge only of one part of the process in which it is involved. We then may conclude that the place where all information is stored is the termite community as a whole. Therefore, here we may talk about a greater knowledge. Such knowledge can only be said to exist at the level of a community of individuals of the same species. This is not the only example. For instance, when flying as a mass, grasshoppers usually fly towards a specific direction. If we take one grasshopper out of this group and put it in a box, it immediately loses its orientation, and panic-stricken, tries to fly in all directions. If we put the box among the flying mass, the grasshopper finds the right direction and begins to fly in a single direction, the direction in which the whole mass flies!

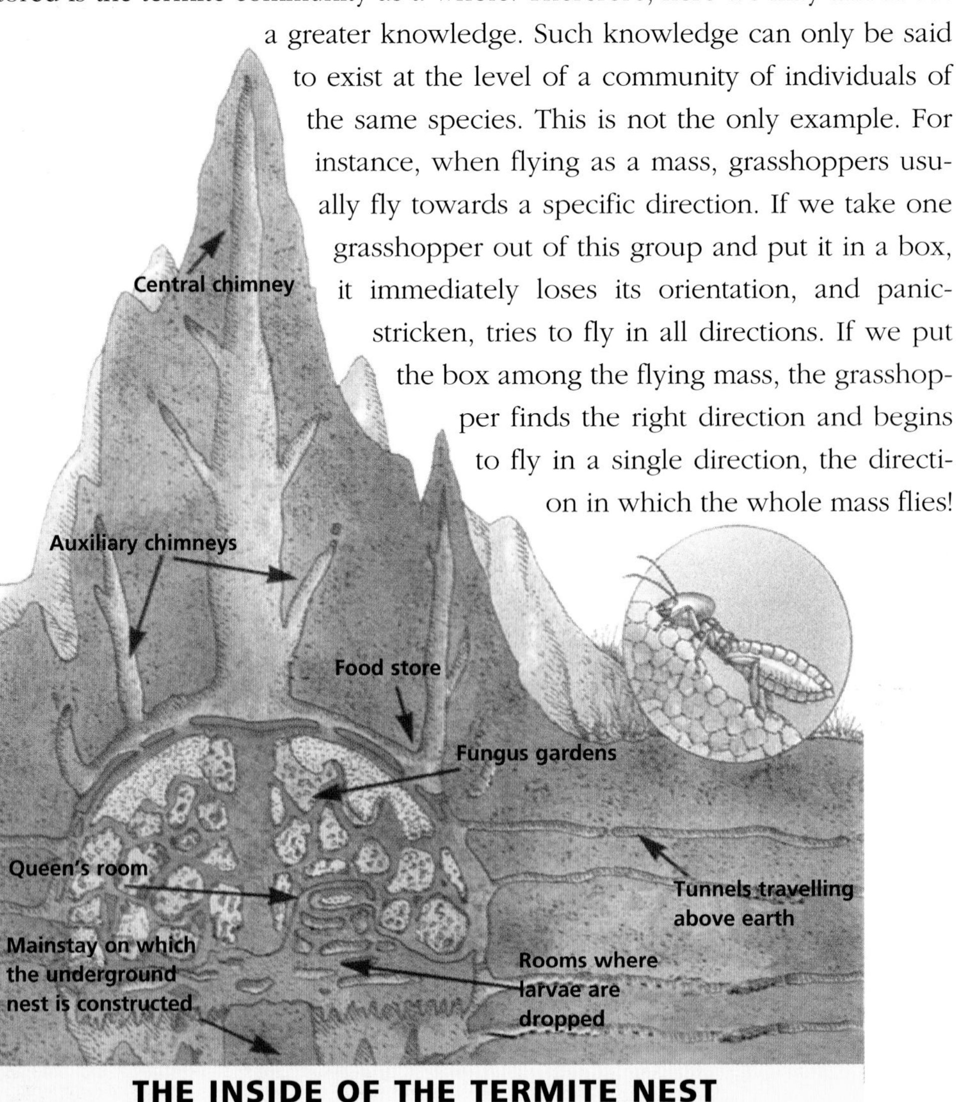

THE INSIDE OF THE TERMITE NEST

Briefly, the information pertaining to the collective organisation and works of individual organisms is revealed only at the communal level. It does not exist individually. In other words, animals that make collective "constructions" such as the bee and the termite are not aware of what they do as individuals. Beyond them all, another wisdom controls them all and creates the perfect outcome, by bringing the work of all together.

We have examined in earlier pages that in the Qur'an, Allah states that production of honey is "inspired" in the bees. This is also true for the work of the termites and other animals.

Definitely, these excellent processes were "taught" to animals and they are programmed to perform this work. Men can manage to make the incredible buildings they construct only after taking years long architectural educations and by using many technical tools. It is evident that these animals that do not possess wisdom and consciousness like men do, were created specifically to do this job and thus to be a means of showing the infinite knowledge and might of their Creator.

The one who is worthy of praise and admiration for the great architectural wonders they construct is surely not these little creatures, but Allah Who created them with this talent.

AGRICULTURE IN THE TOWER

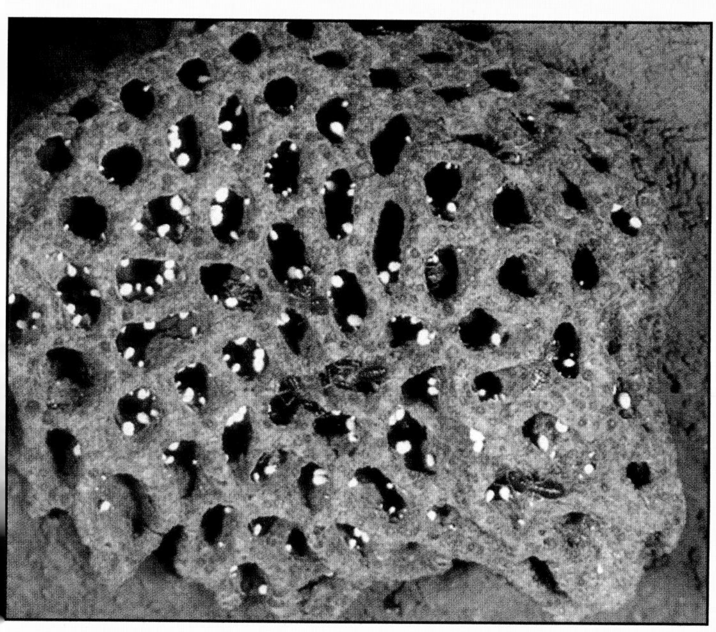

A view from the fungus garden of the termites.

Some termites cultivate mushrooms in the gardens they make in their towers. These mushrooms, however, diffuse heat, by the nature of their life activities, which disturb the temperature balance kept by termites. The termites have to balance this extreme temperature rise. Termites use interesting methods to get rid of the heat they themselves release and from the metabolism of the mushrooms they grow in their garden. The generated heat rises up the main tower (chimney) of the nest. The air circulates and passes to auxiliary chimneys by going through small channels near the walls. Here, oxygen is taken in and the carbon dioxide that is released by the termites and the fungi is given out. Thus, the termite nest works like a huge lung for the whole colony. The air cools as it moves along the capillary channel system.

Consequently, permanently cool and oxygen-rich air flows in at a speed of 12 cm per minute and thus the temperature inside stays constantly at 30°C.

WEAVER ANTS

Weaver ants live in the rainforests of Africa. In contrast to other ants that build their nests under the earth, these ants build their nests from leaves on the tops of trees.

"What is in the heavens and in the earth belongs to Allah. Allah encompasses all things."

(Surat an-Nisa: 126)

Constructed in the face of external attacks, the nest is sometimes so big as to extend over three trees. The nest is prepared to meet all kinds of situations. It has many departments: from private children rooms to watchtowers.

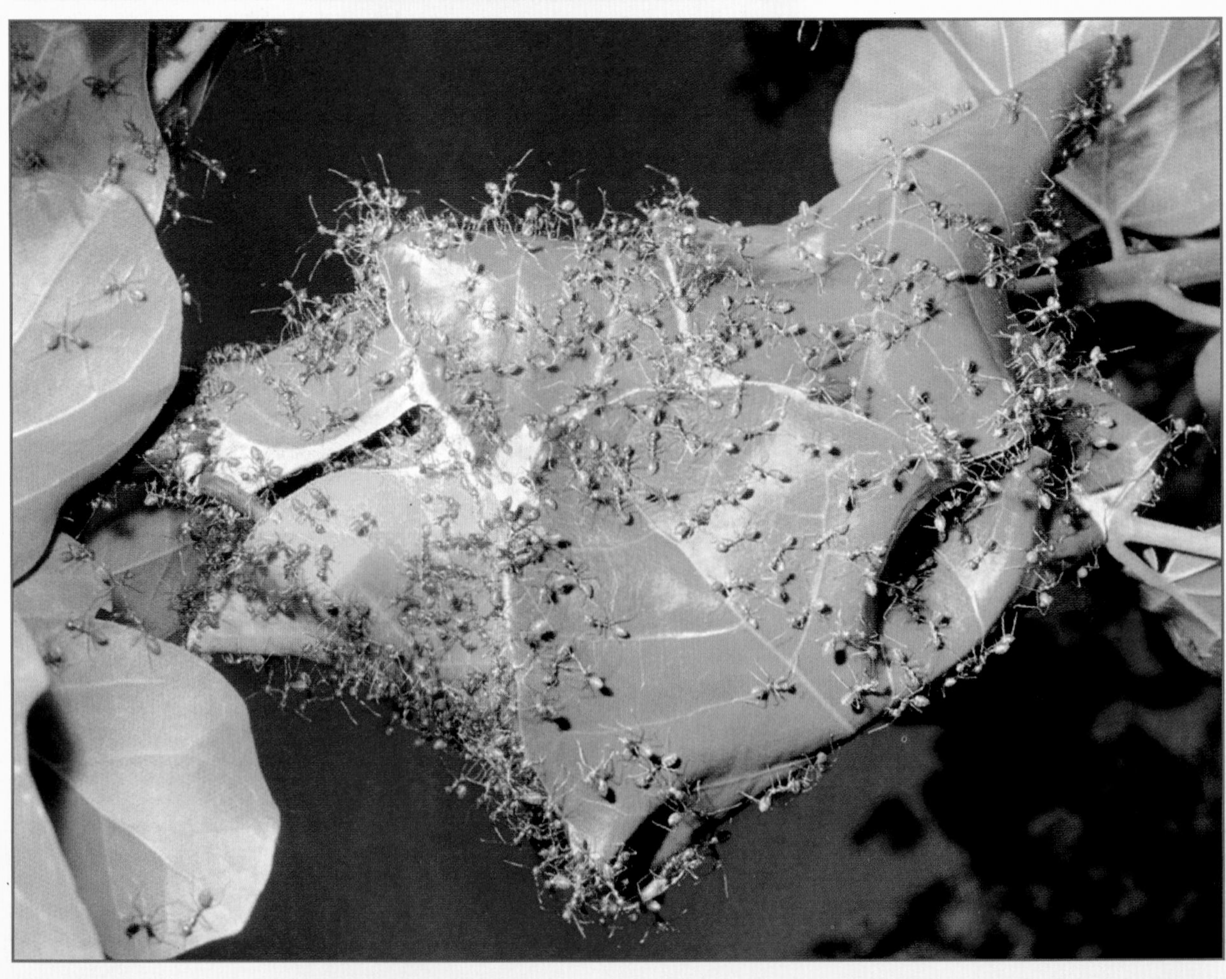

Firstly, ants disperse over the tree on which they plan to settle (see left). After determining the location where they will build a nest, they immediately set to work. They fold the leaves they will use from the sides. In order to bring the leaves together, they make suspension bridges by clamping them together (see right and below). The ant at the head of the chain holds the leaf at its tip and passes it to the second ant clamping on it. This transfer process goes on until the leaf tip reaches the last ant and the two leaves lap over one another.

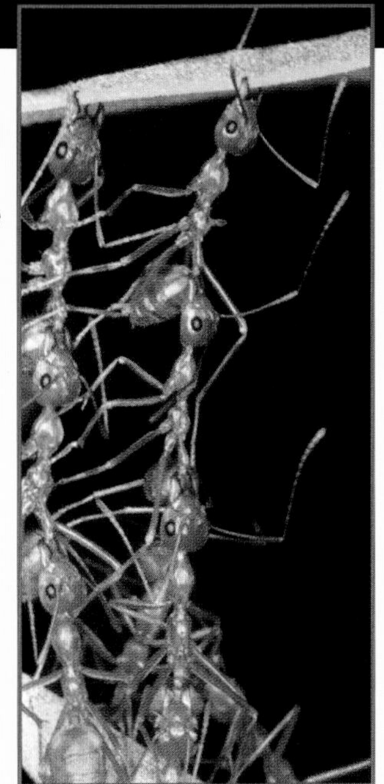

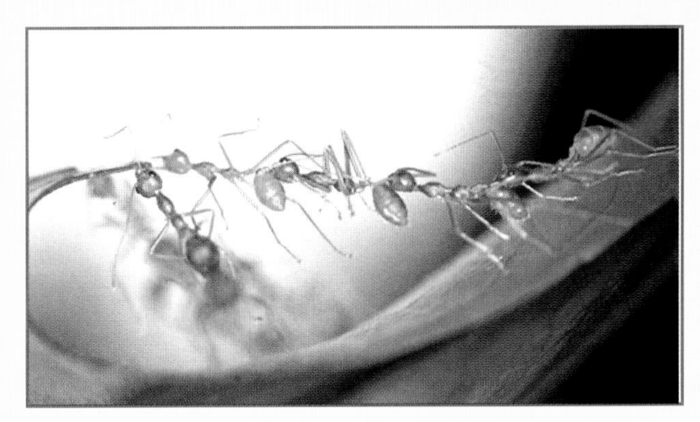

CAN A LARVA MAKE A SEWING MACHINE?

While a few ants hold the tips of leaves with their feet and mouths, the others bring half-developed larvae from the brooding nest.

The larvae, with their saliva, function as a shuttle. When the adult ants suppress the larvae on the leave tips, the secretory glands of the larvae, which produce thread, start to work. The ants bring the larvae back and forth like needles until the leaves are attached to each other tightly. (see below)

THE MYSTERIES IN THE REPRODUCTION OF ANIMALS

That living things can keep their generation going can only be possible through the perfect functioning of their reproductive systems. It is, however, not enough for men and animals to have reproductive systems; they also need a special instinct, namely the sexual instinct, which makes reproduction attractive. Otherwise, despite having the chance to reproduce, most animals would not attempt it. As well as that, once they become aware of the difficulties of birth, laying eggs and the subsequent incubation period, they would avoid involvement in the sexual act, which is the cause of everything that follows.

The sexual drive is not enough by itself either. Although living beings copulate and bring new living beings into the world, their species is still likely to become extinct if they were not created possessing the instinct to protect and care for their young. If parental affection, as possessed by most living species, did not exist, species would become extinct. At this point, those who advocate evolution talk about "the consciousness of breeding generations". According to them, just as every individual spends a considerable effort to protect itself, so must it spend an effort to breed its species. However, it is evident that an animal cannot think, "my generation must continue after me, so I have to do what I can". The animal protects and cares for its offspring not because it hopes for something or expects some future benefits, but because it was created so.

On the contrary, some living things lack such affection and abandon their offspring as soon as they bring them into the world. These animals produce many offspring at a time and some of them survive without any protection. If they were created with a drive to protect their offspring, there would be a population explosion in their species and the balance of nature would be disturbed.

In short, reproduction, the prerequisite for the continuation of life, is a system Allah created for life to continue. Allah is the "Life-Giver". He is the One Who has brought all living things into being and He is the One Who brings new living beings out from those He created. All living things live thanks to Him. They owe their lives not to their parents, as generally supposed, but to Allah Who created their parents as well as them. In the Qur'an, Allah says:

THE DRILLER WASP

This wasp species feeds its offspring with the larvae of another wasp species called the sirex. It faces a problem though: sirex spends its larval period about 4 centimetres beneath a tree bark. For this reason, the mother driller wasp has first to locate the sirex larvae, which it cannot see.

To locate the sirex larvae, the bee uses the very sensitive sensors placed in its body and thus the first problem, namely, finding the location of the larvae, is solved. What about the second?... It overcomes this by drilling the tree bark.

The organ, which the wasp uses to drill the tree bark, is called the "Ovipositor". This special organ is longer than the entire body of the wasp. It is formed by the combination of two appendages coming out of the tail, and it has a sharp end like that of a knife. The end of the 'knife' has a nicked structure in accordance with its purpose.

As soon as the drilling wasp locates the sirex under the bark, it directs its drilling appendages towards the target in the shortest, most direct way possible. The two appendages drill the bark by moving back and forth like a saw. As soon as the wasp reaches the sirex, it places its own egg through its funnel in the larva.

The young wasp starts its life by growing up in the larva found by its mother and left to it both as a source of food and shelter. Is it still necessary to further accentuate that such perfect design can never be the result of random chance, but on the contrary, is the work of a Creator, of Allah, the Owner of eternal wisdom and might?

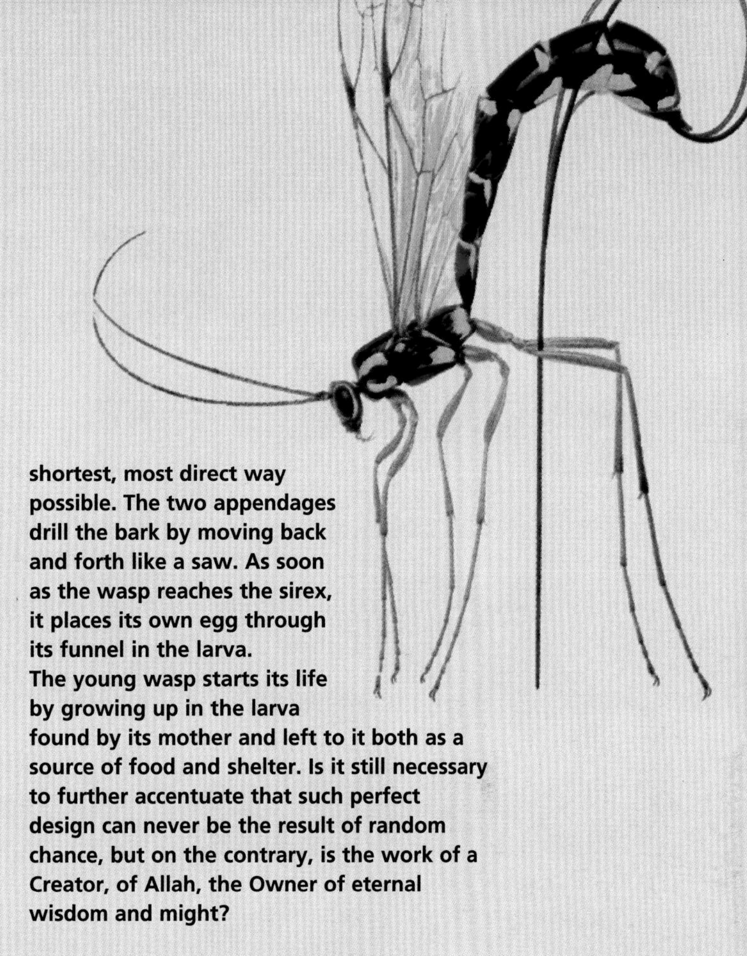

POTTER WASP

The wasp in the picture feeds its larvae in its nest, which it has made of mud with great adeptness.

First, it finds a fleshy caterpillar and stings it at nine key points pertaining to its movement centre. Because of this operation, the caterpillar does not die but is paralysed and can no longer move.

The wasp then very carefully carries the caterpillar, which is as motionless as if it was dead, into its nest.

The paralysed caterpillar meets the wasp larvae's needs for meat until they grow old enough to leave the nest.

It is He Who dispersed you about the earth and you will be gathered to Him. (Surat al-Muminun: 79)

In the following pages, we will review some reproductive systems, which Allah granted some living beings. These living things face great difficulties in guaranteeing the continuation of their species. They unquestionably do what they do, not because they employ logic such as "we have to guarantee the continuity of our species", but from the affection and mercy Allah granted to them.

These animals, that have some striking systems, are only a few examples. In fact, the reproduction of each living thing is a miracle on its own.

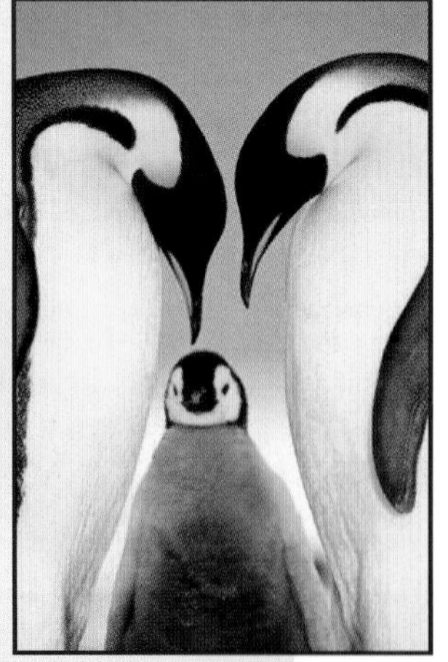

THE PENGUIN: AN ANIMAL CREATED FOR POLAR CLIMATE

The temperature at the Antarctic polar circle where penguins live can sometimes be as low as -40ºC. The bodies of penguins are covered with a thick layer of fat so that they can survive in such a freezing environment. Besides, they have a highly developed digestive system that is able to break food down very rapidly. These two factors furnish penguins with a body temperature of +40º C that makes them indifferent to cold.

EVERYTHING IS FOR THE YOUNG PENGUIN

Penguins incubate during the polar winter. Furthermore, it is not the female but the male penguins that incubate. Apart from the freezing cold falling down to -40º C, the penguin couple are also faced with glaciers at this time of the year. Throughout winter, the glaciers steadily grow, thereby increasing the distance between the incubation site and the coast, where the closest source of food for the penguins is found. This distance may at times be more than 100 km.

Female penguins lay only one egg, leave incubation to their males and return to the sea. During four months of incubation, the male penguin has to resist violent polar storms at times reaching speeds of 100 km per hour. Because it guards the egg, it has no chance to hunt. In any case, the nearest source of food is at a distance of a couple of days' journey. Lying for four full months without eating anything, the male penguin

If nature were indeed the way Darwin said it was, that is, if every individual were concerned only with its own life, then no living thing would spend so much time and energy, and suffer from so much hunger to protect and feed its offspring.

loses half of its weight, but it never leaves the egg. Although it goes without any food for months, it does not go hunting, but resists the hunger.

After the end of four months when the eggs start to crack open, the female penguin suddenly shows up. In the duration, she has not wasted time but worked for her young and stored food for it.

Among hundreds of penguins, the mother easily finds her spouse and offspring. As the mother has constantly hunted in the meantime, it has a full stomach. It empties its stomach and takes over the job of caring for the young.

In spring, the glaciers start to melt and holes emerge in the ice under which the sea appears. The parent penguins soon start to hunt fish in these holes and feed their young.

Feeding the baby is a tough task; sometimes the parents do not eat anything for a long time in order to feed the young. There is no way to make a nest when everything is covered with ice. The only thing the parents can do to protect their offspring from the ice cold is to put it on top of their feet and warm it with their tummy.

Timing is also very important in laying eggs.

Why do the penguins lay eggs in winter, and not in summer? There is one reason for this: if they had laid eggs in summer time, then the development of the offspring would take place in winter time and the seas would be frozen. In that case, the parents would have difficulty in finding food to feed the young due to the inconvenient weather conditions and due to the fact that the seas, the food resource of the penguins, are further away.

In order to protect themselves from the polar climate that is extremely cold, penguins assemble closer together. Thus, the young members of the community get the chance to meet while being protected from the effect of cold winds.

THE HERO OF AN UNUSUAL BIRTH STORY: THE KANGAROO

The reproductive system of kangaroos is quite different from that of other mammals. The kangaroo embryo goes through some stages outside the womb, which normally occur in the womb.

Soon after fertilisation, the blind kangaroo offspring, which is approximately a centimetre, comes into the world. Usually, only one is born at a time. At this stage, it is called "neonate." While all mammals go through this stage in the mother's womb, the kangaroo offspring comes into the world when it is only one centimetre long. It has still not developed: its fore feet are indefinite and its hind feet are comprised of small projections.

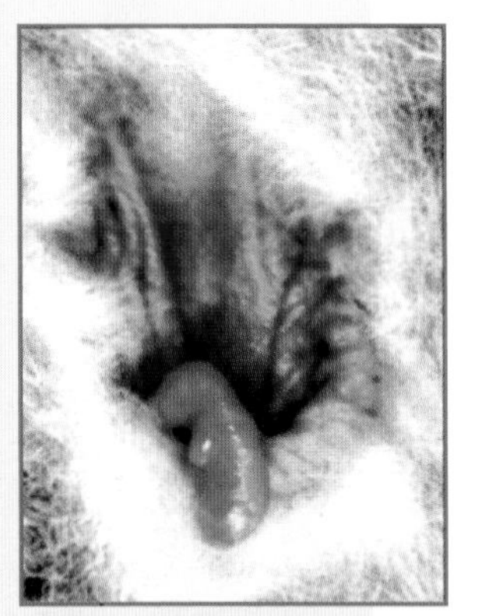

No doubt, the offspring cannot leave its mother in such a state. Coming out of the womb, the neonate starts to move up in its mother's fur with its fore legs and reaches to its mother's pouch after a three-minute journey. To the little kangaroo, the pouch means the same as the womb means to other mammals. Yet, there is an important difference. While others come into the world as babies, the kangaroo is merely an embryo when it comes out of the womb. Its feet, face and many other organs have not yet taken their final shapes.

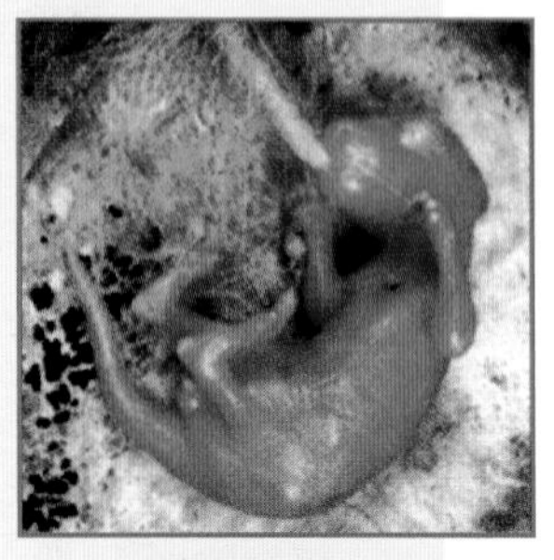

The offspring reaching the mother's pouch attaches itself to one of the four nipples there, and starts to suckle.

At this stage, the mother goes through another ovulation period and a new egg forms in its womb. The female copulates once more and the new egg is fertilised.

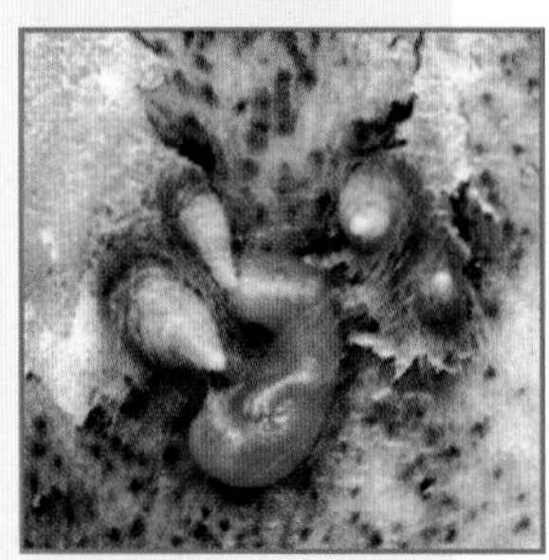

This time the egg does not start to develop immediately. If drought rages in Middle Australia, as is often the case, the fertilised egg in the womb remains undeveloped until the drought is over. If, however, heavy rains fall and if there are rich pastures available, then the development of the egg restarts.

At this stage, we are faced with the question: who makes this calculation; who arranges the development of the egg according to the conditions outside? The egg cannot by any means make this arrangement itself; it is not a complete living being, it has no consciousness, and it is totally unaware of the weather conditions outside. The mother cannot make this arrangement, because, like all other living things, it has no control over the developments taking place in its body. Allah, Who has created both the egg and the mother, definitely controls this extraordinary event..

When weather conditions are convenient, thirty-three days after fertilisation, the new neonate, only as big as a bean, creeps up from the mouth of the womb and reaches the pouch just like its sibling did.

In the meantime, the first neonate in the pouch has grown considerably. It leads its life without doing any harm to its sibling, which is only one centime-

No female becomes pregnant or gives birth except with His knowledge. And no living thing lives long or has its life cut short without that being in a Book. That is easy for Allah.
(Surah Fatir: 11)

tre long. When it is 190 days old, it has grown mature enough to make its first journey outside the pouch. From then on, it starts to spend most of its time outside the pouch and leaves the pouch for good on the 235th day after its birth.

Soon after the birth of its second offspring, the female copulates again. Consequently, the female has three offspring all dependent on her. The first can feed on grass but occasionally comes back to its mother to suckle; the second younger offspring is still developing by suckling; the third is the neonate, which is the youngest.

What is more astonishing than that all three offspring, each in a different stage of development, are dependent on the mother, is that all three offspring are fed by different types of milk according to their sizes.

While the milk the offspring suckles as soon as it reaches the nipple in the pouch is transparent and colourless, it increasingly turns whiter and starts to look like real milk. The amount of fat and other ingredients in the milk increases in parallel with the development of the baby.

As this young one keeps on suckling the milk prepared for its own needs, a more easily digestible milk issues from the nipple that the second baby reaches. Thus, the body of the mother simultaneously produces two types of milk with different ingredients. When the third is born, the number of milk types produced with different ingredients becomes three: highly nutritious milk for the older, and relatively less fatty and nutritious types of milk for the younger. Another point to note here is that each offspring finds the nipple specially prepared for itself. Otherwise, it would suckle milk with an ingredient likely to be harmful to its body, and the milk it suckles would harm it.

This feeding system is very remarkable and it is obviously a special product of creation. The mother cannot, by any means, arrange all these consciously. How can an animal specify the ingredients of milk needed by its young of different sizes? Even if it did, how could it produce it in its own body? How could it distribute these through three different channels?

Doubtless, the kangaroo is not capable of doing any of these. It is not even aware that the milk delivered by its body is of three different types. This wonderful process is unquestionably an outcome of Allah's superior creation.

A NEST OF
WEEDS

Despite its bulky and wild look, the mother crocodile provides the utmost care for its young. It offers safe shelter to its unprotected babies in a special pouch in its mouth.

WHAT KIND OF A MOTHER IS THE CROCODILE?

The care provided by the crocodile, a wild animal of rivers, for its offspring is quite astounding.

First, the animal digs a hole for the incubation of its eggs. The temperature of the hole should never rise above 30°C. A slight rise in temperature would be a threat to the lives of the offspring in the eggs. The crocodile takes precaution that the holes in which it places its eggs are located in rather shady places. This, however, may not in itself be sufficient. For this reason, the female crocodile spends extraordinary efforts to keep the eggs at a constant temperature.

Some crocodile species build nests of weed on cold water, rather than digging holes (as seen in the picture to the left). If the temperature of the nest still rises despite these measures, then the crocodile cools the nest by sprinkling urea on it. When the eggs are about to crack, loud noises arise from the nest. These noises warn the mother that the critical moment has come. The mother crocodile brings the eggs out and helps the offspring pop out of their eggs by using its teeth as tweezers. The safest place for the newly born is the protective pouch in its mother's mouth specially designed to shelter half a dozen newly born crocodiles.

As seen, there is great co-operation and self-sacrifice among animals. For a sensible person, the perfect harmony in nature clearly reveals signs of the being of a superior Creator. That is, the signs of Allah, Who is the Creator of everything in the heavens and on the earth.

THE HEAT TECHNOLOGY OF THE MEGAPODE BIRD

A bird called the "megapode" living in the Pacific islands prepares an interesting "incubation machine" for its offspring.

During the summer season, the female megapode lays one egg every six days. However, the eggs of the megapode are relatively big compared to its size, being almost as big as an ostrich egg. For this reason, the female megapode can only incubate one egg. Therefore, every six days, the new hatched eggs are in danger of dying due to lack of heat. However, this is not a problem for the megapode, because the male megapode is created with the skill to manufacture an incubation machine by using the most abundant materials in nature, that is, sand and earth.

For this purpose, six months before the spawning season comes, the male megapode starts to dig a hole 5 metres in diameter and 1 metre in depth with its gigantic claws. Then, it fills the hole with wet weed and leaves. The main purpose is to use the heat produced by the bacteria in decaying plants to warm the eggs.

However, additional arrangements have to be made for this process to take place. The actual reason why plants decay and release heat is the funnel-shaped hole made by the megapode in the pile of plants. This hole enables rainwater to leak into the nest and keep the organic substances wet. Because of the damp, decay takes place in the plants beneath the sand, and heat is released. Soon before spring, the drought season for Australia starts, and the male begins to air the decayed plant layer. This is to maintain the heat balance. The female bird occasionally visits the hole and checks whether the male is working or not. Finally, the female lays eggs on the sand over the decayed plants.

The male megapode digs a hole for its eggs.

While the male megapode digs a hole for the eggs, the female only supervises without interfering at all.

When the time to hatch comes, the eggs are taken out of the sand.

A SENSITIVE THERMOMETER: THE MALE MEGAPODE

For the development of offspring in the "incubation machine", the temperature should be kept constant at +33°C. In order to achieve this, the male megapode regularly measures the temperature of the sand with its beak, which is as sensitive as a thermometer. If necessary, it opens ventilation holes to reduce the temperature. It is so much so that if a few handfuls of earth are thrown on the sand, the male megapode immediately removes the extra sand with its feet and prevents even the slightest change in temperature. The offspring come into the world under such protective measures. The newly born are so developed that they can fly just a few hours after they pop out of their eggs.

How have these creatures accomplished such a job for millions of years which even men could hardly do? Since we know that animals have no conscious rational intellect as people do, the only explanation of this event is that this creature is specially "programmed" for this task, and originally created able to do it. Otherwise, it is impossible to explain how it could prepare for this job six months in advance, or know the nature of this complex chemical process. Why it embarks on such a difficult task to protect the eggs is another question. The only answer is hidden in the desire to reproduce and protect the young.

The female cuckoo bird lays its eggs next to the eggs of another bird. For this, it observes at length a nest it chooses. As soon as the owner of the nest leaves, it secretly drops an egg in the nest. Meanwhile, it throws one of the eggs in the nest out so that the situation goes unnoticed.

THE CUCKOO BIRD

Did you know that the cuckoo bird lays its eggs in other birds' nests and tricks those birds into looking after its offspring?

When the time to lay eggs comes, the female cuckoo bird seems to race with time. Alert and on watch, the bird hides among the leaves and spies on other birds that build nests. When it sees a familiar bird building a nest, it decides when to lay its own egg. The bird to look after the offspring is now decided upon.

When the cuckoo bird sees that the other bird lays its eggs, it swings into action. As soon as the other bird leaves the nest, the cuckoo immediately flies to the nest and drops its own egg in. Here, it does something very intelligent and throws out one of the actual eggs belonging to the nest. This prevents the owner of the nest from having any doubts.

The mother cuckoo works out a remarkable strategy with perfect timing to guarantee that its offspring makes a safe start in life. The female cuckoo lays not one egg but twenty eggs in a season. Accordingly, it has to find many nursing parents, spy on them and devise good timing to lay its eggs. Since the mother cuckoo lays one egg every two days and it takes five days for each egg to be formed in the ovary, the bird has no time to lose.

Popping out of the egg after an incubation period of twelve days, the cuckoo bird faces its very affectionate - yet not its own - parents as soon as it opens its eyes for the first time after four days. The first thing it does, as soon as it pops out of the egg, is to throw the other eggs out of the nest when the parents are away. The nursing parents carefully feed the offspring, which they take to be theirs. Towards week six when the offspring leaves the nest, we encounter the interesting sight of the cuckoo, a big bird fed by two small birds.

Let us think about why the cuckoo bird leaves its offspring to the care of other birds. Does the mother cuckoo have recourse to such a practice because it is too lazy or because it is not skilful enough to build a nest? Alternatively, is it because that once it used to build nests and look after its own offspring, but then realised that this is a very arduous task, and then it discovered this method? Do you think that a bird can make such a plan on its own? Surely none of these assumptions are true. What this living thing will do is inspired in it. Like all other living things, the cuckoos also do what Allah commands them to.

WHICH IS THE OFFSPRING?

Although six weeks pass by, and the offspring grows to be a few times bigger than it was, the nursing bird meticulously carries out its maternal duty.

The first thing the cuckoo offspring does when it pops out of the egg is to throw other eggs out of the nest. Thus, the nursing parents will feed only the young cuckoo.

THE WAR OF THE WASP "PEPSIS" WITH THE TARANTULA

During the reproductive season, the giant wasp called "pepsis" does not bother with building a nest or incubating, contrary to other animals. It is equipped with a totally different reproductive mechanism by its nature. This wasp feeds and protects its eggs by using the biggest and most poisonous spider on earth called the tarantula.

Tarantulas generally hide themselves in the tunnels they dig underground. This wasp, however, is equipped with special sensors sensitive to the smell of the tarantula. Therefore, it is not so difficult for it to find its prey. The tarantula, however, is not a creature that is often found. For this reason, the wasp sometimes has to walk for hours on the ground to find a single tarantula. During this trip, it does not neglect to clean its sensors regularly so that they do not lose their sensitivity.

When the wasp finds the tarantula, a war breaks out. The main weapon of the tarantula is its fatal poison. At the outset of the struggle, the tarantula immediately bites the wasp. Yet these wasps (pepsis) are protected against the poison of the tarantula by possession of a special antidote and they are not affected by the strong poison of the tarantula owing to that special secretion in their body.

At this stage, the tarantula has nothing more to do against the wasp. It is now the wasp's turn to bite. The wasp bites the tarantula on the upper left part of its stomach and discharges its poison there. It is interesting that the wasp especially chooses this part in the tarantula's body, because this is the most sensitive section of the tarantula. The most interesting part of the event starts after this stage: the poison of the wasp is placed in its body not to kill the tarantula but to paralyse it.

Carrying the paralysed tarantula to a suitable place, the wasp digs a hole there and puts the tarantula in the hole. Then the wasp makes a hole in the stomach of the tarantula and leaves only one egg in it.

Within a few days, the offspring of the pepsis pops out of the egg. The offspring feeds on the flesh of the tarantula and takes shelter in its body until the cocoon period when it will undergo metamorphosis.

The pepsis has to find a tarantula for each one of the twenty eggs it will lay throughout the reproductive season.

This incredible method shows us that the reproductive system of this wasp is specially created in accordance with the nature of the tarantula. Otherwise, it is by no means possible to explain the presence of the antidote in the wasp's body against the poison of the tarantula, or its secreting a fluid that paralyses the tarantula.

The Lord of the East and the West and everything between them if you used your intellect. *(Surat ash-Shu'ara: 28)*

The wasp bites the tarantula on the upper left part of its stomach. This is the most appropriate area for the tarantula to be paralysed.

THE MIGRATION OF BIRDS

In the Qur'an, Allah calls us to give attention to birds with His verse "Have they not looked at the birds above them, with wings outspread and folded back? Nothing holds them up but the All-Merciful. He sees all things." (Surat al-Mulk: 19) In this part, we will particularly review migratory birds; we will describe what perfect balances they establish travelling in the skies, and the systems their bodies are endowed with, and focus on the wonder of Allah's upholding them "in the sky".

HOW DO BIRDS DETERMINE THE TIME OF MIGRATION?

Why and how birds started to migrate and what made them take the "decision of migration" have long been topics of interest. Some scientists hold the reason of migration to be seasonal changes while some others believe the reason to be the search for food. What deserves consideration is how these animals, having no protection, technical outfit, and security but only their bodies, can make these very long-distance flights. Migration requires some special skills like orientation, food storage, and the ability to fly for long periods. It is impossible for an animal not possessing these characteristics to transform into a migratory animal.

One of the experiments made to address this issue is as follows: garden nightingales were subjected to experiments in a lab where internal conditions such as temperature and light could be varied. Internal conditions were arranged differently from external conditions. For instance, if it was winter outside, a spring climate was created in the laboratory and the birds arranged their bodies in accordance with that. The birds stored fat for fuel, just as they do when time for migration approaches. Although birds organised themselves according to the artificial season, and prepared themselves as if they were going to migrate, they did not set out to migrate before it was time. They observed the season outside. This was evidence that birds do not take the decision to start migration according to seasonal conditions.

How, then, do birds determine the time for migration? Scientists have still not found an answer to this question. They believe that living things have "body clocks" that help them to know the time in a closed environment and to differentiate seasonal changes. However, the answer that "birds have body clocks with which they understand the time of migration" is an unscientific answer. What kind of clock is it, which organ of the body does it work with, and how did it come into being? What would happen if this clock were out of order or stayed behind?

Considering that the same system holds true not only for a single migratory bird, but for all migratory animals, more importance must be attributed to these questions.

As is well known, migratory birds do not start migration from the same place, as none of them are found at the same place when the time for migration arrives. Most species first meet at a particular location and then migrate together. How do they arrange such timing? How are these "body-clocks", that birds allegedly have, so harmonious? Is it possible that such a systematic order could come into being spontaneously?

It is impossible for a planned action to take place spontaneously. In addition, neither in birds nor in other migratory animals is there a clock of any kind. All migratory living things do this every year at times determined by them, but they do not do it by observing a body clock. What some people call a body clock is Allah's control over these living beings. Migratory animals follow Allah's orders just like everything in the universe.

USAGE OF ENERGY

Birds consume great energy in flight. For this reason, they need more fuel than all sea-dwelling and land-dwelling animals. For instance, in order to fly the 3,000 km distance between Hawaii and Alaska, a humming bird, weighing a few grams, has to beat its wings 2.5 million times. Despite this, it can remain in the air for as long as 36 hours. Its average speed during this trip is approximately 80 km per hour. During a flight as arduous as that, the quantity of acid in the bird's blood increases excessively and the bird faces the danger of fainting because of its rising body temperature. Some birds deal with this danger by landing. How, then, can those that migrate over enormous oceans save themselves? Ornithologists have observed that under such circumstances, birds spread their wings as wide as possible and so cool down by resting in this manner.

The metabolisms of migratory birds are strong enough to put up with this task. For instance, the metabolic activity in the body of a humming bird, the smallest bird of passage, is 20 times more than that in an elephant. The body temperature of the bird rises to 62° C.

Only five centimetres tall.

The "V" type flight formation.

FLIGHT TECHNIQUES

In addition to having been created ready to endure such arduous flights, birds are also gifted with skills that enable to them to make use of favourable winds.

For instance, storks go up as high as 2,000 m with rising warm air currents, and then glide along swiftly to the next warm air current without beating their wings.

Another flight technique used by bird flocks is the "V" type flight formation. In this technique, big strong birds at the front function as shields against counter air currents and lead the way for the weaker. Aeronautical engineer Dietrich Hummel has proved that with such organisation, a saving of 23% is achieved in the flock in general.

FLIGHT AT HIGH ALTITUDE

Some migrating birds fly at very high altitudes. For instance geese can fly at an altitude of 8,000 m. This is an incredible altitude considering the fact that even at 5,000 metres the atmosphere is 63% less dense than at sea level. Flying at such a height where the atmosphere is so thin, the bird has to beat its wings faster and hence has to find more oxygen.

However, the lungs of these animals are created in such a way as to take maximum benefit from the oxygen available at these heights. Their lungs, which function differently from those of mammals, help them obtain higher level of energy from scarce air.

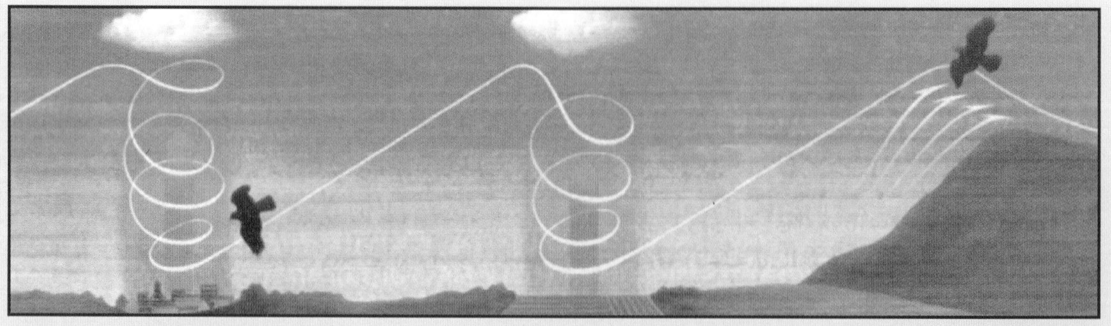

When the bird ascending in the warm air current reaches the top, it glides down swiftly. This helps the bird save a great amount of energy both in ascent and descent.

The above illustration shows the twelve factors beneficial to birds while flying:
1. The sun,
2. Sense of timing,
3. Location of the stars,
4. Ultraviolet rays,
5. Polarised light,
6. Sounds of very low frequency,
7. Sounds such as of waves and thunder coming from very far away,
8. The magnetic field of the earth,
9. Gravity,
10. Meteorological assessment,
11. Favourable winds,
12. Characteristics of the ground below.

A PERFECT SENSE OF HEARING

During migration, birds also take atmospheric phenomena into consideration. For instance, they change direction to avoid a coming storm. Melvin L. Kreithen, an ornithologist who made research into birds' sense of hearing, observed that some birds can hear sounds of extremely small frequencies, which diffuse to great distances in the atmosphere. A migratory bird can therefore hear a storm breaking out over a far away mountain or thunder over an ocean hundreds of kilometres ahead. Besides, it is a known fact that birds are careful to set their routes of migration away from regions where atmospheric conditions are risky.

PERCEPTION OF DIRECTION

How do birds find their direction without the help of a map, a compass or some similar direction finder during their thousands of kilometres long flights?

The first theory put forward regarding this question was that birds memorise the characteristics of the ground beneath them and thus reach their destination without being confused. Yet, experiments have shown that this theory is incorrect.

In an experiment on pigeons addressing this subject, opaque lenses were used to blur the vision of pigeons. Thus, they were prevented from navigating by landmarks on the ground, yet the pigeons could still find their way even if left some kilometres away from their flocks.

Subsequent research has shown that the magnetic field of the earth seems to act on bird species. Various studies have shown that birds have seemingly

THOUSANDS OF KILOMETRES LONG MIGRATION ROUTES

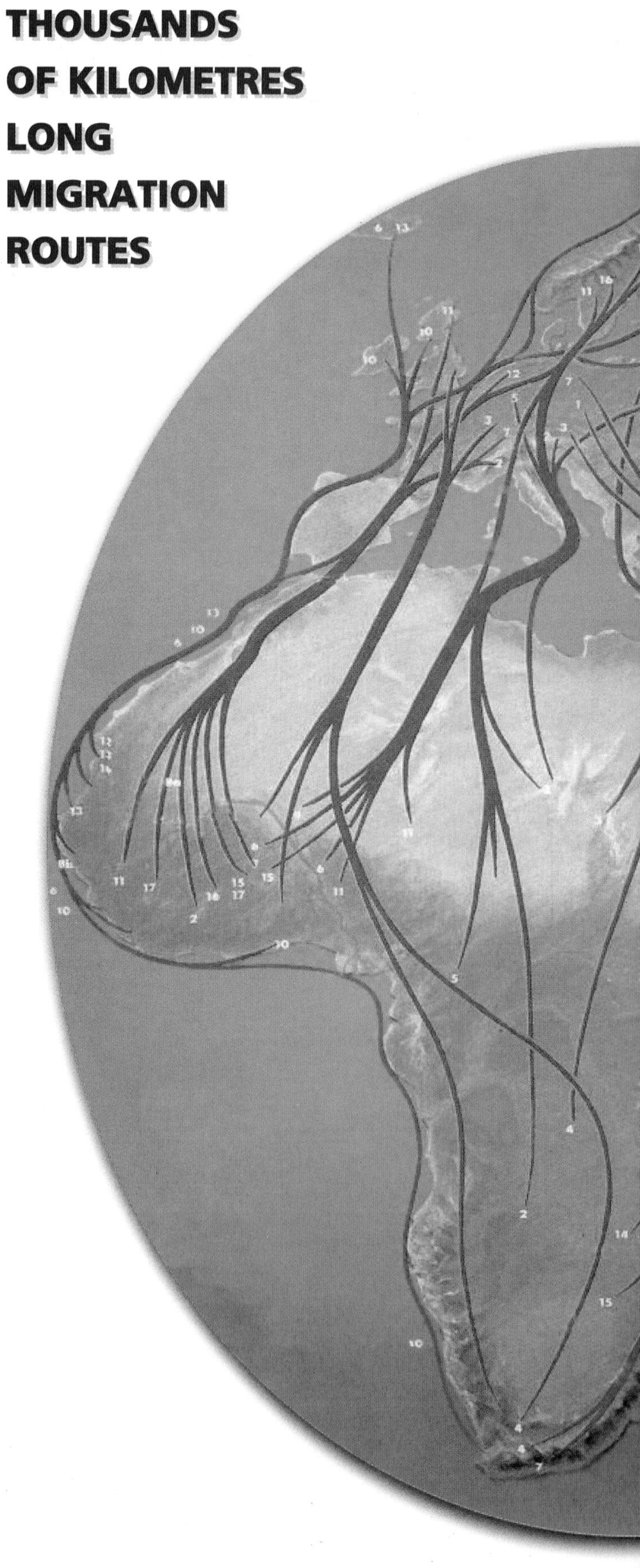

advanced, magnetic receptor systems enabling them to find their way by making use of the magnetic field of the earth. This system helps birds determine their direction by sensing the change in the magnetic field of the earth during their migrations. Experiments reveal that migratory birds can even perceive a 2% variation in the magnetic field of the earth.

Some think that they can explain the subject away by saying that birds have a sort of compass in their bodies. The main question, however, lies just here.

The question is: how do the birds come to be equipped with a "natural compass"? We are aware that the compass is an "invention" and a work of human intelligence. So how does a compass - an apparatus produced by man with his collected knowledge - come to exist in the bodies of birds? Is it likely that some years ago, a bird species, while finding direction, thought about making use of the magnetic field of the earth and invented a magnetic receptor for its own body? Alternatively, was a bird species, years ago, equipped with such a mechanism by "coincidence"? Definitely not....

Neither the bird itself nor a coincidence can add an extremely advanced compass to the body. The bird's body structure, lungs, wings, digestive system and its ability to find direction are the examples of the perfect creation of Allah:

"He is Allah - the Creator, the Maker, the Giver of Form. To Him belong the Most Beautiful Names. Everything in the heavens and earth glorifies Him. He is the Almighty, the All-Wise." (Surat al-Hashr: 24)

"Do you not see that everyone in the heavens and earth glorifies Allah, as do the birds with their outspread wings? Each one knows its prayer and glorification. Allah knows what they do". (Surat an-Nur: 41)

AMAZING JOURNEY OF MONARCH BUTTERFLIES

The migration story of Monarch butterflies, which live in southeast Canada, is more complex than that of the birds.

Monarch butterflies normally live for only 5-6 weeks after they develop from caterpillar. Four generations of Monarch butterflies live within a year. Three of these four generations live in spring and summertime.

With the coming of autumn, the situation changes. Migration starts in autumn and the generation that migrates, lives much longer than the other generations that lived in the same year. The Monarchs that migrate are the fourth generation in the year.

Interestingly enough, the migration starts exactly on the night of the autumn equinox. The butterflies that migrate to the south live six months longer than the previous three generations. They need to live exactly this long to complete their journey and return.

The butterflies that go down to the south do not disperse after they pass across the Tropic of Cancer and leave the cold weather behind. After migrating over half of the American continent, millions of butterflies settle down in the middle of Mexico. Here the ridges of volcanic mountains are covered with a great variety of flora. Located at a height of 3,000 metres, this place is warm enough for the subsistence of the butterflies. For a period of four months, from December to March, they eat nothing. As the fat stored in their bodies nourishes them, they only drink water.

Flowers that bloom in the spring are quite important for the Monarchs. After a four-month fast, for the first time, in the spring they give themselves a nectar feast. They now have stored enough energy to return to North America. This generation, which lives a two-month life span extended to eight months, is no different from the three earlier generations in other respects. They mate at the end of March before setting out to their journey. On the equinox, the colony starts flying back to the north. Soon after they complete their journey and arrive in Canada, they die. However, before they die, they give birth to a new generation, which is necessary for the perpetuation of their species.

The newly born generation is the first generation of the year and lives about one and a half months long. Then comes the second and third generations.

When thousands of Monarchs perch on a tree, the tree becomes invisible.

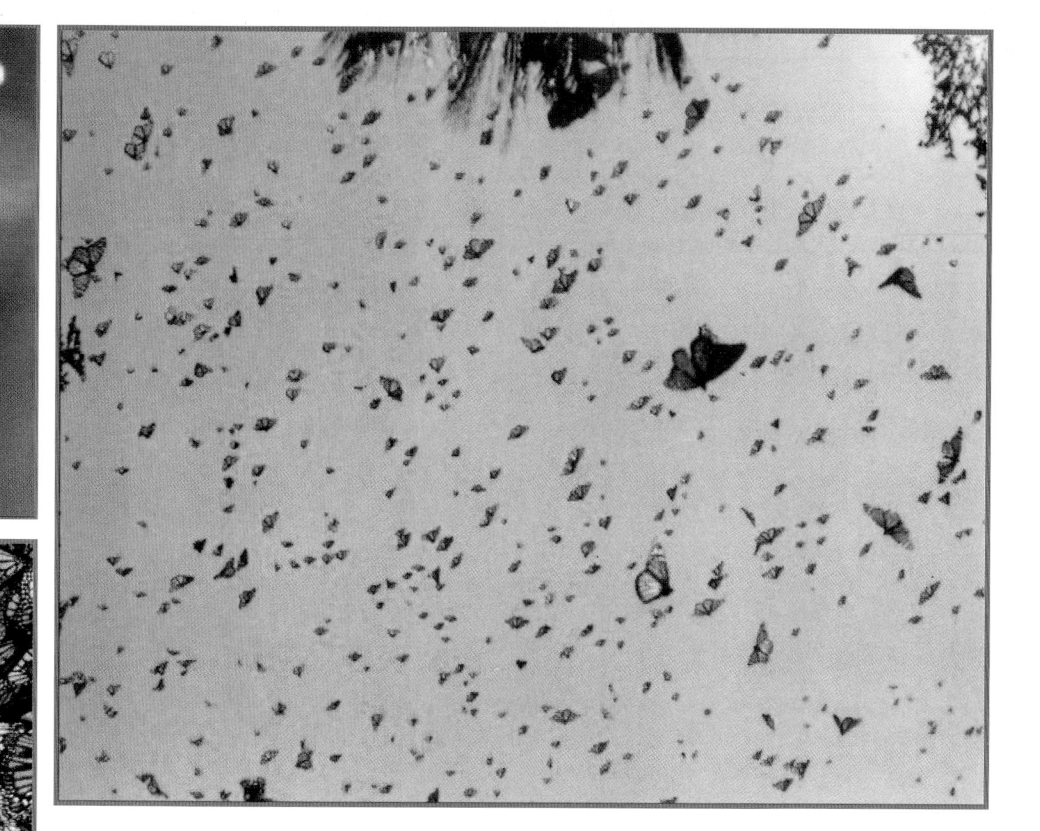

When it comes to the fourth generation, migration starts over again. This generation will live six months longer than the others will, and the chain will continue in the same way.

This interesting system provokes many questions: how is that the fourth of every four generations lives six months longer? How does this long-lived generation always coincide with winter and has done so for thousands of years? How do these butterflies always start migrating at the equinox, and how do they attune themselves so sensitively, or are they using a calendar?

No doubt, there are no answers to these questions through "evolution" or other variants on that theory. The butterflies must have borne these interesting characteristics from the time they came into existence. If the first fourth generation of Monarchs on earth did not have the characteristic to live long, then all the butterflies would die within that winter and these animals would become extinct.

Monarchs must have borne this extraordinary characteristic from the time they were created. "Coincidences" unquestionably do not have such a faculty as could arrange the generations of the animal according to migration. On the other hand, it is also unlikely that butterflies decided to make their fourth generations live longer and arranged their metabolisms, DNA and genes accordingly.

Obviously, the Monarchs were created possessing such features.

NATURE AND TECHNOLOGY

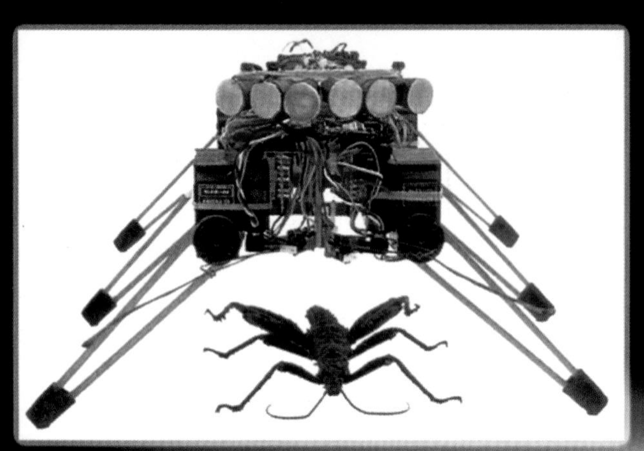

Robots and Bugs

Scientists working on robot technology do not fall short in observing bugs during their research. Those robots, which are made by taking the legs of bugs as reference, have a firmer balance when standing on the floor. Such robots, having sucker mechanisms placed on the tips of their feet, can walk on walls and ceilings like flies.

Each passing day, man makes new progress in technology, produces wonders in design and production. Human beings can design and produce new products with the skills Allah grants them. This point deserves particular attention, because Allah gives them this skill, so people have no right to be puffed up with pride or arrogant.

Nature is one of the pieces of evidence for this. Anyone, who looks around carefully, can see that Allah has gifted nature with countless wonders. Everywhere, every living being, from plants to animals, on land and in sea, is equipped with amazing features. In this chapter, where living beings that serve as examples of technology are presented, the purpose is to show that the things people think they have attained with their own skill already exist in nature and to remind us how wrong it is for man to be boastful.

Some designs produced by man after years of research, effort and technological development have existed in nature for millions of years. Scientists, who realise this, have been observing nature for a very long time and they make use of it in their inventions. They have started to develop new models by referring to the examples in nature. They have realised with some astonishment that there is a great difference between the techniques they use and the perfect techniques used in nature. This has led them to accept the existence of a superior Owner of Wisdom Who rules over nature. They understand that all these subtleties could not have been formed by coincidence. The owner of this supe-

The Velcro Bandage and the Burr

The Swiss engineer Georges de Mestral developed a new buttoning system called the Velcro Bandage by imitating burrs.
After spending a great deal of effort in getting rid of these parts of plants sticking to his clothes, Mestral thought to use the system of these plants in the clothing industry. He formed the same clasping system in an overcoat by putting the hooks of this part of the plant on one side and the curls of an animal's coat on the other.
Due to the flexibility of the hooks and curls, the system attaches and detaches easily, without wearing out. This is why the suits of astronauts are today equipped with Velcro bandages.

rior wisdom whose existence they have grasped through science is unquestionably Allah, the Sustainer of the heavens and the earth.

For instance, after dolphins were studied, a projection called the "dolphin snout" was added to ships' bows, which were initially produced in a "V" shape. Designers understood that the structure of the dolphin's snout is ideal for the best hydrodynamic cutting through water. No doubt, not only the structure of the snout, but all the features of the dolphin are ideal, because each one of them is the work of Allah Who is the **"Maker" (Surat al-Hashr: 24)**

In this chapter, we will review models, which designers produced by imitating nature as in the example of the dolphin. We will draw attention to the excellence of the creation of Allah. These features of living beings, each one of which is a wonder of design, are very important for appreciating the might of Allah. The features of living beings here covered have existed for millions of years, that is, since they were created. Man, however, has only been able to imitate some of their features in the last couple of centuries. For those who can see the evidence of the might of Allah, everything in nature is endowed with such features. This is stated in a verse:

> **(These are) an instruction and a reminder for every penitent human being. (Surah Qaf: 8)**

CONCORDE AND THE DOLPHIN

Dolphin snouts also served as a model for the designers of the Concorde. In a study conducted by engineers to reduce air friction on the outer surface of the Concorde, the spindle-shaped snout of the dolphin inspired them. The tail fin of the fish works as an engine in the water. Similarly, Concorde's motors were placed at the rear as is the driving motor-like fin of the dolphin and a very good result was obtained.

THE BOW OF THE SHIP AND THE DOLPHIN

The snout of the dolphin was taken as a model for the bows of modern ships.

Instead of the V-shaped bows, a structure similar to the snout of dolphins is used in big ships constructed today. This type of bow splits the water surface more efficiently, thus helps faster sailing with less energy consumption. The dolphin snout-type bows save up to 25% of fuel.

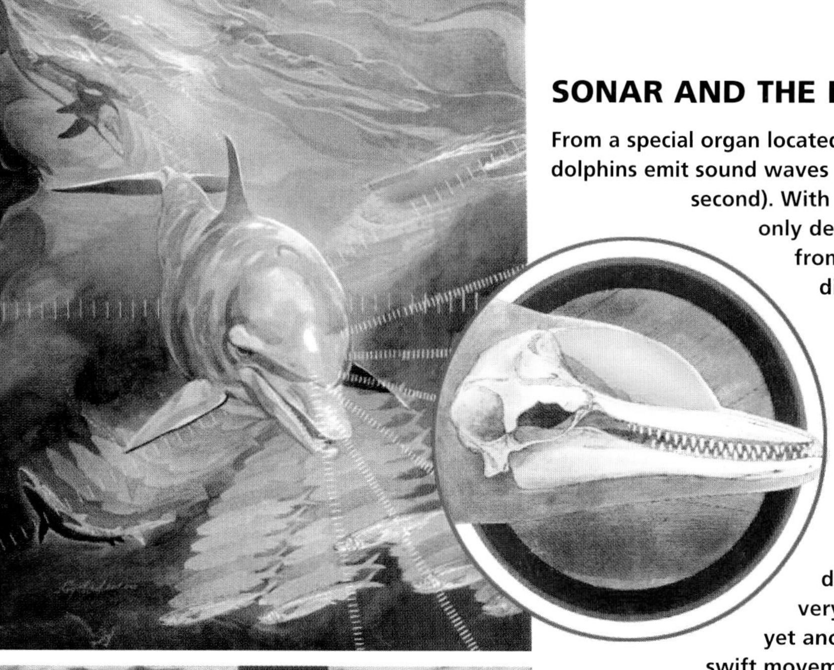

SONAR AND THE DOLPHIN

From a special organ located on the front part of their head, dolphins emit sound waves with 200,000 hertz (vibrations per second). With the help of these vibrations, they not only detect obstacles in their way but also, from the quality of the echo, estimate the direction, distance, speed, size and shape of the object in question. The working principle of sonar is the same as this faculty of dolphins.

SUBMARINES AND THE DOLPHIN

The shuttle-shaped body structure of dolphins earns them the ability to move very swiftly in water. Scientists discovered yet another feature that plays a big role in the swift movement of the fish:
The skin of the dolphin is made up of three layers. The outer layer is very thin and flexible. The inner layer is thick and made up of flexible hair which makes this layer look like a plastic-haired comb. The third layer in the middle is made of a sponge-like substance. A sudden pressure likely to effect the rapidly swimming dolphin is cushioned as it is transmitted into the inner layers.
After a four-year research, German submarine engineers managed to make a synthetic coating with the same feature. This coating was made up of two rubber layers and between the layers were bubbles similar to the skin cells of the dolphin. A 250% increase in the speed of submarines was observed in those in which these coatings were used.

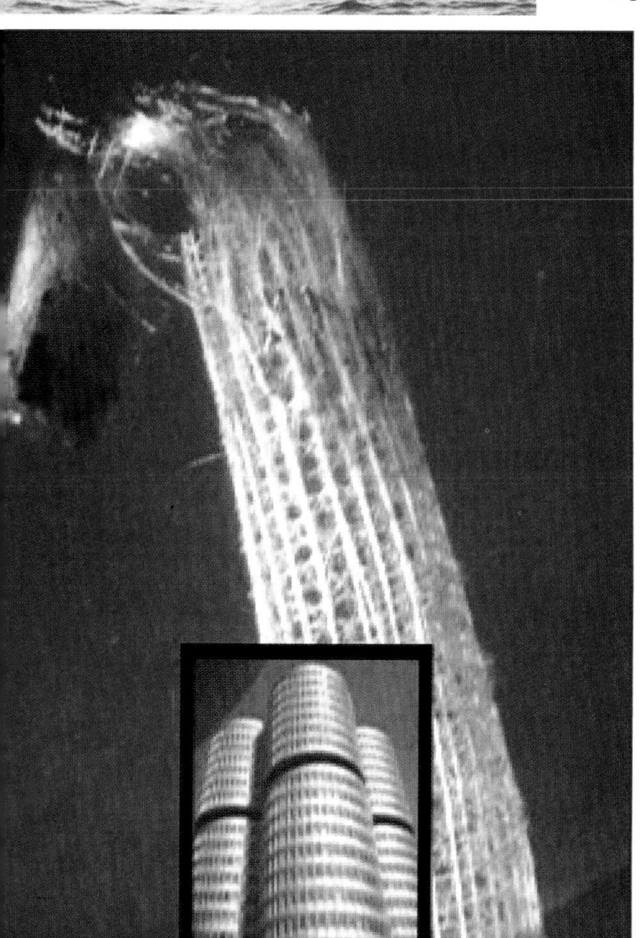

HEAT INSULATED CHIMNEYS AND THE NETTLE

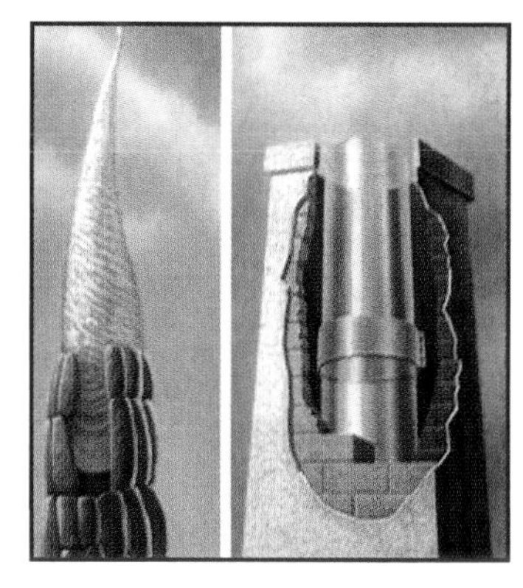

The insides of the nettle are coated with a hard layer made up of lime and silica. This special layer protects the plant against the caustic liquid produced by the plant. A German company has started to apply this protective quality of the nettle to the construction of factory chimneys.

THE SKELETON OF THE SPONGE

The sea sponge has an interwoven skeletal structure made up of glass-fibres and slim pin-like structures. This skeleton protects the sponge from all kinds of aquatic conditions. The BMW building, which is constructed by a similar technique, is, however, quite infirm in comparison with the skeletal structure of the sponge living in its aquatic medium.

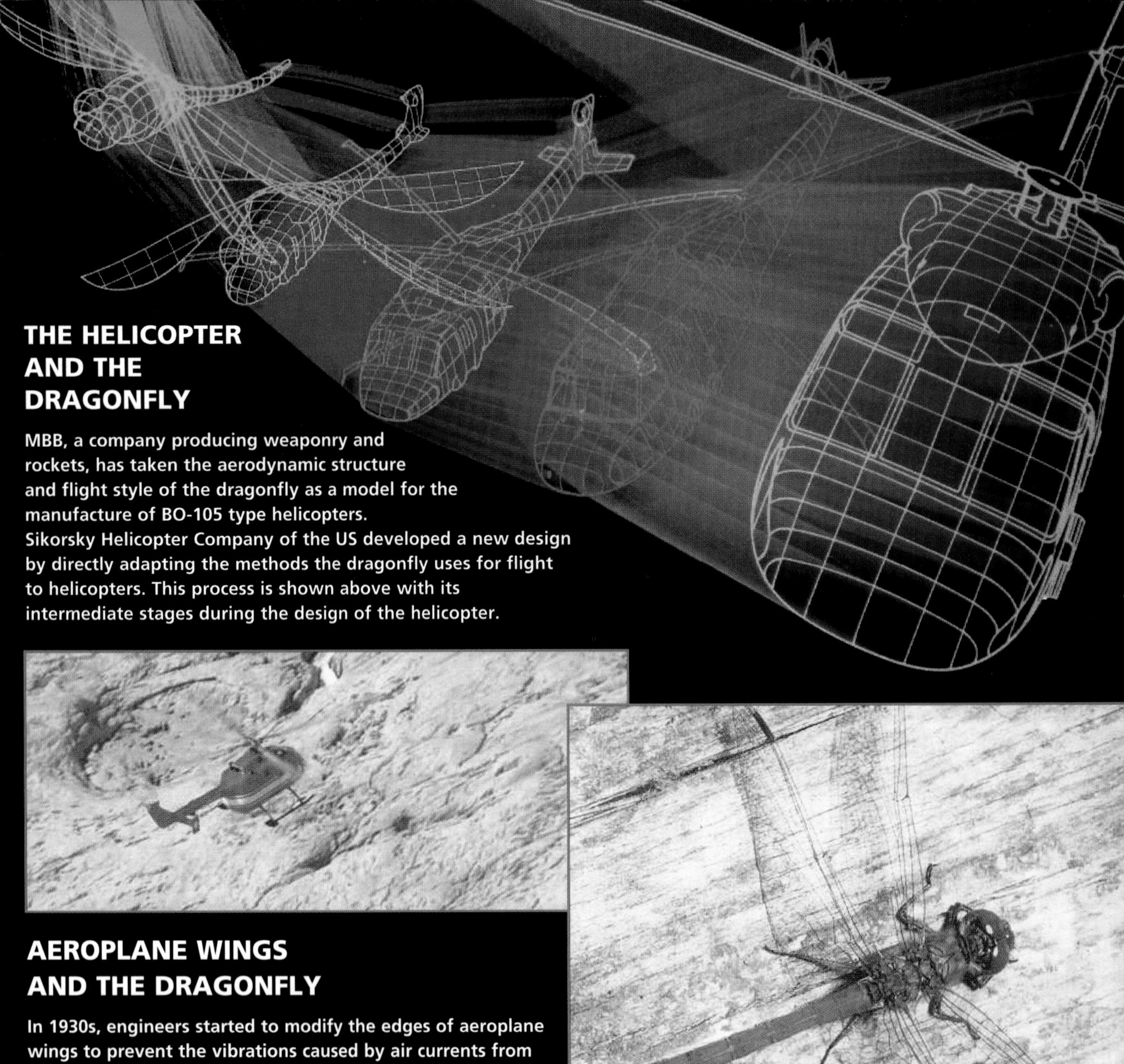

THE HELICOPTER AND THE DRAGONFLY

MBB, a company producing weaponry and rockets, has taken the aerodynamic structure and flight style of the dragonfly as a model for the manufacture of BO-105 type helicopters.
Sikorsky Helicopter Company of the US developed a new design by directly adapting the methods the dragonfly uses for flight to helicopters. This process is shown above with its intermediate stages during the design of the helicopter.

AEROPLANE WINGS AND THE DRAGONFLY

In 1930s, engineers started to modify the edges of aeroplane wings to prevent the vibrations caused by air currents from harming the vehicle. Twenty years later, scientists found out that this system had already been present in the wings of the dragonfly. The small black cells at the tip of the wings of the dragonfly serve the same function as the weight on the tip of aeroplane wings.

THE VULTURE AND THE AEROPLANE

The vulture opens the feathers at the tip of its wings like the fingers of a hand and thus diminishes the air whirlpools formed by its wings. (left) The picture above shows a model that is prepared to apply the same aerodynamic structure to aeroplanes.

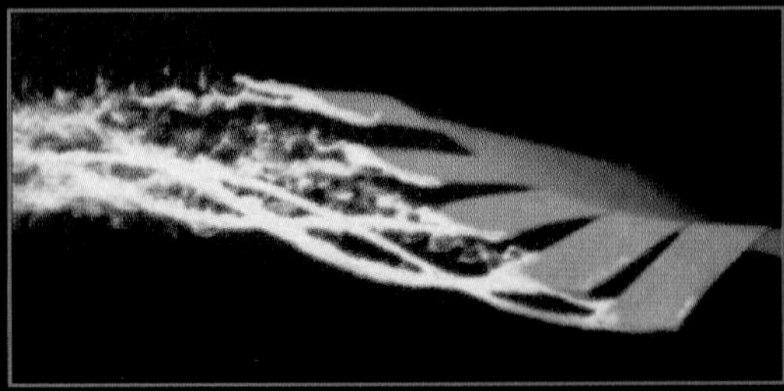

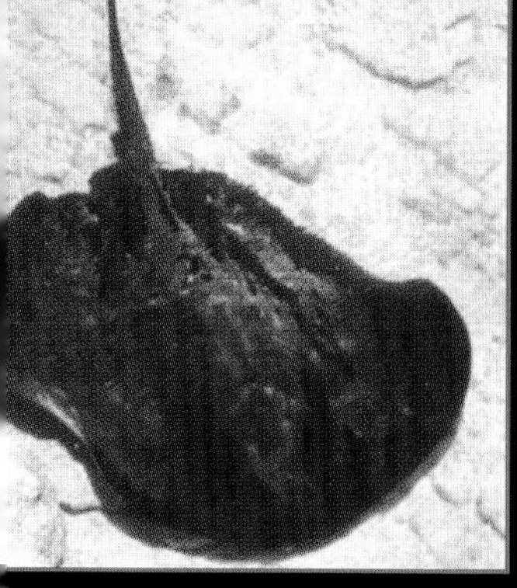

RADAR AND THE BAT

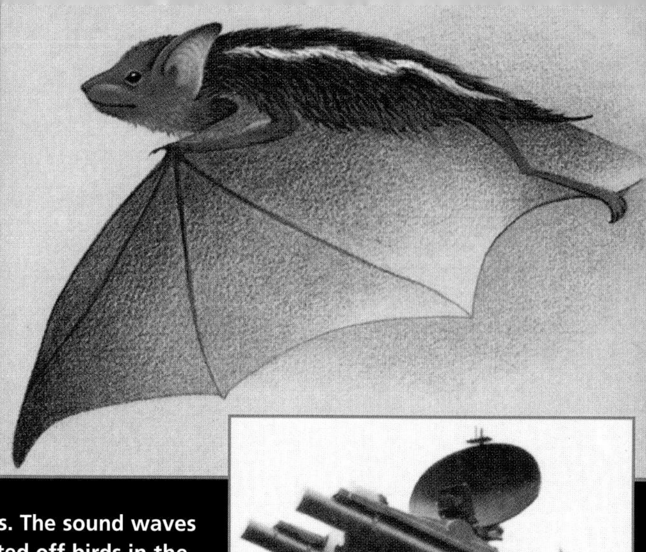

Having such weak sight as to be considered "blind", bats emit very high frequency sound waves called ultrasound. These sounds, which are over 20,000 hertz (cycles per second), are inaudible to human beings. The sound waves emitted by bats are reflected off birds in the air, animals on the ground and other objects that stand in the bat's way. The bat determines its direction and orientation according to these reflected vibrations. Radars work on the same principle.

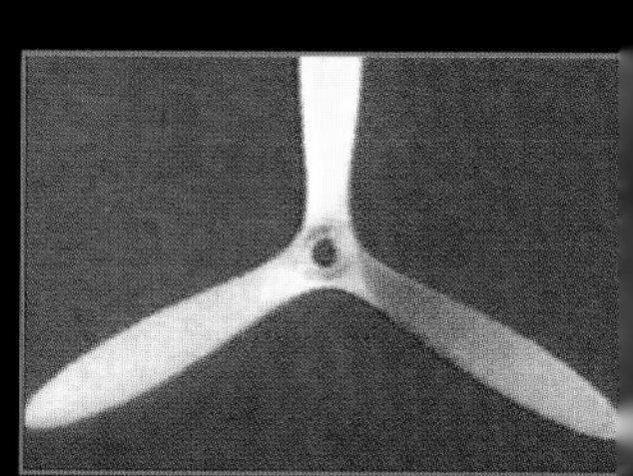

IE AEROPLANE ID THE CATFISH

flat shape of the catfish, which is y effective hydrodynamically, has a model for aeroplane design. ay, flat-shaped models are nmonly used both in the aments industry and civil aviation. instance, the "Orient Express" del by McDonald Douglas looks like tfish. Twice as fast as sound, the shape of this new model keeps air stance during flight to a minimum.

THE CHICORY SEED AND THE PARACHUTE

The seeds of the wild chicory plant make a long trip floating in the air by means of winds. The principle of parachutes is the same as that of this plant.

THE MAPLE SEED AND THE PROPELLER

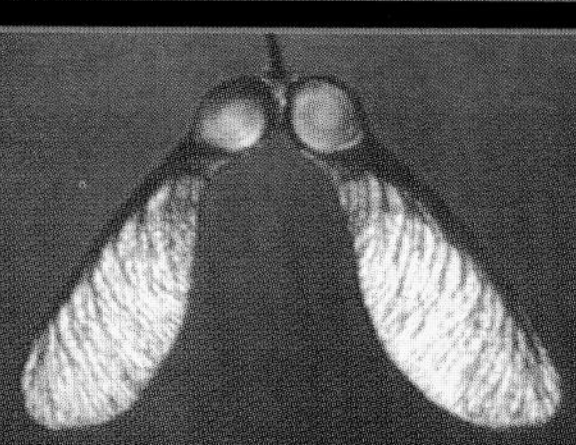

The shape of the maple seed causes it to rotate around itself very rapidly as it falls to the ground. This shape inspired Sir George Cayley, one of the first experts on aviation.

SUBMARINE AND THE NAUTILUS

en it wants to dive, the nautilus fills the little chambers in its y with water. When it wants to surface, it pumps a special it produces into these little cells and discharges the water. The same type of chambers as those in the nautilus are utilised in submarines, where water taken in is discharged via water engines.

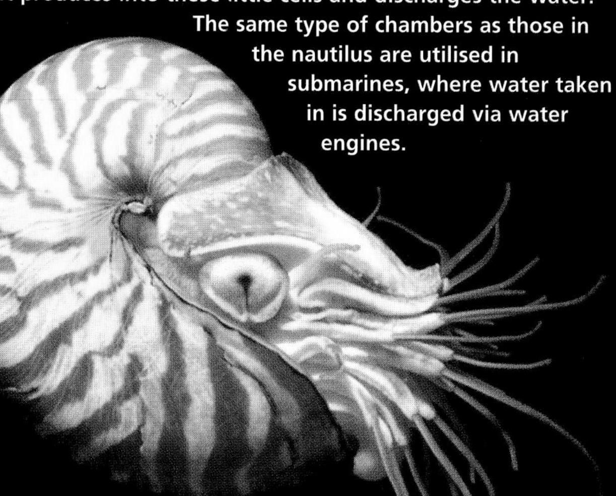

THE MOUTH OF FLY AND THE ZIP

t has only been a century since zips were invented. Yet, flies have been using the zip system, for the hundreds of thousands of years since they were created, to lock their lower lips.
he proboscis expands at its tip thus helping to disclose the natural zip.

THE TELESCOPE AND THE BEE AND HONEYCOMB

Honeycombs serve as models for the frames of telescopes.
The lens of a space telescope, which is designed to collect X-rays emitted by heavenly bodies, is manufactured from hexagonal mirrors, in imitation of beehives.
The reason why hexagonal mirrors are used is that with this shape, no area is wasted, and combinations of hexagons reinforce the general structure. In addition, a sequence made up of hexagons provides a wide field of view and a high quality telescope. Interestingly enough, the eyes of bees have been made of hexagonal units for millions of years since they were created, just as this telescope.

THE BUTTERFLY AND THE HOSE-PIPE

The butterfly's proboscis is an advanced tool equipped with numerous technical details. At moments of rest, the proboscis is coiled up like a watch's helical spring. When the butterfly wants to feed, a special muscle in the proboscis swings into action. When the proboscis is unwrapped to take the shape of a pipe, it can even suck the flower's nectar from the deepest petals.
he straws we use to drink beverages also have the same system.

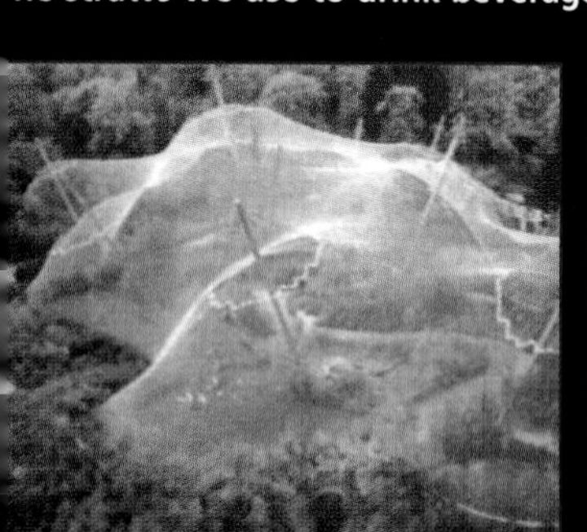
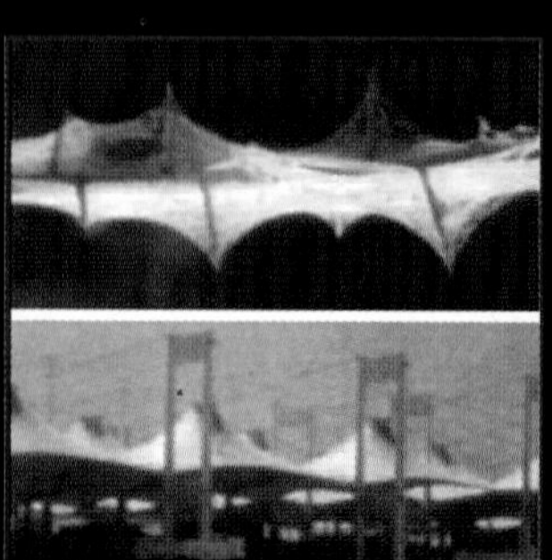

ARCHITECTURE AND THE COBWEB

he tight structure of the cobweb made by the dew spider does not ermit the web to be torn. In our day, this feature of the web has een discovered by civil engineers, who use the same system with ne help of barbed wire. The Hajj Terminal in Jeddah Airport, and Munich Zoo are just two buildings constructed making use of this rinciple.

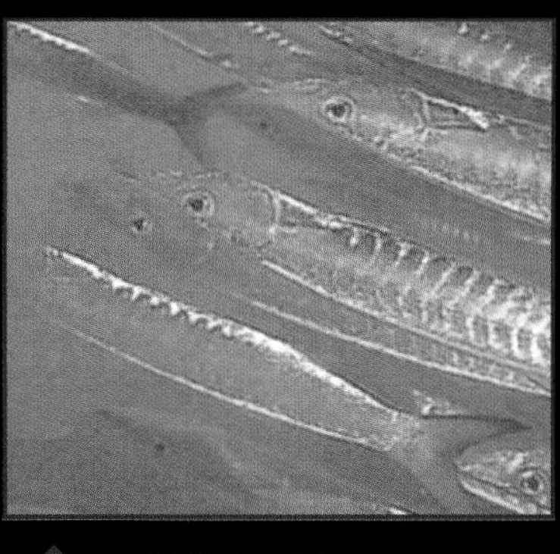

FLUIDITY AND THE BLUE TROUT

New York firemen add a substance called 'Yolioks', which is similar to the viscous gelatinous substance produced by the blue trout, to the tank water of their vehicles. This substance increases the speed of water flow at the hosepipe's nozzle. This system increases the water's pouring volume by 50%. The mucoid fluid covering the blue trout's skin reduces friction in the same manner, and helps these fish proceed easily in water despite strong water resistance.

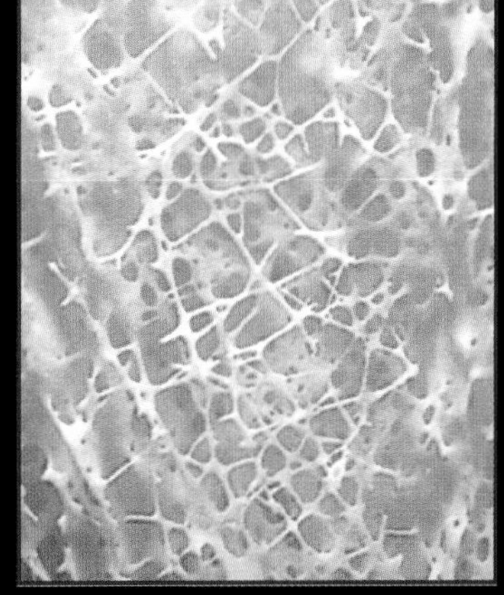

THE EIFFEL TOWER AND THE HUMAN BONE

While designing the famous tower, Maurice Koechlin, assistant to Eiffel, the architect of the tower, was inspired by the femur, the lightest and strongest bone of the human body. The result has been a self-ventilated and strong structure. The femur, which has been a source of inspiration for the tower, is in the shape of a pipe and has a fusiform internal structure, i.e. in which the bone narrows in the middle and expands at each end. This structure provides flexibility and lightness for the bones, yet does not cause them to lose a bit of their strength. In buildings that are constructed in this way, construction material is saved, and the construction's skeletons gain firmness and flexibility.

THE SNORKEL AND GNAT LARVAE

The gnat larva that develops in water satisfies its need for oxygen through an air pipe reaching to the water surface. The hair around the pipe prevents water from leaking in just as the stopper on the top of the snorkel does.

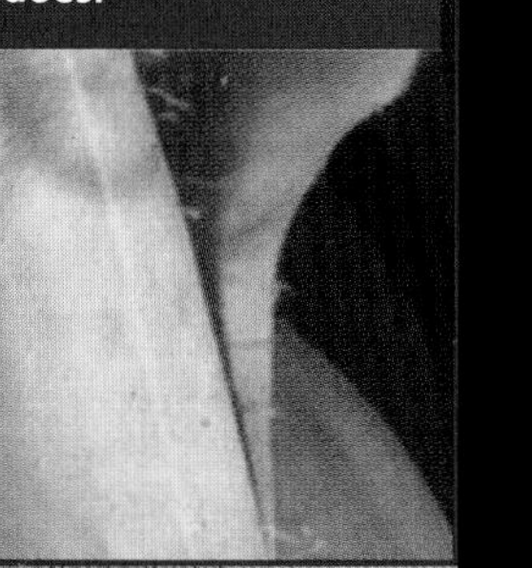

THE ROBOT AND THE WORM

Researchers from Amiens University took the worm as a model and manufactured a worm-like robot consisting of independent components. This robot can proceed in canals, in which man cannot move, to detect water leakages or make measurements.

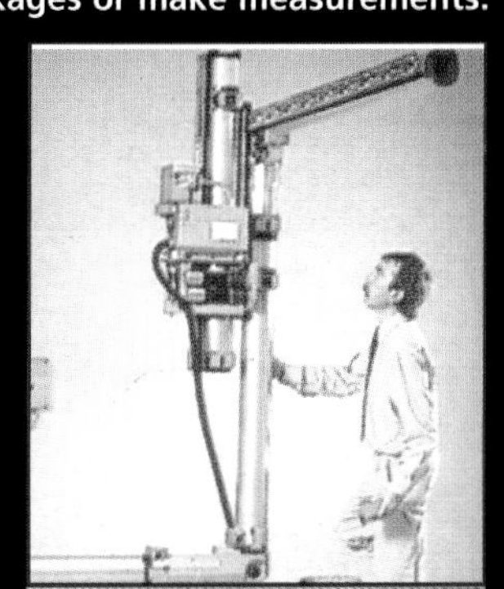

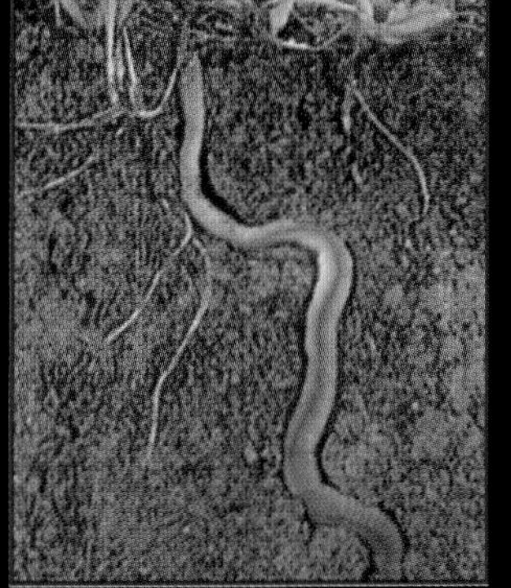

THE CROCUS FLOWER AND THE SENSITIVE THERMOMETER

The crocus is a flower equipped with a bio-thermometer. This plant opens, when the temperature rises to a favourable degree and then starts to close again, when it falls below it. The Schott Company, which imitated this flower's sensitivity to temperature, produced thermometers measuring temperature changes of even 0.001^{o} C. (Bild Der Wissenschaft, February 1990)

THE CORN ROOT AND LIGHT CONDUCTING GLASS CABLES

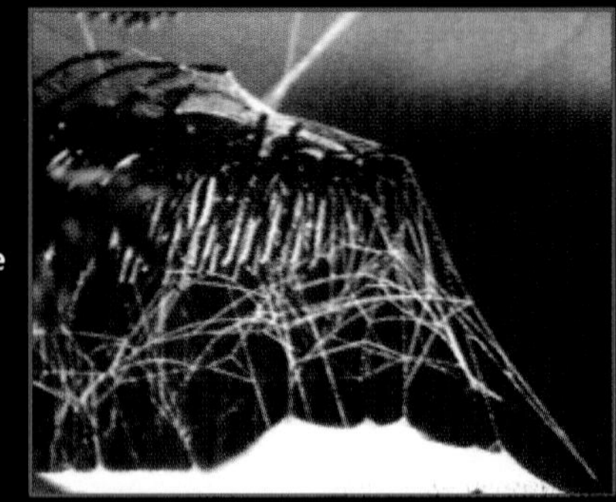

An equivalent of light-conducting glass cables already existed thousands of years ago. Researchers, however, have only recently discovered that cables can convey light. The shoot of corn seed can conduct daylight to the deepest place of the root and it helps develop the corn seeds. Fibre optics, which has this light-conducting feature, is extensively used in many areas from traffic signs to inter-computer data transfer.

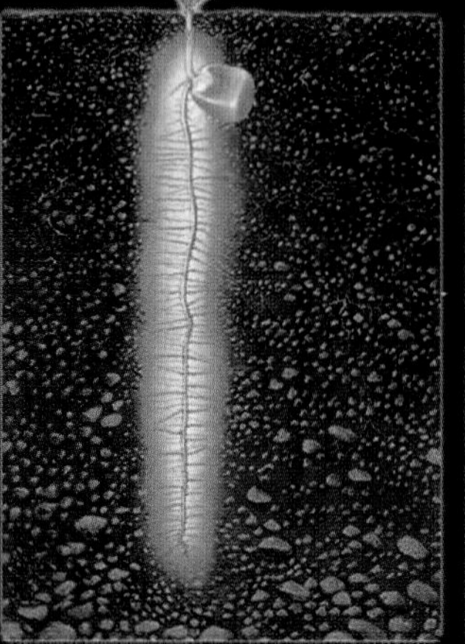

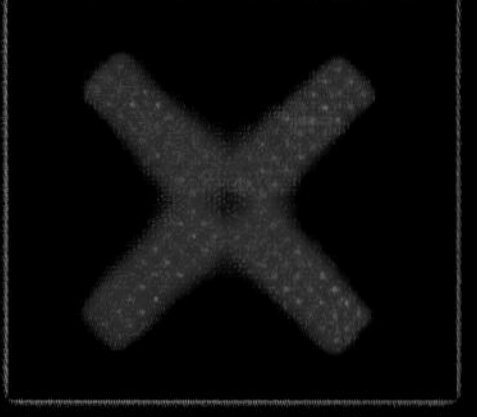

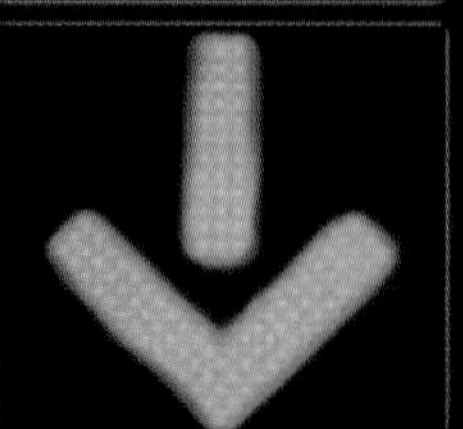

THE MUNICH OLYMPIC STADIUM AND THE COBWEB

In the construction of the ceiling coatings of the Munich Olympic Stadium, the structure of the crested lark spider's home, which it makes by stretching web on grasses and bushes, is taken as a model.

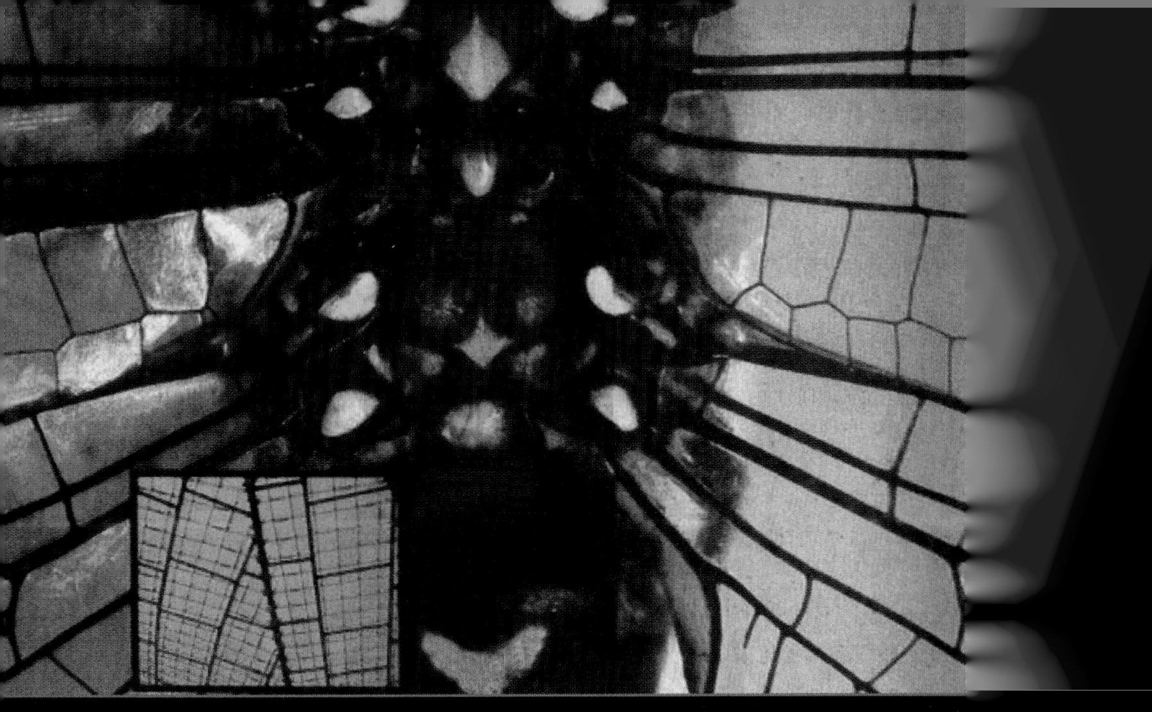

THE MUNICH OLYMPIC STADIUM AND THE DRAGONFLY'S WINGS

Despite its thinness, the dragonfly's wing is very strong because it is made up of approximately 1,000 compartments. Owing to this divided structure, the wings of the animal are not torn and they resist air pressure. The roof of the Munich Olympic Stadium is constructed according to the same principle (see little photograph).

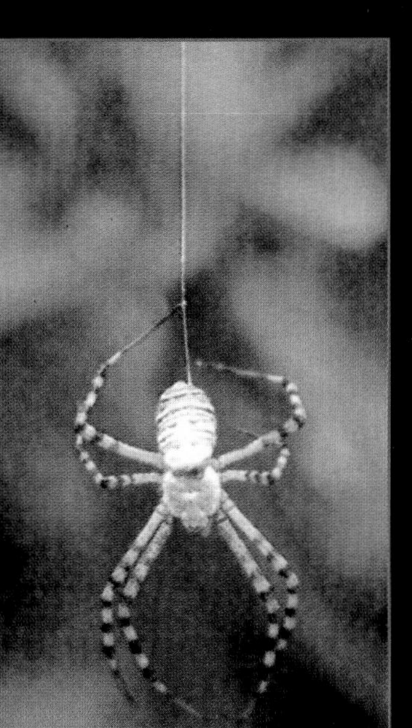

THE SPIDER AND THE THREAD INDUSTRY

Scientists still work to imitate the thread of the spider, which is thin, yet far stronger than steel ropes of the same thickness.

He is the Orig
heavens and
...He created
and He has k
all things. Th
your Lord.
god but Him,
of everything.
Him. He is r
for ever
(Surat al-An'a

STRAW AND THE SKELET STRUCTURE BUILDING

The interior webbed structure of straw make flexible and strong. The same construction techn is used in the skeletal

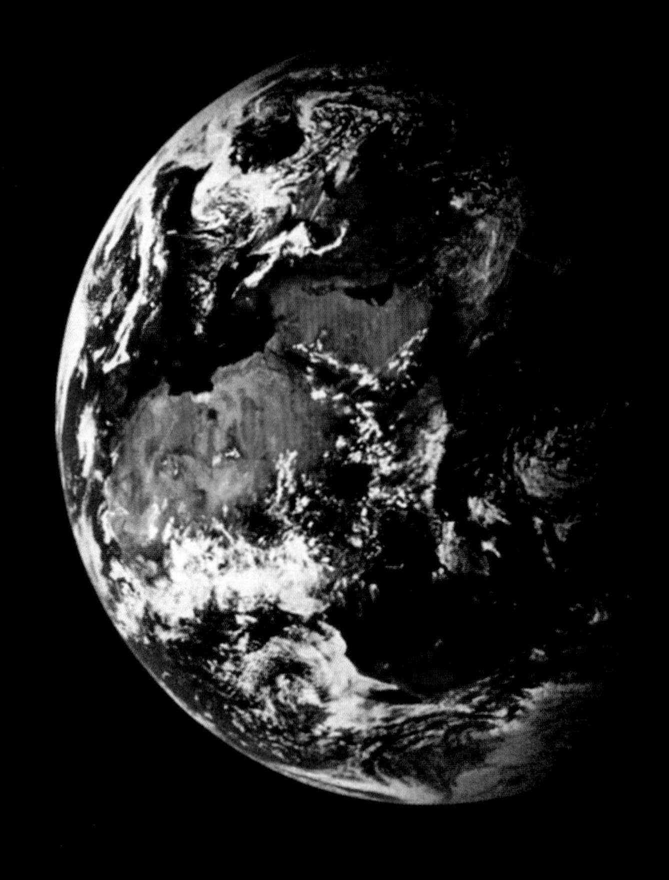

Do you not see that Allah has subjected
to you everything in the heavens and earth
and has showered His blessings upon you,
both outwardly and inwardly? Yet there are people
who argue about Allah without knowledge
or guidance or any illuminating Book.

(Surah Luqman: 20)

A PLANET CREATED FOR MANKIND

Materialist philosophy offers a single explanation of the order and balance in the universe: it is coincidence. According to this claim, the whole universe is shaped through coincidences.

However, when we investigate the universe only briefly, we see that this claim is completely unreal. Coincidence only leads to chaos whereas order, rather than chaos, prevails in the universe. This order proves to us the being and eternal power of Allah, Who created the universe out of nothing and then gave it a shape.

When we explore the universe, we encounter numerous examples of order. The world we live in is only one of those. With all its features, the world is created with extremely delicate balances making it suitable for the survival of living beings.

The distance of the earth from the sun, the inclination of its axis to its orbit, the balances in the atmosphere, the rotational speed of the earth around its axis and around the sun, the functions of oceans and mountains on the earth, the features of living beings and the interactions of all those, are just a few elements of this ecological balance.

When earth is compared with other planets, it becomes even more evident that it is especially designed for man. Water, for instance, is a compound that is very rarely found in space. The liquid form of water exists only in our planet out of all the planets in the solar system. Moreover, 70% of the world is covered with water. Millions of varieties of living beings live in this medium. The freezing of water, its capacity to attract and store heat, the existence of very large masses of water in the form of oceans, and the even distribution of heat across the world are all exclusive characteristics of the earth. No other planet has such a liquid mass in constant circulation.

The axis of the earth makes a 23-degree inclination to its orbit. Seasons are formed due to this inclination. If this inclination were a little more or less than it is now, temperature differences between seasons would reach extremes and unbearably hot summers and extremely cold winters would take place on the earth.

The earth's rotation around its axis is at the most appropriate speed for living beings. When we look at other planets in the solar system, we see that they also experience night and day. However, because the time differences are far bigger than those in the world, the temperature differences between day and night are very high. The fierce wind activity in the atmospheres of other planets is not experienced in the world's atmosphere thanks to this balanced rotation.

The gases making up the atmosphere and their concentration in the atmosphere are extremely important for the existence not only of human beings but also of all living beings on the earth. The formation of the gasses in the atmosphere in just the right proportions that remain constant is made possible by the co-existence of numerous delicate balances.

Hundreds of points can be listed in addition to the above mentioned features. Even the examples quoted so far, however, reveal to us a certain reality:

The world in which we live is very specially constructed for the survival of living beings. It is the product not of coincidence but of a conscious order.

This perfect order prevailing throughout the universe leads us to a single conclusion: a Creator with infinite power and wisdom, that is, Allah, Who is the Possessor of all worlds, created the universe.

THE GREAT BALANCE IN THE ATMOSPHERE

There are four basic gasses in the atmosphere. These are nitrogen (78%), oxygen (21%), argon (less than 1%), and carbon dioxide (0.03%). Gasses in the atmosphere fall into two groups: "those that are reactive" and "those that are non-reactive". Analysis on reactive gasses reveals that the reactions they enter into are essential for life whereas non-reactive gasses produce compounds that are destructive for life when they enter into reaction. For instance, argon and nitrogen are inactive gasses. They can be involved in very few chemical reactions. However, if these could react easily, like oxygen, the oceans would turn into nitric acid, for example.

On the other hand, oxygen reacts with other atoms, organic compounds, and even rocks. These reactions yield the most basic molecules of life such as water and carbon dioxide.

In addition to the reactivity of gasses, their present concentrations are also highly critical for life.

Let us look at oxygen, for instance. Oxygen is the most abundant reactive gas in our atmosphere. The high oxygen concentration of our atmosphere is one of the features that distinguish earth from other planets in the solar system in which even minute amounts of oxygen are not present.

If there were more oxygen in the atmosphere, oxidation would take place quicker and rocks and metals would be eroded sooner. Hence, the earth would be eroded and disintegrate, and animate life would face a great threat. If we had a little less oxygen, respiration would become harder, and less of the ozone gas would be produced. Changes in the amount of ozone would be fatal for life. Less ozone would cause the solar ultra-violet rays to reach the world in greater intensity causing living things to vanish. More ozone would prevent the sun's heat reaching the earth and thus be fatal.

Carbon dioxide has similar delicate balances. Plants absorb the sun's radiation via this gas, mix it with water, form bicarbonate that dissolves rocks, and leave it in oceans. They also break this gas down and release oxygen back into the atmosphere. Thus, oxygen, an essential for living beings, is constantly released into the atmosphere. This gas also helps the world maintain a "greenhouse effect" keeping its present temperature constant.

If there were less carbon dioxide, the amount of plant-life on land and in the sea would be reduced, leaving less food for animals. There would be less bicarbonate in the oceans, thus causing an increase in acidity. An increase in carbon dioxide in the atmosphere would expedite the chemical erosion of land forming a detrimental alkali residue in oceans. In addition, the greenhouse effect would increase, thus causing the surface temperature of the earth to rise and life on earth to be destroyed.

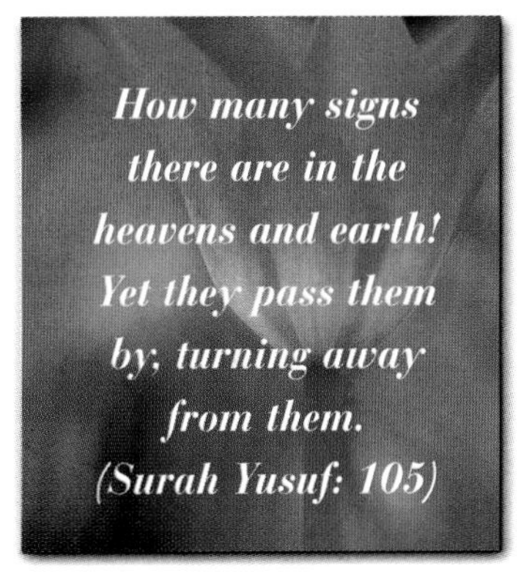

How many signs there are in the heavens and earth! Yet they pass them by, turning away from them.
(Surah Yusuf: 105)

As seen, the existence of the atmosphere has great importance for the continuation of life on earth. A number of astrophysical conditions have to co-exist for the atmosphere to be maintained.

A) The earth's surface has to remain at a certain moderate temperature, within definite limits. For this:

1. The earth has to be a certain distance from the sun. This distance plays a role in the quantity of heat energy reaching the earth from the sun. A slight deviation in the earth's orbit around the sun – either drawing closer or farther – would cause great changes in the heat reaching the earth from the sun. Calculations show that a 13% decrease in the heat reaching the earth would cause it to be covered with an ice layer 1,000 metres thick. A slight increase in energy, on the other hand, would cause all living things to be scorched.

2. The temperature should be homogeneous across the earth. For this, the world has to rotate about its axis at a certain speed (1,670 km/hr at the equator). If the earth's speed of rotation were to exceed a certain limit, the atmosphere would grow extremely warm, increasing the gas molecules' velocity of

escape from the earth and causing the atmosphere to be dispersed in space and to vanish.

If the earth's velocity of rotation were slower than required, then gas molecules' velocity of escape from the earth would decrease and they would also disappear through being absorbed by the earth because of the effect of gravitation.

3. The 23°27' inclination of the earth's axis prevents the excess heat between the poles and the equator liable to pose an obstacle to the formation of the atmosphere. If this inclination had not existed, the temperature difference between the polar zones and the equator would increase enormously, making it impossible for a life-supportive atmosphere to exist.

Mankind! Worship your Lord, who created you and those before you, so that hopefully you will have taqwa. It is He who made the earth a couch for you, and the sky a dome. (Surat al-Baqarah: 21-22)

B) A layer is needed to prevent the dispersion of generated heat:

To keep the earth's surface temperature at a constant level, temperature loss must be prevented, particularly at nights. For this purpose, there is a need for a compound to prevent heat loss from the atmosphere. This need is met by introducing carbon dioxide in the atmosphere. Carbon dioxide covers the earth like a quilt and prevents the loss of heat to space.

C) On earth, there are certain structures maintaining the balance of heat between the poles and the equator:

There is a heat difference of 120°C between the poles and the equator. If such a heat difference had existed on a more even surface, there would be tremendous atmospheric movement, and heavy storms with speed of 1,000 km per hour would turn the world upside down. Because of these storms, the equilibrium in the atmosphere would soon be destroyed and the atmosphere would dissipate.

However, the earth is uneven and that blocks potential powerful air currents that might have arisen due to the heat difference. The unevenness starts with the Himalayas between the Indian sub-continent and China, continues with the Taurus Mountains in Anatolia, and reaches the Alps in Europe through mountain-chains joining the Atlantic Ocean in the west and the Pacific Ocean in the east. In the oceans, the excess heat formed at the equator is channelled to north and south due to the properties of liquids, thus balancing the heat differences.

As seen, the existence of air, one of the basic elements of life, has become possible only with the establishment of thousands of physical and ecological balances. Moreover, the establishment of those conditions alone on our planet is not sufficient for the continuation of life on earth. If the world were to exist in its present state with its geophysical structure and its motion in space, yet have a different position in the galaxy, the balance would still be upset.

For instance, a smaller star instead of the sun would cause the earth to grow extremely cold, and a bigger star would scorch the earth.

It is sufficient to look at the dead planets in space in order to understand that the earth is not a result of random coincidence. The conditions essential for life are too complicated to have been formed "on their own" and at random, and, certainly within the solar system, the earth alone is especially created for life.

THE NITROGEN BALANCE AND BACTERIA

The nitrogen cycle is another evidence that the earth is especially designed for human life.

Nitrogen is one of the basic elements found in the tissues of all living organisms. Although 78% of the atmosphere consists of nitrogen, human beings and animals cannot absorb it directly. It is the main function of bacteria to meet our need for nitrogen.

The nitrogen cycle starts with the gas nitrogen (N_2) in the air. Bacteria living in some plants transform nitrogen in the air into ammonia (NH_3). Other

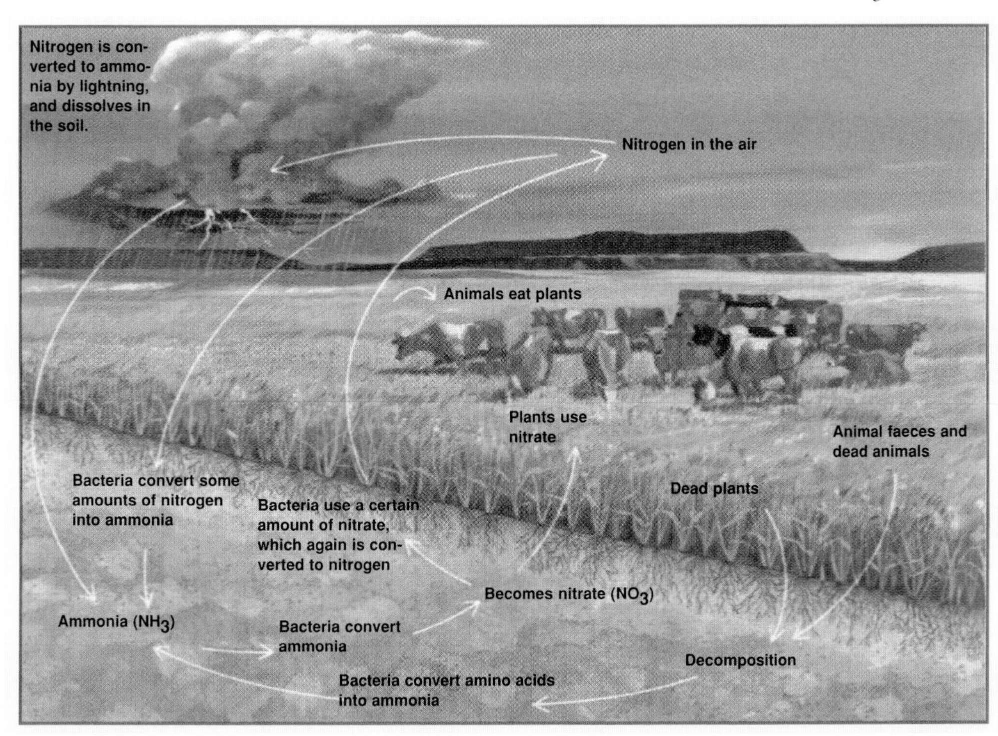
Nitrogen is converted to ammonia by lightning, and dissolves in the soil.
Nitrogen in the air
Animals eat plants
Plants use nitrate
Animal faeces and dead animals
Dead plants
Bacteria convert some amounts of nitrogen into ammonia
Bacteria use a certain amount of nitrate, which again is converted to nitrogen
Becomes nitrate (NO_3)
Ammonia (NH_3)
Bacteria convert ammonia
Decomposition
Bacteria convert amino acids into ammonia

types of bacteria, on the other hand, transform ammonia into nitrate (NO_3). (Lightning also plays an important role in the transformation of the nitrogen in the air into ammonia.)

At the next stage, living things that produce their own food, such as green plants, absorb nitrogen. Animals and human beings that cannot produce their own food can meet their nitrogen need only by eating these plants.

The nitrogen in animals and human beings returns to nature through their faeces and their corpses which bacteria decompose. While doing so, bacteria not only perform the task of cleaning but also release ammonia, the main source of nitrogen. While a certain amount of ammonia is converted to carbon by some other bacteria and mixes with the air, another part is converted to nitrate by other types of bacteria. Plants use them and the cycle continues.

The lack of bacteria in this cycle alone would bring the end of life. Without bacteria, plants could not meet their need for carbon and would soon become extinct. It is not possible to talk of life in a place where no plants exist.

THE EARTH'S PRESERVED AND PROTECTED ROOF: THE ATMOSPHERE

Though we are generally not aware of them, many meteorites fall on the earth as well as on other planets. The reason why these meteorites, which form giant craters when they fall on other planets, do not harm the earth is that the atmosphere exerts very strong friction on the falling meteors. Meteors cannot withstand this friction for long and lose immense mass by being burned. Thus, capable of causing great disasters, this danger is averted thanks to the atmosphere.

In the Qur'an, this characteristic in the creation of the atmosphere is explained: "**We made the sky a preserved and protected roof yet still they**

The Van Allen radiation belts.

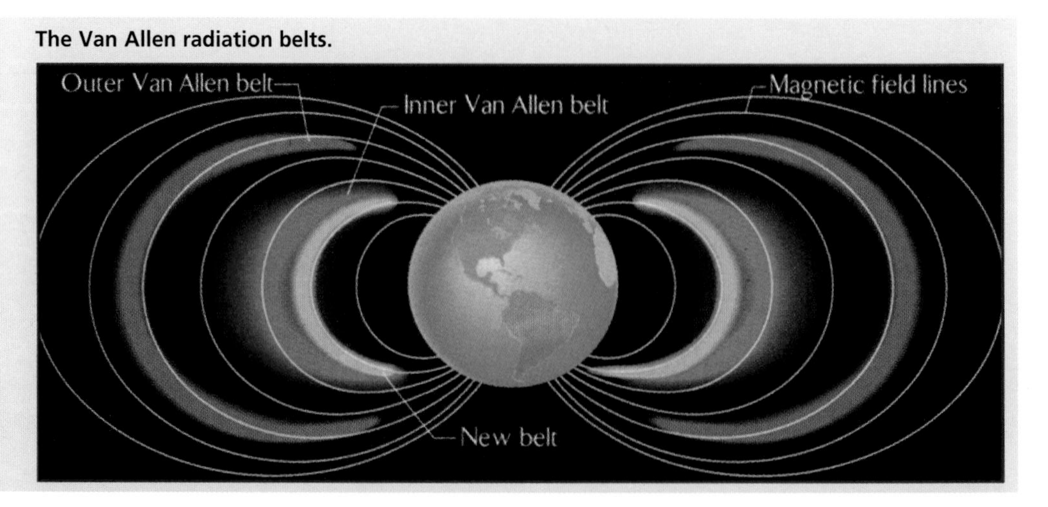

If the atmosphere did not have a protective shield, the earth would be left defenceless against showers of meteors.

turn away from Our signs." (Surat al-Anbiya: 32)

One of the most important indications that the sky is "a preserved and protected roof" is the magnetic field surrounding the earth. The top layer of the atmosphere is made up of a magnetic zone called the "Van Allen Belt". This zone is formed by the qualities of the earth's core.

The core of the earth contains heavy magnetic elements like iron and nickel. What is more important, however, is that the core is composed of two distinct structures. The inner core is solid while the outer core is liquid. The outer layer floats on top of the inner layer, creating a magnetic effect on heavy metals, which in turn forms a magnetic field. The Van Allen Belt is an extension of this magnetic zone reaching the outer layer of the atmosphere. This magnetic field shields the earth against possible dangers from space.

One of the most serious of these dangers is the "solar winds". Apart from heat, light and radiation, the sun sends the earth a wind made up of protons and electrons moving at a speed of 1.5 million kilometres per hour.

Solar winds cannot pass through the Van Allen Belts, which create magnetic fields at a distance of 40,000 miles from the earth. When the solar wind, in the form of a rain of particles, runs into this magnetic field, it decomposes and flows around this field.

The atmosphere absorbs most of the X-rays and ultraviolet rays emitted by the sun. Without this absorption, life on earth would be impossible.

The atmospheric zones surrounding us only let harmless rays, radio waves, and visible light reach the earth. If our atmosphere did not have such impermeability, we could neither use radio waves for communication nor have daylight, which is the basis of life.

The ozone layer surrounding the earth prevents harmful ultraviolet rays from the sun from reaching the earth. Ultraviolet rays from the sun are so charged with energy that they could kill all living things on earth. For this reason, to make life possible on earth, the ozone layer is another especially created part of the "preserved and protected roof" of the sky.

Ozone is produced from oxygen. While there are two oxygen atoms in the (O_2) molecules of oxygen gas, there are three oxygen atoms in the (O_3) molecules of ozone gas. Ultraviolet rays coming from the sun add one more atom to the oxygen molecule to form the ozone molecule. The ozone layer, which is formed by the action of ultraviolet, arrests fatal ultraviolet rays and thus constitutes one of the most basic conditions of life on earth.

Briefly, if the earth's core did not have the quality of forming magnetic field, and the atmosphere did not have the structure and density to filter harmful rays, life on earth would be out of the question. It is, no doubt, impossible for any human being or any other living being to have ordered those. It is evident that Allah has created those protective features that are critically essential for human life, and that He created the sky as a "preserved and protected roof".

That other planets lack such "preserved and protected roofs" is another indication that the earth is specially designed for human life. For instance, the entire core of the planet Mars is solid and therefore there is no protective magnetic shield around it. Because Mars is not as big as the earth, not enough pressure has been generated to form the liquid part of the core. In addition, being the right size alone is not enough for the formation of a magnetic field around a planet. For instance, the diameter of Venus is almost the same as that of the earth. Its mass is only 2% less than the earth's and its weight is almost the same as the earth's. Therefore, both in terms of pressure and for other reasons, it is inevitable that a metallic liquid part should form in the core of Venus. However, there is no magnetic field around Venus, the reason being the relatively slower rotation of Venus as compared to earth. While earth completes its rotation about its axis in one day, Venus does so in 243 days.

The sizes of the moon and other neighbouring planets and their distances to the earth are also important for the existence of the magnetic field constituting the "preserved and protected roof" of the earth. If one of these planets was bigger than its actual size, it would cause it to have a greater gravitational force. A neighbouring planet with such a large gravitational force would change the velocity of the liquid and solid parts of the earth's core and prevent the formation of a magnetic field in its present form.

Briefly, the sky's having the quality of a "preserved and protected roof" requires that many variables such as the structure of the earth's core, its rotational speed, the distance between planets, and the masses of planets converge at the most correct point.

THE WATER CYCLE AND LIFE

Each moment, millions of cubic metres of water are carried from the oceans to the atmosphere and then to the land. Life depends on this giant water cycle. If we had attempted to arrange this cycle, we would not have been able to succeed even if we had used all the technology in the world. Through evaporation, however, we obtain water, the first and foremost condition of life, without any extra cost or energy. Each year 45 million cubic metres of water evaporate from the oceans. The evaporated water is carried by winds over the lands in the form of clouds. Each year, 3-4 million cubic metres of water are carried from oceans to lands, and therefore to us.

Simply put, water, over whose cycle we have no control, and without which we cannot live more than a few days, is sent to us in a very special way.

The Qur'an reminds us that this is one of the most evident signs for which man should be "grateful":

Have you thought about the water that you drink? Is it you who sent it down from the clouds or are We the Sender? If We wished We could

Do you not see that Allah sends down water from the sky and threads it through the earth to emerge as springs and then by it brings forth crops of varying colours, which then wither and you see them turning yellow and then He makes them into broken stubble? There is a reminder in that for people of intelligence. (Surat az-Zumar: 21)

It is He who sends down water from the sky. From it you drink and from it come the shrubs among which you graze your herds. And by it He makes crops grow for you and olives and dates and grapes and fruit of every kind. There is certainly a sign in that for people who reflect. (Surat an-Nahl: 10-11)

have made it bitter, so will you not give thanks? (Surat al-Waqi'ah: 68-70)

RAIN IS SENT DOWN IN MEASURED AMOUNTS

In the eleventh verse of Surat az-Zukhruf, rain is defined as water sent down in "measured amounts". "It is He (Allah) Who sends down water in measured amounts from the sky."

Indeed, rain falls on the earth in an unerring measure.

The first of the measures related to rain is its speed of descent. When dropped from a height of 1,200 metres, an object having the same weight and size as a rain-drop would continuously accelerate and fall on the ground at a speed of 558 km/h. The average raindrop, however, fall at only 10-12 km/h.

The reason for this is that the raindrop has a special form that increases the frictional effect of the atmosphere and helps it fall on the ground more slowly. A glance at the figures below is sufficient to understand the disaster the earth would face every time it rained if rain raindrops were in a different form, or the atmosphere did not have the quality of friction.

The minimum altitude of rain clouds is 1,200 metres. The effect caused by a single drop falling from that height is equal to a 1 kg object dropped from 15 cm. There are also rain clouds at altitudes of 10,000 metres. In this case, a single drop would have an effect equal to a 1 kg object dropped from 110 cm.

It is estimated that in one second, approximately 16 million tons of water evaporate from the earth. This number is equal to the amount of water that drops on the earth in one second. In one year, this figure amounts to 505×10^{12} tons. Water continuously circulates in a balanced cycle according to a "measure".

THE FORMATION OF RAIN

Only after weather radar was invented was it possible to discover the stages by which rain is formed. According to this, the formation of rain takes place in three stages. First, the formation of wind; second, the formation of clouds; third, the emergence of raindrops.

What is related in the Qur'an about the formation of rain shows great parallels with these discoveries:

It is Allah Who sends the winds (1st Stage) **which stir up clouds which He spreads about the sky however He wills. He forms them into dark**

clumps (2nd Stage) **and you see the rain come pouring out from the middle of them** (3rd stage)**. When He makes it fall on those of His slaves He wills, they rejoice! (Surat ar-Rum: 48)**

FIRST STAGE: "It is Allah Who sends the winds..."

Countless air bubbles formed by the foaming of the oceans continuously burst and cause water particles to be ejected towards the sky. These particles which are rich in salt, are then carried away by winds and ascend in the atmosphere. These particles, which are called aerosols, function as water traps, and form cloud drops by collecting around themselves the water vapour, which ascends from the seas as tiny drops.

SECOND STAGE: " ... which stir up clouds which He spreads about the sky however He wills. He forms them into dark clumps..."

The clouds form from water vapour that condenses around the salt crystals or dust particles in the air. Because the water drops in these clouds are very small (with a diameter between 0.01 and 0.02 mm), the clouds are suspended

On the surfaces of oceans, each moment, countless tiny air bubbles formed by the foaming burst, and numerous water drops, which are rich in salt, are ejected into the atmosphere. By the action of the winds carrying away these drops, the atmosphere collects twenty-seven million tons of salt a day. These salts are to constitute the central core around which the raindrop later forms.

Water particles surround salt crystals that are carried from oceans to clouds and so, form raindrops. Becoming heavier than air, drops leave from the clouds, and start to fall on the ground as rain.

in the air and they spread in the sky. Thus, the sky is covered with clouds.

THIRD STAGE: "...and you see the rain come pouring out from the middle of them."

The water particles that surround salt crystals and dust particles thicken and form raindrops, so, the drops which become heavier than air leave the clouds, and start to fall on the ground as rain.

THE RAIN MADE SWEET

The Qur'an draws our attention to the rain's being "sweet":

Have you thought about the water that you drink? Is it you who sent it down from the clouds or are We the Sender? If We wished We could have made it bitter, so will you not give thanks? (Surat al-Waqi'ah: 68-70)

...and (did We not) give you sweet fresh water to drink? (Surat al-Mursalat: 27)

It is He Who sends down water from the sky. From it you drink and from it come the shrubs among which you graze your herds. (Surat an-Nahl: 10)

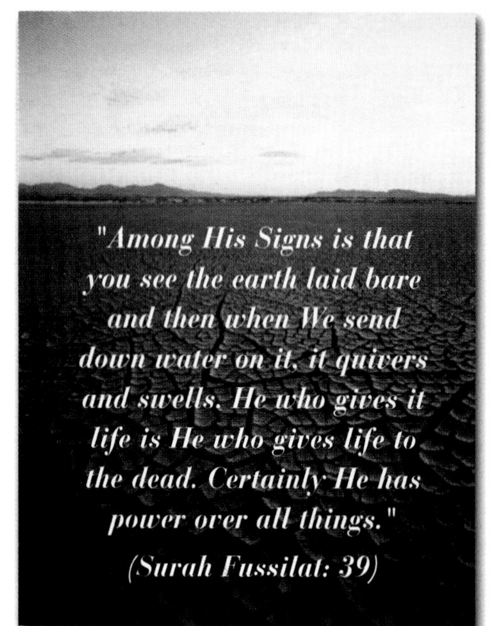

"Among His Signs is that
you see the earth laid bare
and then when We send
down water on it, it quivers
and swells. He who gives it
life is He who gives life to
the dead. Certainly He has
power over all things."
(Surah Fussilat: 39)

As we know, the source of rainwater is evaporation and 97% of evaporation takes place from "salty" oceans. Rainwater, however, is sweet. The reason why rain is sweet is because of another physical law that Allah established. According to this law, no matter whether water evaporates from salt seas, or mineralised lakes, or from within mud, it does not contain any foreign material. It falls on the ground pure and clean according to Allah's ordinance **"...And We send down from heaven pure water" (Surat al-Furqan: 48)**

RAINS THAT GIVE LIFE TO A DEAD LAND

In the Qur'an, many verses call our attention the rain's function of "bringing a dead land to life". **"...And We send down from heaven pure water so that by it We can bring a dead land to life and give drink to many of the animals and people We created." (Surat al – Furqan: 48-49)**

In addition to furnishing the earth with water, which is an inevitable need of living beings, rain also has a fertilising effect.

Raindrops that reach the clouds after being evaporated from the seas contain certain substances "that will give life" to a dead land. These "life-giving" drops are called "surface tension drops". Surface tension drops form on the top level of the sea's surface, which is called the micro layer by biologists. In this layer, which is thinner than one tenth of a millimetre, there are many organic leftovers from the pollution caused by microscopic algae and zooplankton. Some of these leftovers select and collect within themselves some elements which are very rare in sea water, such as phosphorus, magnesium, potassium and some heavy metals like copper, zinc, cobalt and lead. These "fertiliser"-laden drops are lifted up into the sky by the winds and after a while they drop on the ground inside the raindrops. Seeds and plants on the earth find numerous metallic salts and elements essential for their growth here in these raindrops. This event is revealed in another verse:

"And We sent down blessed water from the sky and made gardens grow by it and grain for harvesting." (Surah Qaf: 9)

The salts that fall in rain are small examples of certain conventional fertilisers (calcium, magnesium, potassium, etc.) used for increasing fertility. The heavy metals found in these types of aerosols, on the other hand, are other elements that increase fertility in the development and production of plants.

Briefly, rain is an important fertiliser. A barren land can be furnished with all the essential elements for plants, over a hundred-year period, just by these fertilisers dropped with rain. Forests also develop and are fed with the help of these sea-based aerosols.

In this way, 150 million tons of fertiliser falls on the total land surface every year. If there were no natural fertilisation like this, there would be very little vegetation on the earth, and the ecological balance would be impaired.

It is He who made the earth a cradle for you and threaded pathways for you through it and sent down water from the sky by which We have brought forth various different types of plants. (Surah Ta Ha: 53)

THE USE OF FREEZING FROM ABOVE

One of the most interesting and important qualities of water is that, unlike other substances, its solid state is lighter than its liquid state – that is, ice is lighter than water. For this reason, seas start freezing from above, because the frozen layer is lighter than the liquid part of the water. Thus, the risk that the sea would totally freeze causing life to cease to exist is eliminated, because the frozen layer which rises above insulates the liquid part remaining below the sea from the cold weather outside.

If ice were heavier than water (which is what would normally be expect-

ed), then seas would start freezing from the bottom. In this case, the insulation referred to above would not occur, all of the seas would freeze and life in water would be destroyed. Since ice takes up more space than water, the frozen seas would take up more space than before and cause the water on the top to rise and overflow.

In addition, that water's heaviest state is +4°C is very important for life. In seas, water reaching +4°C sinks to the bottom as it is at its heaviest. For this reason, the bottom of the seas that are covered with icebergs is always in a liquid state, and has a temperature of +4°C in which living beings can survive. Similarly, in wintertime, the bottoms of lakes and rivers covered with an icy layer are also life supportive.

WATER'S LATE WARMING UP AND FREEZING

Another feature of water is its slow evaporation and freezing. It is a known fact that in the summer months, the sand that rapidly warms up during the day also rapidly cools down at night. The temperature of seawater, on the other hand, only varies two to three degrees between day and night. The reason for this is that water somehow maintains its temperature in sudden rises and falls in temperature, and delays evaporation and freezing. When this quality of water is considered at the level of the entire world, it can be seen that water, either in liquid form or as steam, in oceans and the atmosphere, has the most important role in the earth's temperature. Waters that cover the earth prevent overheating by absorbing the heat in that part of the world exposed to the sun. Similarly, in those parts that are not subjected to the sun as directly as elsewhere, oceans and other waters function, with the heat they possess, as a radiator and prevent the temperature from falling too low. This way, the temperature difference between day and night always remains within reasonable limits which human beings and other living things can tolerate. If the amount of water on the earth were less than the land area, then the temperature difference between night and day would increase a great deal, transforming the earth into a desert and making life impossible or, at least very difficult.

THE WEIGHT OF CLOUDS

Clouds can be incredibly heavy. For instance, in a storm cloud called "Cumulo-nimbus" up to 300,000 tons of water accumulates.

The establishment of an order whereby a mass of 300,000 tons can rest in the sky is no doubt quite amazing. A verse in the Qur'an draws our attention to the weight of clouds:

"It He is Who sends out the winds, bringing advance news of His mercy, so that when they have lifted up the heavy clouds, We dispatch them to a dead land and send down water to it, by means of which We bring forth all kinds of fruit. In the same way We will bring forth the dead, so that hopefully you will pay heed." (Surat al-A'raf: 57)

And He has made everything in the heavens and everything on the earth subservient to you. It is all from Him. There are certainly signs in that for people who reflect. (Surat al-Jathiyah: 13)

WINDS

"...and the varying direction of the winds, there are signs for people who use their intellect." (Surat al-Jathiyah: 5)

Wind is the air current formed between different temperature zones. Varying temperatures in the atmosphere give rise to different air pressures, making the air continuously flow from high pressure to low. If the difference between pressure centres, that is, temperatures in the atmosphere, is too high, then the air current, that is, the wind becomes very strong. This is how such highly destructive winds as hurricanes are formed.

What is interesting is that despite highly divergent zones of temperature and pressure such as the equator and the poles, our world is not continually

exposed to very strong winds thanks to some barriers and "regulations". If the giant air current, which otherwise would likely have been formed between the poles and the equator, had not been softened by the means that will be described below, the earth would have been turned into a dead planet constantly exposed to heavy storms.

Principally, altitude differences on earth break the force of the winds. Highly differing altitudes give rise to warm and cold front systems. Seen on the lower slopes of mountains, these systems cause new winds. Thus, the bi-centred system between the equator and the pole transforms into a multi-centred system thanks to cliffs, and winds are softened by being channelled in different directions. The mountain chains on the earth's crust function like giant air corridors. Corridors help the winds spread air evenly across the earth.

The inclination of the world's axis also has a great role in the softening of the winds. If the axis of the earth had been exactly perpendicular to its orbit, the earth would have suffered from violent storms throughout. However, the equator of our planet is tilted at an angle of 23°27' with respect to its plane of orbit. Thus, the temperature does not always remain the same in the regions between the two poles and changes according to seasons. This means that the air pressure is brought into balance and that therefore the force of the wind is lessened. As the temperature difference between the equator and the two poles decreases, the winds blow warmer.

In addition, two gas layers have been created around the planet to balance the temperature difference. The ozone and carbon dioxide layers balance the temperature of the atmosphere. The ozone layer absorbs "excessive" sunrays. Carbon dioxide, on the other hand, has an opposite function: it retains the acquired heat and thus prevents cooling.

All of this material shows us that man owes his life to a great system containing increasingly complex sub-systems. The whole universe is created to make human life possible.

VERSES OF THE QUR'AN AND THE UNIVERSE

In the 88th verse of Surat al-Isra, Allah refers to the divine nature of the Qur'an: **"Say: 'If both men and jinn banded together to produce the like of this Qur'an, they could never produce anything like it, even if they backed each other up.'" (Surat al-Isra: 88)**

Allah sent the Qur'an to people fourteen centuries ago. Some facts that could only be discovered with the technology of the 20th century were stated in the Qur'an fourteen centuries ago. This plainly shows us that the Qur'an is one of the most important pieces of evidence that let us acknowledge Allah's being.

In the Qur'an, there are many pieces of evidence that the Qur'an is from Allah and that mankind can never produce anything like it. One of these pieces of evidence is that the verses of the Qur'an exist in our universe:

In accordance with the verse **"We will show them Our Signs on the horizon and within themselves until it is clear to them that it is the truth. Is it not enough for your Lord that He is a witness of everything?" (Surah Fussilat: 53)**, much of the information given in the Qur'an finds its correlate in the external world. For Allah has created everything in the universe and, therefore, possesses complete knowledge of it. He, also, has revealed the Qur'an. For this reason, a great deal of the information and analyses given in the Qur'an, will be seen and recognised by wise, conscientious believers who have insight.

However, it should not be forgotten that the Qur'an is not a "book of science". The purpose of the revelation of the Qur'an is stated thus in the verses:

> **"Alif Lam Ra This is a Book We have sent down to you so that you can bring mankind from the darkness to the light, by the permission of their Lord, to the path of the Almighty, the Praiseworthy." (Surah Ibrahim: 1)**
>
> **"...as guidance and a reminder for people of intelligence." (Surat Ghafir: 54)**

In brief, Allah sends the Qur'an to believers as a guide. It explains to them how to be slaves of Allah and seek His good pleasure.

The Qur'an, however, also gives some basic information on certain subjects

He Who created the seven heavens in layers. You will not find any flaw in the creation of the All-Merciful. Look again – do you see any gaps? Then look again and again. Your sight will return to you dazzled and exhausted! (Surat al- Mulk: 3-4)

such as the creation of the universe, the birth of man, the structure of the atmosphere, and the balances in the heavens and on the earth. That these pieces of information are in harmony with the most recent findings of modern science is important in the sense that it again confirms that the Qur'an is "the Word of Allah". For according to the verse **"Will they not ponder the Qur'an? If it had been from other than Allah, they would have found many inconsistencies in it" (Surat an-Nisa: 82)**, there is perfect harmony between the statements of the Qur'an and the external world.

In the following pages we will dwell on the extraordinary parallels between the pieces of information about the universe given by the Qur'an and science.

THE BIG BANG THEORY AND WHAT IT TEACHES

The questions of how the seamless universe originated, where it leads to, and how the laws maintaining its order and balance work have always been topics of interest.

The prevailing materialist opinion for some centuries until the early 20th century was that the universe had infinite dimensions, that it had existed since eternity, and that it would continue to exist forever. According to this view, called the "static universe model", the universe has neither a beginning nor an end.

Laying the groundwork for materialist philosophy, this view denied the existence of the Creator while it maintained that the universe is a constant, stable, and unchanging collection of matter. However, the 20th century's developing science and technology demolished primitive concepts such as the static universe model. Today, on the brink of the 21st century, modern physics has come to the conclusion, with many experiments, observations and calculations, that the universe had a beginning and that it was created out of nothing and began with a big explosion.

In addition, it is maintained that the universe, contrary to the claims of materialists, is not stable and constant, but that it is in constant motion, change, and expansion. Today, these facts are admitted by the world of science. Now, let us look at how these very important facts are brought to light by the world of science.

THE EXPANSION OF THE UNIVERSE

In 1929, at the California Mount Wilson observatory, an American astronomer by the name of Edwin Hubble made one of the greatest discoveries in the history of astronomy. While he observed the stars with a giant telescope, he found out that the light emitted by them was shifted to the red end of the spectrum and that this shift was more pronounced the further a star was from the earth. This discovery had an electrifying effect on the world of science, because according to the recognised rules of physics, the spectra of light beams travelling towards the point of observation tend towards violet while the spectra of the light beams moving away from the point of observation tend towards red. Hubble's observations showed that the light from stars tends towards red. This means that they are constantly moving away from us.

Before long, Hubble made another very important discovery: Stars and galaxies move away not only from us, but also from one another. The only conclusion that can be made about a universe where everything moves away from everything else is that the universe constantly "expands".

To better understand, the universe can be thought of as the surface of a balloon being blown up. Just as the points on the surface of a balloon move apart from each other as the balloon is inflated, so do the objects in space move apart from each other as the universe keeps expanding. In fact, this had been theoretically discovered even earlier. Albert Einstein, who is considered one of the most renowned scientists of the century, had originally concluded during his work on General Relativity that his equations showed that the universe could not be static. However, he artificially altered his equations by the addition of a 'constant' to produce a static model of the universe because that was the dominant idea of the time. Einstein was later to identify his act as "the greatest mistake of his career".

Everything in the heavens and the earth glorifies Allah. He is the Almighty, the All-Wise. The kingdom of the heavens and the earth belongs to Him. He gives life and causes to die. He has power over all things.
(Surat al- Hadid: 1-2)

What importance, then, did the fact that the universe expands have to the existence of the universe?

The expansion of the universe implies that the universe would prove to have originated from a single point. Calculations show that this "single point" that harboured all the matter of the universe must have had "zero volume" and "infinite density". The universe had come about by the explosion of this single point with zero volume. This great explosion that marked the beginning of the universe was named the "Big Bang" and the theory took its name from that.

It has to be said that "zero volume" is a theoretical expression used for descriptive purposes. Science can define the concept of "nothingness", which is beyond the limits of human comprehension, only by expressing it as "a point with zero volume". In truth, "a point with no volume" means "nothingness". The universe has come into being from nothingness. In other words, it was created.

This great fact, which was discovered by modern physics only towards the end of this century, was announced to us in the Qur'an fourteen centuries ago:

He created the heavens and the earth (from nothing). (Surat al-An'am: 101)

When we compare the statement in the verse with the Big Bang theory, we see that there is a striking resemblance. However, the Big Bang was introduced as a scientific theory only in the 20th century.

The expansion of the universe is one of the most important pieces of evidence that the universe was created out of nothing. Although this was not discovered by science until the 20th century, Allah has informed us of this reality in the Qur'an revealed 1,400 years ago:

It is We Who have built the universe with (Our creative) power, and, verily, it is We Who are steadily expanding it. (Surat adh-Dhariyat: 47)

In 1948, George Gamov came up with another idea concerning the Big Bang. He stated that after the formation of the universe from a big explosion, a surplus of radiation, left over from this explosion, should have existed in the universe. Moreover, this radiation ought to be uniformly diffused across the universe.

This evidence which "ought to have existed" was soon to be found. In 1965, two researchers, by the name of Arno Penzias and Robert Wilson, discovered these waves by chance. This radiation, called "cosmic background radiation", did not seem to radiate from a particular source but rather pervaded the whole of space. Thus, it was understood that the heat waves that were radiating uniformly from every direction in space were left over from the initial stages of the Big Bang. Penzias and Wilson were awarded a Nobel Prize for their discovery.

In 1989, NASA sent the Cosmic Background Explorer (COBE) satellite into space to do research on cosmic background radiation. It took only eight minutes for the sensitive scanners on this satellite to confirm the measurements of Penzias and Wilson. COBE had found the remains of the big explosion that had taken place at the outset of the universe.

Another important piece of evidence for the Big Bang was the amount of hydrogen and helium in space. In the latest calculations, it was understood that the hydrogen-helium concentration in the universe agreed with the theoretical calculations of the hydrogen-helium concentration remaining from the Big Bang. If the universe had no beginning and if it had existed since eternity, its hydrogen should have been completely consumed and converted to helium.

All of this compelling evidence caused the Big Bang theory to be embraced by the scientific community. The Big Bang model was the latest point reached by cosmologists concerning the beginning and formation of the universe.

Defending the steady-state theory alongside Fred Hoyle for years, Dennis Sciama described the final position they had reached after all the evidence for the Big Bang theory was gathered. Sciama said that he had taken part in the heated debate between the defenders of the steady-state theory and those who tested that theory with the hope of refuting it. He added that he had defended the steady-state theory, not because he deemed it valid but because he wished that it were valid. Fred Hoyle stood out against all objections as evidence against this theory began to unfold. Sciama went on to say that he had first taken a stand along with Hoyle but as evidence began to pile up, he had to admit that the game was over and that the steady-state theory had to be dismissed.

Prof. George Abel from the University of California also said that currently available evidence shows that the universe originated billions of years ago with the Big Bang. He concedes that he has no choice but to accept the Big Bang theory.

With the Big Bang's victory, the concept of "eternal matter" that constituted the basis of the materialist philosophy was thrown into the trash-heap of history. What, then, was before the Big Bang and what was the power that brought the universe into "being" with this big explosion when it was previously "non-existent"? This question certainly implies, in Arthur Eddington's words, the "philosophically unfavourable" fact (unfavourable for the materialists), that is, the existence of the Creator. Renowned atheist philosopher Anthony Flew comments on the issue:

> Notoriously, confession is good for the soul. I will therefore begin by confessing that the Stratonician atheist has to be embarrassed by the contemporary cosmological consensus. For it seems that the cosmologists are providing a scientific proof of what St. Thomas contended could not be proved philosophically; namely, that the universe had a beginning. So long as the universe can be comfortably thought of as being not only without end but also without beginning, it remains easy to urge that its brute existence, and whatever are found to be its most fundamental features, should be accepted as the explanatory ultimates. Although I believe that it remains still correct, it certainly is neither easy nor comfortable to maintain this position in the face of the Big Bang story.

Many scientists who are not blindly conditioned to be atheists have admitted the role of the almighty Creator in the creation of the universe. This Creator must be a being Who has created both matter and space/time, yet Who is independent of them. Well-known astrophysicist Hugh Ross has this to say:

> If time's beginning is concurrent with the beginning of the universe, as the space-theorem says, then the cause of the universe must be some entity operating in a time dimension completely independent of and pre-existent to the time dimension of the cosmos. This conclusion is powerfully important to our understanding of who God is and who or what God isn't. It tells us that God is not the universe itself, nor is God contained within the universe.

Matter and space/time are created by the almighty Creator Who is independent of all these notions. This Creator is Allah Who is the Lord of the heavens and the earth.

Allah has let us know the scientific pieces of evidence of this in His Book, which He sent to us fourteen centuries ago as the manifest evidence of His being.

THE PERFECTION IN THE UNIVERSE

He Who created the seven heavens in layers. You will not find any flaw in the creation of the All-Merciful. Look again – do you see any gaps? Then look again and again. Your sight will return to you dazzled and exhausted! (Surat al-Mulk: 3-4)

Countless billions of stars and galaxies in the universe move in their separate orbits yet in total harmony. Stars, planets and satellites revolve both around their own axes and within the systems to which they belong. Furthermore, sometimes galaxies consisting of almost 200-300 billions stars flow through each other. During this transition in some of the very famous examples observed by astronomers, no collisions occur to cause havoc in the great order in the universe.

Across the universe, the magnitude of the velocities is difficult to comprehend when compared with our earthly standards. Magnitudes in space are enormous when compared with the measurements we employ on earth. Stars and planets, with masses of billions or trillions of tons, galaxies, and galaxy clusters, with sizes in numerical values that can only be represented numerically by mathematicians, move in space at tremendous velocities.

For instance, the earth rotates about its axis at a mean velocity of about 1,670 km an hour. When we remember that the fastest bullet has an average velocity of 1,800 km an hour, it becomes clear how fast the earth is moving despite its giant size.

The earth's orbital velocity around the sun is about sixty times that of the bullet's: 108,000 km an hour. (If it were possible to manufacture a vehicle that

He is the Originator of the heavens and the earth. How could He have a son when He has no wife? He created all things and He has knowledge of all things. That is Allah, your Lord. There is no god but Him, the Creator of everything. So worship Him. He is responsible for everything. Eyesight cannot perceive Him but He perceives eyesight. He is the All-Penetrating, the All-Aware. Clear insights have come to you from your Lord. Whoever sees clearly, does so to his own benefit. Whoever is blind, it is to his own detriment.

(Surat al-An'am: 101-104)

could move so fast, it would orbit the earth in twenty-two minutes.)

These figures, however, only relate to the earth. The solar system is even more amazing. The velocity of this system is at a level which pushes the limits of logic. In the universe, as systems increase in size, velocities also increase. The solar system revolves around the centre of the galaxy at 720,000 km an hour. The velocity of the "Milky Way" itself, comprising some 200 billion stars, is 950,000 km an hour in space.

This overwhelming speed actually shows that our lives on the earth are lived on the knife-edge. Normally, it would be quite likely for huge accidents to occur in such a complex system. However, as Allah says in the verse, in this system is no "flaw" or "want of proportion". The universe, just as everything within it, is not left "on its own" and it operates according to the balance Allah has established.

ORBITS AND THE ROTATING UNIVERSE

One of the most important causes of the great balance in the universe is unquestionably that the heavenly bodies follow certain orbits or 'spheres'. Though unknown until recently, these orbits are emphasised in the Qur'an:

It is He Who created night and day and the sun and moon, each one swimming in an orbit. (Surat al-Anbiya: 33)

Stars, planets and satellites revolve both around their own axes and within the systems to which they belong, and the larger universe works in a subtle order just like the gears of a machine.

The orbits in the universe are not confined to the motions of certain celestial bodies. Our solar system and the galaxies have a great activity around other centres as well. Each year, the earth and the Solar system move 500 million kilometres away from their location of the previous year. It has been computed that even a minor deviation of the celestial bodies from their orbits would lead to results that would turn the system upside down. For instance, let us look at what a 3 millimetre deviation above or below the normal in the world's orbit would cause:

"While rotating around the sun, the earth follows such an orbit that, every 18 miles, it only deviates 2.8 millimetres from a direct course. The orbit followed by the earth never changes, because even a deviation of 3 millimetres would cause catastrophic disasters: if the deviation were 2.5 mm instead of 2.8 mm, then the orbit would be very large, and all of us would freeze. If the deviation were 3.1 mm, we would be scorched to death." (Bilim ve Teknik, July 1983)

THE SUN

Being 150 million km away from the earth, the sun uninterruptedly provides us with our required energy.

In this celestial body with its huge energies, hydrogen atoms are continuously converted into helium. Each second, 616 million tons of hydrogen is converted to 612 million tons of helium. During that, the energy released is equivalent to the explosion of 500 million hydrogen bombs.

Life on earth is made possible by the energy from the sun. The permanence of the balance on earth and 99% of the energy needed for life are provided by the sun. Half of this energy is visible and comes in the form of light. The rest of the energy is in the form of ultraviolet rays, which are invisible, and in the form of heat.

Another feature of the sun is its dilating itself periodically like a bell. This is repeated every five minutes and the surface of the sun moves 3 km closer to the earth and further away from it at a speed of 1,080 km per hour.

The sun is only one of the 200 billion stars comprising the Milky Way. Although 325,500 times bigger than the earth, it is considered one of the small stars in the universe. It is at a distance of 30 thousand light years from the centre of the Milky Way, which has a diameter of 125 thousand light years. (1 light year = 9,460,800,000,000 km.)

THE JOURNEY OF THE SUN

And the sun runs to its resting place. That is the decree of the Almighty, the All-Knowing. (Surah Yasin: 38)

According to the calculations of astronomers, the sun, due to the activity of our galaxy, travels at a speed of 720,000 km per hour towards the Solar Apex, a place on the celestial sphere close to the star Vega. (This means that approximately, it travels a distance of 720,000x24=17,280,000 km a day, as does our earth which is dependent on it.)

SEVEN LAYERS OF HEAVENS

"It is Allah Who created the seven heavens and of the earth the same number." (Surat at-Talaq: 12)

Throughout the Qur'an, Allah mentions the seven heavens or skies. When we examine the composition of the earth's atmosphere, we find that it is made up of seven layers. In the atmosphere, interfaces divide the layers from one another. According to Encyclopaedia Americana (9/188), the following layers are one on top of another depending on temperature:

1st Layer TROPOSPHERE: Its thickness reaches 8 km at the poles and 17 km at the equator. This layer contains a great amount of clouds. The temperature goes down 6.5° C a kilometre depending on altitude. In one part of it, called the tropopause, where there are fast air currents, the temperature stays constant at -57°C.

2nd Layer STRATOSPHERE: It reaches an altitude of 50 km. Here, ultraviolet light is absorbed causing heat to be released and the temperature to rise to 0°C. During this absorption, the ozone layer, which has vital importance for the earth, is formed.

3rd Layer MESOSPHERE: Its altitude reaches up to 85 km. Here, the temperature drops to -100° C.

4th Layer THERMOSPHERE: Temperature rises at a decelerating pace.

5th Layer IONOSPHERE: Gases in this region are found in ionic form. Because radio waves are reflected back by the ionosphere, communication on earth becomes possible.

6th Layer EXOSPHERE: Being between 500 km and 1000 km, the characteristics of this layer change according to the activities of the sun.

7th Layer MAGNETOSPHERE: This is the area in which the earth's magnetic field lies and which looks like a great void. Energetically charged subatomic particles are retained in regions called the Van Allen radiation belts.

THE MOUNTAINS PREVENTING THE EARTHQUAKES

It is Allah Who created the heavens with no support – you can see them – and cast firmly embedded mountains on the earth so that it would not move under you, and scattered about in it creatures of every kind. (Surah Luqman: 10)

Have We not made the earth a flat carpet and the mountains its pegs? (Surat an-Naba: 6-7)

The information obtained by geological investigation of mountains is in full accord with the verses of the Qur'an. One of the most significant characteristics of mountains is their rising at the conjunction points of the earth's plates, which are closely pressed together as they draw close to one another, and their "fixing" them. Having this attribute, mountains may be likened to nails that keep wood pieces together.

In addition to this, the pressure exerted by mountains on the earth's crust prevents the impact of magma activity at the centre of the earth from reaching the earth's surface and thus crushing the earth's crust.

THE SEAS' NOT MINGLING WITH ONE ANOTHER

"He has let loose the two seas, converging together, with a barrier between them they do not break through." (Surat ar-Rahman: 19-20)

In the verse above, it is stressed that two bodies of water meet together, yet do not mingle with one another due to a barrier. How is this possible? Normally, what would be expected is that the waters of the two seas mingle with one another when they meet together and that the proportions of salts and the temperatures of each of them would tend to balance. The case, however, is different. For instant, although the Mediterranean Sea and the Atlantic Ocean, and the Red Sea and the Indian Ocean physically meet together, their waters do not mingle with one another. The reason for this is a barrier between them. This barrier is a force known as the "surface tension".

THE TWO CODES IN IRON

Iron is one of the four most abundant elements in the world and for ages, it has been one of the most vital metals for mankind. The verse referring to iron is as follows:

"...And We sent down iron in which there lies great force and which has many uses for mankind." (Surat al-Hadid: 25)

This verse incorporates two very interesting mathematical codes.

"Al-Hadid" (Iron) is the 57th surah of the Qur'an. The numerical value (in the "Abjad" system of Arabic in which each letter has a numerical value) of the letters of the word "Al-Hadid" is the same: 57.

The numerical value (Abjad) of the word "Hadid" (iron) alone, without the definite article "al", is 26 and 26 is the atomic number of iron.

The theory of evolution is a philosophy and a conception of the world that produces false hypotheses, assumptions and imaginary scenarios in order to explain the existence and origin of life in terms of mere coincidences. The roots of this philosophy go back as far as antiquity and ancient Greece.

All atheist philosophies that deny creation, directly or indirectly embrace and defend the idea of evolution. The same condition today applies to all the ideologies and systems that are antagonistic to religion.

The evolutionary notion has been cloaked in a scientific disguise for the last century and a half in order to justify itself. Though put forward as a supposedly scientific theory during the mid-19th century, the theory, despite all the best efforts of its advocates, has not so far been verified by any scientific finding or experiment. Indeed, the "very science" on which the theory depends so greatly has demonstrated and continues to demonstrate repeatedly that the theory has no merit in reality.

Laboratory experiments and probabilistic calculations have definitely made it clear that the amino acids from which life arises cannot have been formed by chance. The cell, which supposedly emerged by chance under primitive and uncontrolled terrestrial conditions according to evolutionists, still cannot be synthesised even in the most sophisticated, high-tech laboratories of the 20th century. Not a single "transitional form", creatures which are supposed to show the gradual evolution of advanced organisms from more primitive ones as neo-Darwinist theory claims, has ever been found anywhere in the world despite the most diligent and prolonged search in the fossil record.

Striving to gather evidence for evolution, evolutionists have unwittingly proven by their own hands that evolution cannot have happened at all!

The person who originally put forward the theory of evolution, essentially in the form that it is defended today, was an amateur English biologist by the name of Charles Robert Darwin. Darwin first published his ideas in a book entitled *The Origin of Species by Means of Natural Selection* in 1859. Darwin claimed in his book that all living beings had a common ancestor and that they evolved from one another by means of natural selection. Those that best adapted to the habitat transferred their traits to subsequent generations, and by accumulating over great epochs, these advantageous qualities transformed individuals into totally different species from their ancestors. The human being was thus the most developed product of the mechanism of natural selection. In short, the origin of one species was another species.

Darwin's fanciful ideas were seized upon and promoted by certain ideological and political circles and the theory became very popular. The main reason was that the level of knowledge of those days was not yet sufficient to reveal that Darwin's imaginary scenarios were false. When Darwin put forward his assumptions, the disciplines of genetics, microbiology, and biochemistry did not yet exist. If they had, Darwin might easily have recognised that his theory was totally unscientific and thus would not have attempted to advance such meaningless claims: the information determining species already exists in the genes and it is impossible for natural selection to produce new species by altering genes.

While the echoes of Darwin's book reverberated, an Austrian botanist by the name of Gregor Mendel discovered the laws of inheritance in 1865. Although little known before the end of the century, Mendel's discovery gained great importance in the early 1900s with the birth of the science of genetics. Some time later, the structures of genes and chromosomes were discovered. The discovery, in the 1950s, of the DNA molecule, which incorporates genetic information, threw the theory of evolution into a great crisis, because the origin of the immense amount of information in DNA could not possibly be explained by coincidental happenings.

Besides all these scientific developments, no transitional forms, which were supposed to show the gradual evolution of living organisms from primitive to advanced species, have ever been found despite years of search.

These developments ought to have resulted in Darwin's theory being banished to the dustbin of history. However, it was not, because certain circles insisted on revising, renewing, and elevating the theory to a scientific platform. These efforts gain meaning only if we realise that behind the theory lie ideological intentions rather than scientific concerns.

Nevertheless, some circles that believed in the necessity of upholding a theory that had reached an impasse soon set up a new model. The name of this new model was neo-Darwinism. According to this theory, species evolved as a result of mutations, minor changes in their genes, and the fittest ones survived through the mechanism of natural selection. When, however, it was proved that the mechanisms proposed by neo-Darwinism were invalid and minor changes were not sufficient for the formation of living beings, evolutionists went on to look for new models. They came up with a new claim called "punctuated equilibrium" that rests on no rational or scientific grounds. This model held that living beings suddenly evolved into another species without any transitional forms. In other words, species with no evolutionary "ancestors" suddenly appeared. This was a way of describing creation, though evolutionists would be loath to admit this. They tried to cover it up with incomprehensible scenarios. For instance, they said that the first bird in history could all of a sudden inexplicably have popped out of a reptile egg. The same theory also held that carnivorous land-dwelling animals could have turned into giant whales, having undergone a sudden and comprehensive transformation.

Charles Darwin

These claims, totally contradicting all the rules of genetics, biophysics, and biochemistry are as scientific as fairy-tales of frogs turning into princes! Nevertheless, being distressed by the crisis that the neo-Darwinist assertion was in, some evolutionist paleontologists embraced this theory, which has the distinction of being even more bizarre than neo-Darwinism itself.

The only purpose of this model was to provide an explanation for the gaps in the fossil record that the neo-Darwinist model could not explain. However, it is hardly rational to attempt to explain the gap in the fossil record of the evolution of birds with a claim that "a bird popped all of a sudden out of a reptile egg", because, by the evolutionists' own admission, the evolution of a species to another species requires a great and advantageous change in genetic information. However, no mutation whatsoever improves the genetic information or adds new information to it. Mutations only derange genetic information. Thus, the "gross mutations" imagined by the punctuated equilibrium model, would only cause "gross", that is "great", reductions and impairments in the genetic information.

The theory of punctuated equilibrium was obviously merely a product of the imagination. Despite this evident truth, the advocates of evolution did not hesitate to honour this theory. The fact that the model of evolution proposed by Darwin could not be proved by the fossil record forced them to do so.

Darwin claimed that species underwent a gradual change, which necessitated the existence of half-bird/half-reptile or half-fish/half-reptile freaks. However, not even one of these "transitional forms" was found despite the extensive studies of evolutionists and the hundreds of thousands of fossils that were unearthed.

Evolutionists seized upon the model of punctuated equilibrium with the hope of concealing this great fossil fiasco. As we have stated before, it was very evident that this theory is a fantasy, so it very soon consumed itself. The model of punctuated equilibrium was never put forward as a consistent model, but rather used as an escape in cases that plainly did not fit the model of gradual evolution. Since evolutionists today realise that complex organs such as eyes, wings, lungs, brain and others explicitly refute the model of gradual evolution, in these particular points they are compelled to take shelter in the fantastic interpretations of the model of punctuated equilibrium.

Is there any Fossil Record to Verify the Theory of Evolution?

The theory of evolution argues that the evolution of a species into another species takes place gradually, step-by-step over millions of years. The logical inference drawn from such a claim is that monstrous living organisms called "transitional forms" should have lived during these periods of transformation. Since evolutionists allege that all living things evolved from each other step-by-step, the number and variety of these transitional forms should have been in the millions.

If such creatures had really lived, then we should see their remains everywhere. In fact, if this thesis is correct, the number of intermediate transitional forms should be even greater than the number of animal species alive today and their fossilised remains should be abundant all over the world.

Since Darwin, evolutionists have been searching for fossils and the result has been for them a crushing disappointment. Nowhere in the world – neither on land nor in the depths of the sea – has any intermediate transitional form between any two species ever been uncovered.

Darwin himself was quite aware of the absence of such transitional forms. It was his greatest hope that they would be found in the future. Despite his hopefulness, he saw that the biggest stumbling block to his theory was the missing transitional forms. This is why, in his book *The Origin of Species*, he wrote:

> Why, if species have descended from other species by fine gradations, do we not everywhere see innumerable transitional forms? Why is not all nature in confusion, instead of the species being, as we see them, well

A 320-million-year-old cockroach fossil

> defined?... But, as by this theory innumerable transitional forms must have existed, why do we not find them embedded in countless numbers in the crust of the earth?... But in the intermediate region, having intermediate conditions of life, why do we not now find closely-linking intermediate varieties? This difficulty for a long time quite confounded me.[1]

Darwin was right to be worried. The problem bothered other evolutionists as well. A famous British paleontologist, Derek V. Ager, admits this embarrassing fact:

> The point emerges that if we examine the fossil record in detail, whether at the level of orders or of species, we find – over and over again – not gradual evolution, but the sudden explosion of one group at the expense of another.[2]

The gaps in the fossil record cannot be explained away by the wishful thinking that not enough fossils have yet been unearthed and that these missing fossils will one day be found. Another evolutionist paleontologist, T. Neville George, explains the reason:

> There is no need to apologise any longer for the poverty of the fossil record. In some ways, it has become almost unmanageably rich and discovery is outpacing integration... The fossil record nevertheless continues to be composed mainly of gaps.[3]

Life Emerged on Earth Suddenly and in Complex Forms

When terrestrial strata and the fossil record are examined, it is seen that living organisms appeared simultaneously. The oldest stratum of the earth in which fossils of living creatures have been found is that of the "Cambrian", which has an estimated age of 530-520 million years.

Living creatures that are found in the strata belonging to the Cambrian period emerged in the fossil record all of a sudden without any pre-existing ances-

A 360-million-year-old trilobite fossil

tors. The vast mosaic of living organisms, made up of such great numbers of complex creatures, emerged so suddenly that this miraculous event is referred to as the "Cambrian Explosion" in scientific literature.

Most of the organisms found in this stratum have highly advanced organs like eyes, or systems seen in organisms with a highly advanced organisation such as gills, circulatory systems, and so on. There is no sign in the fossil record to indicate that these organisms had any ancestors. Richard Monestarsky, the editor of *Earth Sciences* magazine, states about the sudden emergence of living species:

> A half-billion years ago the remarkably complex forms of animals that we see today suddenly appeared. This moment, right at the start of Earth's Cambrian Period, some 550 million years ago, marks the evolutionary explosion that filled the seas with the world's first complex creatures. The large animal phyla of today were present already in the early Cambrian and they were as distinct from each other then as they are today.[4]

Not being able to find answers to the question of how earth came to overflow with thousands of different animal species, evolutionists posit an imaginary period of 20 million years before the Cambrian Period to explain how life originated and "the unknown happened". This period is called the "evolutionary gap". No evidence for it has ever been found and the concept is still conveniently nebulous and undefined even today.

In 1984, numerous complex invertebrates were unearthed in Chengjiang, set in the central Yunnan plateau in the high country of southwest China. Among them were trilobites, now extinct, but no less complex in structure than any modern invertebrate.

The Swedish evolutionist paleontologist, Stefan Bengston, explains the situation as follows:

> If any event in life's history resembles man's creation myths, it is this sud-

The Most Cherished Pieces of Evidence of Evolution are Proven to be Invalid

A one hundred and thirty-five million-year-old Archaeopteryx fossil, the alleged ancestor of birds, which is said to have evolved from dinosaurs (above). Research on the fossil showed it, on the contrary, to be an extinct bird that had once flown but later lost that ability.

A four hundred and ten million-year-old Coelacanth fish fossil (below). Evolutionists claimed that it was the transitional form proving the transition of this fish from water to land. The fact that more than forty living examples of this fish have been caught in the last fifty years reveals that this is still a perfectly ordinary fish and that it is still living.

den diversification of marine life when multicellular organisms took over as the dominant actors in ecology and evolution. Baffling (and embarrassing) to Darwin, this event still dazzles us.[5]

The sudden appearance of these complex living beings with no predecessors is no less baffling (and embarrassing) for evolutionists today than it was for Darwin 135 years ago. In nearly a century and a half, they have advanced not one step beyond the point that stymied Darwin.

As may be seen, the fossil record indicates that living things did not evolve from primitive to advanced forms, but instead emerged all of a sudden and in a perfect state. The absence of the transitional forms is not peculiar to the Cambrian period. Not a single transitional form verifying the alleged evolutionary "progression" of vertebrates – from fish to amphibians, reptiles, birds, and mammals – has ever been found. Every living species appears instantaneously and in its current form, perfect and complete, in the fossil record.

In other words, living beings did not come into existence through evolution. They were created.

EVOLUTION FORGERIES

Deceptions in Drawings

The fossil record is the principal source for those who seek evidence for the theory of evolution. When inspected carefully and without prejudice, the fossil record refutes the theory of evolution rather than supporting it. Nevertheless, misleading interpretations of fossils by evolutionists and their prejudiced representation to the public have given many people the impression that the fossil record indeed supports the theory of evolution.

The susceptibility of some findings in the fossil record to all kinds of interpretations is what best serves the evolutionists' purposes. The fossils unearthed are most of the time unsatisfactory for reliable identification. They usually consist of scattered, incomplete bone fragments. For this reason, it is very easy to distort the available data and to use it as desired. Not surprisingly, the reconstructions (drawings and models) made by evolutionists based on such fossil remains are prepared entirely speculatively in order to confirm evolutionary theses. Since people are readily affected by visual information, these imaginary reconstructed models are employed to convince them that the reconstructed creatures really existed in the past.

Evolutionist researchers draw human-like imaginary creatures, usually setting out from a single tooth, or a mandible fragment or a humerus, and present them to the public in a sensational manner as if they were links in human evolution. These drawings have played a great role in the establishment of the image of "primitive men" in the minds of many people.

These studies based on bone remains can only reveal very general characteristics of the creature concerned. The distinctive details are present in the soft tissues that quickly vanish with time. With the soft tissues speculatively interpreted, everything becomes possible within the boundaries of the imagination of the reconstruction's producer. Earnst A. Hooten from Harvard University explains the situation like this:

Continuously running into such skilfully drawn half-man half-ape creatures in books or other publications, the public becomes convinced that man evolved from the ape or some similar creature. These drawings, however, are outright forgeries.

> To attempt to restore the soft parts is an even more hazardous undertaking. The lips, the eyes, the ears, and the nasal tip leave no clues on the underlying bony parts. You can with equal facility model on a Neanderthaloid skull the features of a chimpanzee or the lineaments of a philosopher. These alleged restorations of ancient types of man have very little if any scientific value and are likely only to mislead the public... So put not your trust in reconstructions.[6]

Studies Made to Fabricate False Fossils

Unable to find valid evidence in the fossil record for the theory of evolution, some evolutionists have ventured to manufacture their own. These efforts, which have even been included in encyclopaedias under the heading "evolution forgeries", are the most telling indication that the theory of evolution is an ideology and a philosophy that evolutionists are hard put to defend. Two of the most egregious and notorious of these forgeries are described below.

Piltdown Man

Charles Dawson, a well-known doctor and amateur paleoanthropologist, came forth with a claim that he had found a jawbone and a cranial fragment in a pit in the area of Piltdown, England, in 1912. Although the skull was human-like, the jawbone was distinctly simian. These specimens were christened the

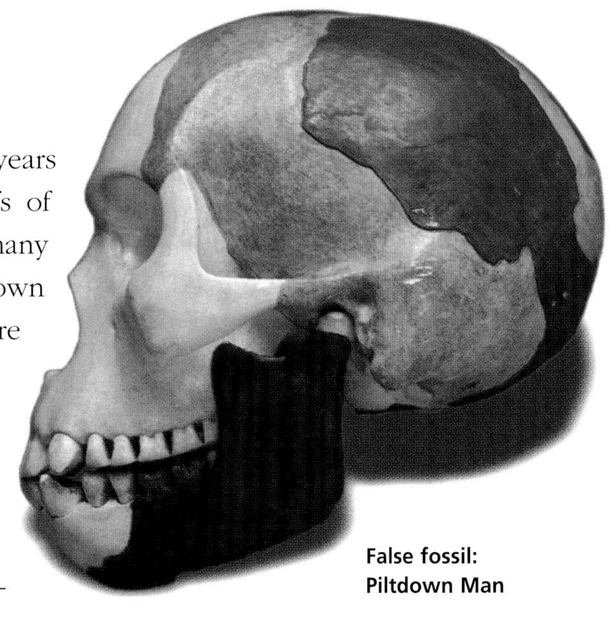

False fossil:
Piltdown Man

"Piltdown Man". Alleged to be 500 thousand years old, they were displayed as absolute proofs of human evolution. For more than 40 years, many scientific articles were written on the "Piltdown Man", many interpretations and drawings were made and the fossil was presented as crucial evidence of human evolution.

In 1949, scientists examined the fossil once more and concluded that the "fossil" was a deliberate forgery consisting of a human skull and the jawbone of an orang-utan.

Using the fluorine dating method, investigators discovered that the skull was only a few thousand years old. The teeth in the jawbone, which belonged to an orang-utan, had been artificially worn down and the "primitive" tools that had conveniently accompanied the fossils were crude forgeries that had been sharpened with steel implements. In the detailed analysis completed by Oakley, Weiner and Clark, they revealed this forgery to the public in 1953. The skull belonged to a 500-year-old man, and the mandibular bone belonged to a recently deceased ape! The teeth were thereafter specially arranged in an array and added to the jaw and the joints were filed in order to make them resemble that of a man. Then all these pieces were stained with potassium dichromate to give them a dated appearance. (These stains disappeared when dipped in acid.) Le Gros Clark, who was a member of the team that disclosed the forgery, could not hide his astonishment:

> The evidences of artificial abrasion immediately sprang to the eye. Indeed so obvious did they seem it may well be asked: how was it that they had escaped notice before? [7]

Nebraska Man

In 1922, Henry Fairfield Osborn, the director of the American Museum of Natural History, declared that he had found a molar tooth fossil in western Nebraska near Snake Brook belonging to the Pliocene period. This tooth allegedly bore the common characteristics of both man and ape. Deep scientific arguments began in which some interpreted this tooth to be that of Pithecanthropus erectus while others claimed it was closer to that of modern human beings. This fossil, which aroused extensive debate, was popularly named "Nebraska Man". It was also immediately given a "scientific name": "Hesperopithecus Haroldcooki".

This picture was drawn based on a single tooth and it was published in the *Illustrated London News* of 24th July 1922. However, evolutionists were extremely disappointed when it was revealed that this tooth belonged neither to an ape-like creature nor to a man, but to an extinct species of pig.

Many authorities gave Osborn their support. Based on this single tooth, reconstructions of Nebraska Man's head and body were drawn. Moreover, Nebraska Man was even pictured with a whole family.

In 1927, other parts of the skeleton were also found. According to these newly discovered pieces, the tooth belonged neither to a man nor to an ape. It was realised that it belonged to an extinct species of wild American pig called Prosthennops.

Did Men and Apes Come from a Common Ancestor?

According to the claims of the theory of evolution, men and modern apes have common ancestors. These creatures evolved in time and some of them became the apes of today, while another group that followed another branch of evolution became the men of today.

Evolutionists call the so-called first common ancestors of men and apes "Australopithecus" which means "South African ape". Australopithecus, nothing but an old ape species that has become extinct, has various types. Some of them are robust, while others are small and slight.

Evolutionists classify the next stage of human evolution as "Homo", that is "man". According to the evolutionist claim, the living beings in the Homo series are more developed than Australopithecus, and not very much different from modern man. The modern man of our day, Homo sapiens, is said to have formed at the latest stage of the evolution of this species.

The fact of the matter is that the beings called Australopithecus in this imaginary scenario fabricated by evolutionists really are apes that became extinct, and the beings in the Homo series are members of various human races that lived in the past and then disappeared. Evolutionists arranged various ape and human fossils in an order from the smallest to the biggest in order to form a "human evolution" scheme. Research, however, has demonstrated that these fossils by no means imply an evolutionary process and some of these alleged ancestors of man were real apes whereas some of them were real humans.

Now, let us have a look at Australopithecus, which represents to evolutionists the first stage of the scheme of human evolution.

Australopithecus: Extinct Apes

Evolutionists claim that Australopithecus are the most primitive ancestors of modern men. These are an old species with a head and skull structure similar to that of modern apes, yet with a smaller cranial capacity. According to the claims of evolutionists, these creatures have a very important feature that authenticates them as the ancestors of men: bipedalism.

The movements of apes and men are completely different. Human beings are the only living creatures that move freely about on two feet. Some other animals do have a limited ability to move in this way, but those that do have bent skeletons.

According to evolutionists, these living beings called Australopithecus had the ability to walk in a bent rather than an upright posture like human beings. Even this limited bipedal stride was sufficient to encourage evolutionists to project onto these creatures that they were the ancestors of man.

However, the first evidence refuting the allegations of evolutionists that Australopithecus were bipedal came from evolutionists themselves. Detailed studies made on Australopithecus fossils forced even evolutionists to admit that these looked "too" ape-like. Having conducted detailed anatomical research on Australopithecus fossils in the mid-1970s, Charles E. Oxnard likened the skeletal structure of Australopithecus to that of modern orang-utans:

> An important part of today's conventional wisdom about human evolution is based on studies of teeth, jaws and skull fragments of australopithecine fossils. These all indicate that the close relation of the australopithecine to the human lineage may not be true. All these fossils are different from gorillas, chimpanzees and men. Studied as a group, the australopithecine seems more like the orang-utan. [8]

What really embarrassed evolutionists was the discovery that Australopithecus could not have walked on two feet and with a bent posture. It would have been physically very ineffective for Australopithecus, allegedly bipedal but with a bent stride, to move about in such a way because of the enormous energy demands it would have entailed. By means of computer simulations conducted in 1996, the English paleoanthropologist Robin Crompton also demonstrated that such a "compound" stride was impossible. Crompton reached the following conclusion: a living being can walk either upright or on all fours. A type of in-between stride cannot be sustained for long periods because of the extreme energy consumption. This means that Australopithecus could not have been both bipedal and have a bent walking posture.

Probably the most important study demonstrating that Australopithecus could not have been bipedal came in 1994 from the research anatomist Fred Spoor and his team in the Department of Human Anatomy and Cellular Biology at the University of Liverpool, England. This group conducted studies on the bipedalism of fossilised living beings. Their research investigated the involuntary balance mechanism found in the cochlea of the ear, and the findings showed conclusively that Australopithecus could not have been bipedal. This precluded any claims that Australopithecus was human-like.

The Homo Series: Real Human Beings

The next step in the imaginary human evolution is "Homo", that is, the human series. These living beings are humans who are no different from modern men, yet who have some racial differences. Seeking to exaggerate these differences, evolutionists represent these people not as a "race" of modern man but as a different "species". However, as we will soon see, the people in the Homo series are nothing but ordinary human racial types.

According to the fanciful scheme of evolutionists, the internal imaginary evolution of the Homo species is as follows: First Homo erectus, then Homo sapiens archaic and Neanderthal Man, later Cro-Magnon Man and finally modern man.

Despite the claims of evolutionists to the contrary, all the "species" we have enumerated above are nothing but genuine human beings. Let us first examine Homo erectus, who evolutionists refer to as the most primitive human species.

The most striking evidence showing that Homo erectus is not a "primitive" species is the fossil of "Turkana Boy", one of the oldest Homo erectus remains. It is estimated that the fossil was of a 12-year-old boy, who would have been 1.83 meters tall in his adolescence. The upright skeletal structure of the fossil is no different from that of modern man. Its tall and slender skeletal structure totally complies with that of the people living in tropical regions in our day. This fossil is one of the most important pieces of evidence that Homo erectus is simply another specimen of the modern human race. Evolutionist paleontologist Richard Leakey compares Homo erectus and modern man as follows:

> One would also see differences in the shape of the skull, in the degree of protrusion of the face, the robustness of the brows and so on. These differences are probably no more pronounced than we see today between the separate geographical races of modern humans. Such biological variation

arises when populations are geographically separated from each other for significant lengths of time.[9]

Leakey means to say that the difference between Homo erectus and us is no more than the difference between Negroes and Eskimos. The cranial features of Homo erectus resulted from their manner of feeding, and genetic emigration and from their not assimilating with other human races for a lengthy period.

Another strong piece of evidence that Homo erectus is not a "primitive" species is that fossils of this species have been unearthed aged twenty-seven thousand years and even thirteen thousand years. According to an article published in *Time* – which is not a scientific periodical, but nevertheless had a sweeping effect on the world of science – Homo erectus fossils aged twenty-seven thousand years were found on the island of Java. In the Kow swamp in Australia, some thirteen thousand year-old fossils were found that bore Homo Sapiens-Homo Erectus characteristics. All these fossils demonstrate that Homo erectus continued living up to times very close to our day and were nothing but a human race that has since been buried in history.

Archaic Homo Sapiens and Neanderthal Man

Archaic Homo sapiens is the immediate forerunner of contemporary man in the imaginary evolutionary scheme. In fact, evolutionists do not have much to say about these men, as there are only minor differences between them and modern men. Some researchers even state that representatives of this race are still living today, and point to the Aborigines in Australia as an example. Like Homo sapiens, the Aborigines also have thick protruding eyebrows, an inward-inclined mandibular structure, and a slightly smaller cranial volume. Moreover, significant discoveries have been made hinting that such people lived in Hungary and in some villages in Italy until not very long ago.

Evolutionists point to human fossils unearthed in the Neander valley of Holland which have been named Neanderthal Man. Many contemporary researchers define Neanderthal Man as a sub-species of modern man and call it "Homo sapiens neandertalensis". It is definite that this race lived together with modern humans, at the same time and in the same areas. The findings testify that Neanderthals buried their dead, fashioned musical instruments, and had cultural affinities with the Homo sapiens sapiens living during the same period. Entirely modern skulls and skeletal structures of Neanderthal fossils are not open to any speculation. A prominent authority on the subject, Erik Trinkaus from New Mexico University writes:

Detailed comparisons of Neanderthal skeletal remains with those of modern humans have shown that there is nothing in Neanderthal anatomy that conclusively indicates locomotor, manipulative, intellectual, or linguistic abilities inferior to those of modern humans.[10]

In fact, Neanderthals even had some "evolutionary" advantages over modern men. The cranial capacity of Neanderthals was larger than that of the modern man and they were more robust and muscular than we are. Trinkaus adds: "One of the most characteristic features of the Neanderthals is the exaggerated massiveness of their trunk and limb bones. All of the preserved bones suggest a strength seldom attained by modern humans. Furthermore, not only is this robustness present among the adult males, as one might expect, but it is also evident in the adult females, adolescents, and even children."

To put it precisely, Neanderthals are a particular human race that assimilated with other races in time.

All of these factors show that the scenario of "human evolution" fabricated by evolutionists is a figment of their imaginations, and that men have always been men and apes always apes.

Can Life Result from Coincidences as Evolution Argues?

The theory of evolution holds that life started with a cell that formed by chance under primitive earth conditions. Let us therefore examine the composition of the cell with simple comparisons in order to show how irrational it is to ascribe the existence of the cell – a structure which still maintains its mystery in many respects, even at a time when we are about to set foot in the 21st century – to natural phenomena and coincidences.

With all its operational systems, systems of communication, transportation and management, a cell is no less complex than any city. It contains power stations producing the energy consumed by the cell, factories manufacturing the enzymes and hormones essential for life, a databank where all necessary information about all products to be produced is recorded, complex transportation systems and pipelines for carrying raw materials and products from one place to another, advanced laboratories and refineries for breaking down imported raw materials into their usable parts, and specialised cell membrane proteins for the control of incoming and outgoing materials. These constitute only a small part of this incredibly complex system.

Far from being formed under primitive earth conditions, the cell, which in its composition and mechanisms is so complex, cannot be synthesised in even the most sophisticated laboratories of our day. Even with the use of amino acids, the building blocks of the cell, it is not possible to produce so much as a single organelle of the cell, such as mitochondria or ribosome, much less a whole cell. The first cell claimed to have been produced by evolutionary coincidence is as much a figment of the imagination and a product of fantasy as the unicorn.

Proteins Challenge Coincidence

And it is not just the cell that cannot be produced: the formation, under natural conditions, of even a single protein of the thousands of complex protein molecules making up a cell is impossible.

Proteins are giant molecules consisting of amino acids arranged in a particular sequence in certain quantities and structures. These molecules constitute the building blocks of a living cell. The simplest is composed of 50 amino acids; but there are some proteins that are composed of thousands of amino acids. The absence, addition, or replacement of a single amino acid in the structure of a protein in living cells, each of which has a particular function, causes the protein to become a useless molecular heap. Incapable of demonstrating the "accidental formation" of amino acids, the theory of evolution founders on the point of the formation of proteins.

We can easily demonstrate, with simple probability calculations anybody can understand, that the functional structure of proteins can by no means come about by chance.

There are twenty different amino acids. If we consider that an average-sized protein molecule is composed of 288 amino acids, there are 10^{300} different combinations of acids. Of all of these possible sequences, only "one" forms the desired protein molecule. The other amino-acid chains are either completely useless or else potentially harmful to living things. In other words, the probability of the coincidental formation of only one protein molecule cited above is "1 in 10^{300}". The probability of this "1" occurring out of an "astronomical" number consisting of 1 followed by 300 zeros is for all practical purposes zero; it is impossible. Furthermore, a protein molecule of 288 amino acids is rather a modest one compared with some giant protein molecules consisting of thousands of amino acids. When we apply similar probability calculations to these giant protein molecules, we see that even the word "impossible" becomes inadequate.

If the coincidental formation of even one of these proteins is impossible, it is billions of times more impossible for approximately one million of those proteins to come together by chance in an organised fashion and make up a complete human cell. Moreover, a cell is not merely a collection of proteins. In addition to proteins, cells also include nucleic acids, carbohydrates, lipids, vitamins, and many other chemicals such as electrolytes, all of which are arranged harmoniously and with design in specific proportions, both in terms of structure and function. Each functions as a building block or component in various organelles.

As we have seen, evolution is unable to explain the formation of even a single protein out of the millions in the cell, let alone explain the cell.

Prof. Dr. Ali Demirsoy, one of the foremost authorities of evolutionist thought in Turkey, in his book *Kalitim ve Evrim* (Inheritance and Evolution), discusses the probability of the accidental formation of Cytochrome-C, one of the essential enzymes for life:

> The probability of the formation of a Cytochrome-C sequence is as likely as zero. That is, if life requires a certain sequence, it can be said that this has a probability likely to be realised once in the whole universe. Otherwise, some metaphysical powers beyond our definition should have acted in its formation. To accept the latter is not appropriate to the goals of science. We therefore have to look into the first hypothesis.[11]

After these lines, Demirsoy admits that this probability, which he accepted just because it was "more appropriate to the goals of science", is unrealistic:

> The probability of providing the particular amino acid sequence of Cytochrome-C is as unlikely as the possibility of a monkey writing the history of humanity on a typewriter – taking it for granted that the monkey pushes the keys at random.[12]

The correct sequence of proper amino acids is simply not enough for the formation of one of the protein molecules present in living things. Besides this, each of the twenty different types of amino acid present in the composition of proteins must be left-handed. Chemically, there are two different types of amino acids called "left-handed" and "right-handed". The difference between them is the mirror-symmetry between their three dimensional structures, which is similar to that of a person's right and left hands. Amino acids of either of these two types are found in equal numbers in nature and they can bond perfectly well with one another. Yet, research uncovers an astonishing fact: all proteins present in the structure of living things are made up of left-handed amino acids. Even a single right-handed amino acid attached to the structure of a protein renders it useless.

Let us for an instant suppose that life came into existence by chance as evolutionists claim. In this case, the right and left-handed amino acids that were generated by chance should be present in nature in roughly equal amounts. The question of how proteins can pick out only left-handed amino acids, and how not even a single right-handed amino acid becomes involved in the life process is something that still confounds evolutionists. In the *Britannica Science Encyclopaedia*, an ardent defender of evolution, the authors indicate that the amino acids of all living organisms on earth and the building blocks of complex polymers such as proteins have the same left-handed asymmetry. They add that this is tantamount to tossing a coin a million times and always getting heads. In the same encyclopaedia, they state that it is not possible to understand why molecules become left-handed or right-handed and that this choice is fascinatingly related to the source of life on earth.[13]

It is not enough for amino acids to be arranged in the correct numbers, sequences, and in the required three-dimensional structures. The formation of a protein also requires that amino acid molecules with more than one arm be linked to each other only through certain arms. Such a bond is called a "peptide bond". Amino acids can make different bonds with each other; but proteins comprise those and only those amino acids that join together by "peptide" bonds.

Research has shown that only 50 % of amino acids, combining at random, combine with a peptide bond and that the rest combine with different bonds that are not present in proteins. To function properly, each amino acid making up a protein must join with other amino acids with a peptide bond, as it has only to be chosen from among the left-handed ones. Unquestionably, there is no control mechanism to select and leave out the right-handed amino acids and personally make sure that each amino acid makes a peptide bond with the other.

Under these circumstances, the probabilities of an average protein molecule comprising five hundred amino acids arranging itself in the correct quantities and in sequence, in addition to the probabilities of all of the amino acids it contains being only left-handed and combining using only peptide bonds are as follows:

– The probability of being in the right sequence = $1/20^{500}$ =$1/10^{650}$

– The probability of being left-handed = $1/2^{500}$ =$1/10^{150}$

– The probability of combining using a "peptide bond" = $1/2^{499}$ =$1/10^{150}$

TOTAL PROBABILITY = $1/10^{950}$ that is, "1" probability in 10^{950}

As you can see above, the probability of the formation of a protein molecule comprising five hundred amino acids is "1" divided by a number formed by placing 950 zeros after a 1, a number incomprehensible to the human mind. This is only a probability on paper. Practically, such a possibility has "0" chance of realisation. In mathematics, a probability smaller than 1 over 10^{50} is statistically considered to have a "0" probability of realisation.

The probability of an average protein molecule comprising five hundred amino acids being arranged in the correct proportion and sequence in addition to the probability of all of the amino acids it contains being only left-handed and being combined only with peptide bonds is "1" divided by 10^{950}. We can write this number, which is formed by putting 950 zeros after 1, as follows:

$$10^{950} =$$

100,000,000,000,000,000,000,000,000,000,000,000,000,000,000,000,000,000,000,
000,000,000,000,000,000,000,000,000,000,000,000,000,000,000,000,000,000,000,
000,000,000,000,000,000,000,000,000,000,000,000,000,000,000,000,000,000,000,
000,000,000,000,000,000,000,000,000,000,000,000,000,000,000,000,000,000,000,
000,000,000,000,000,000,000,000,000,000,000,000,000,000,000,000,000,000,000,
000,000,000,000,000,000,000,000,000,000,000,000,000,000,000,000,000,000,000,
000,000,000,000,000,000,000,000,000,000,000,000,000,000,000,000,000,000,000,
000,000,000,000,000,000,000,000,000,000,000,000,000,000,000,000,000,000,000,
000,000,000,000,000,000,000,000,000,000,000,000,000,000,000,000,000,000,000,
000,000,000,000,000,000,000,000,000,000,000,000,000,000,000,000,000,000,000,
000,000,000,000,000,000,000,000,000,000,000,000,000,000,000,000,000,000,000,
000,000,000,000,000,000,000,000,000,000,000,000,000,000,000,000,000,000,000,
000,000,000,000,000,000,000,000,000,000,000,000,000,000,000,000,000,000,000,
000,000,000,000,000,000,000,000,000,000,000,000,000,000,000,000,000,000,000,
000,000,000,000,000,000,000,000,000,000,000,000,000,000,000,000,000,000,000,
000,000,000,000,000,000,000,000,000,000,000,000,000,000,000,000,000,000,000,
000,000,000,000,000,000,000,000,000,000,000,000,000

While the improbability of the formation of a protein molecule made up of five hundred amino acids reaches such an extent, we can further proceed to push the limits of the mind to higher levels of improbability. In the "haemoglobin" molecule, a vital protein, there are five hundred and seventy-four amino acids, which is a much larger number than that of the amino acids making up the protein mentioned above. Now consider this: in only one out of the billions of red blood cells in your body, there are "280,000,000" (280 million) haemoglobin molecules. The supposed age of the earth is not sufficient to afford the formation of even a single protein, let alone a red blood cell, by the method of "trial and error". The conclusion from all this is that evolution falls into a terrible abyss of improbability right at the stage of the formation of a single protein.

Looking for Answers to the Generation of Life

Well aware of the terrible odds against the possibility of life forming by chance, evolutionists were unable to provide a rational explanation for their beliefs, so they set about looking for ways to demonstrate that the odds were not so unfavourable.

They designed a number of laboratory experiments to address the question of how life could generate itself from non-living matter. The best known and most respected of these experiments is the one known as the "Miller Experiment" or "Urey-Miller Experiment", which was conducted by the American researcher Stanley Miller in 1953.

With the purpose of proving that amino acids could have come into existence by accident, Miller created an atmosphere in his laboratory that he assumed would have existed on primordial earth (but which later proved to be unrealistic) and he set to work. The mixture he used for this primordial atmosphere was composed of ammonia, methane, hydrogen, and water vapour.

Miller knew that methane, ammonia, water vapour and hydrogen would not react with each other under natural conditions. He was aware that he had to inject energy into the mixture to start a reaction. He suggested that this energy could have come from lightning flashes in the primordial atmosphere and, relying on this supposition, he used an artificial electricity discharge in his experiments.

Miller boiled this gas mixture at 100 ^{0}C for a week, and, in addition, he introduced an electric current into the chamber. At the end of the week, Miller analysed the chemicals that had been formed in the chamber and observed that three of the twenty amino acids, which constitute the basic elements of proteins, had been synthesised.

This experiment aroused great excitement among evolutionists and they promoted it as an outstanding success. Encouraged by the thought that this experiment definitely verified their theory, evolutionists immediately produced new scenarios. Miller had supposedly proved that amino acids could form by themselves. Relying on this, they hurriedly hypothesised the following stages. According to their scenario, amino acids had later by accident united in the proper sequences to form proteins. Some of these accidentally formed proteins placed themselves in cell membrane-like structures, which "somehow" came into existence and formed a primitive cell. The cells united in time and formed living organisms. The greatest mainstay of the scenario was Miller's experiment.

However, Miller's experiment was nothing but make-believe, and has since been proven invalid in many respects.

The Invalidity of Miller's Experiment

Nearly half a century has passed since Miller conducted his experiment. Although it has been shown to be invalid in many respects, evolutionists still advance Miller and his results as absolute proof that life could have formed spontaneously from non-living matter. When we assess Miller's experiment critically, without the bias and subjectivity of evolutionist thinking, however, it is evident that the situation is not as rosy as evolutionists would have us think. Miller set for himself the goal of proving that amino acids could form by themselves in earth's primitive conditions. Some amino acids were produced, but the conduct of the experiment conflicts with his goal in many ways, as we shall now see.

✦ Miller isolated the amino acids from the environment as soon as they were formed, by using a mechanism called a "cold trap". Had he not done so, the conditions of the environment in which the amino acids formed would immediately have destroyed the molecules.

It is quite meaningless to suppose that some conscious mechanism of this sort was integral to earth's primordial conditions, which involved ultraviolet radiation, thunderbolts, various chemicals, and a high percentage of free oxygen. Without such a mechanism, any amino acid that did manage to form would immediately have been destroyed.

✦ The primordial atmospheric environment that Miller attempted to simulate in his experiment was not realistic. Nitrogen and carbon dioxide would have been constituents of the primordial atmosphere, but Miller disregarded this and used methane and ammonia instead.

Why? Why were evolutionists insistent on the point that the primitive atmosphere contained high amounts of methane (CH_4), ammonia (NH_3), and water vapour (H_2O)? The answer is simple: without ammonia, it is impossible to synthesise an amino acid. Kevin McKean talks about this in an article published in *Discover* magazine:

> Miller and Urey imitated the ancient atmosphere of earth with a mixture of methane and ammonia. According to them, the earth was a true homogeneous mixture of metal, rock and ice. However in the latest studies, it is understood that the earth was very hot at those times and that it was composed of melted nickel and iron. Therefore, the chemical atmosphere of that time should have been formed mostly of nitrogen (N_2), carbon dioxide (CO_2) and water vapour (H_2O). However these are not as appropriate as methane and ammonia for the production of organic molecules.[14]

After a long period of silence, Miller himself also confessed that the atmospheric environment he used in his experiment was not realistic.

✦ Another important point invalidating Miller's experiment is that there was enough oxygen to destroy all the amino acids in the atmosphere at the time when evolutionists thought that amino acids formed. This oxygen concentration would definitely have hindered the formation of amino acids. This situation completely negates Miller's experiment, in which he totally neglected oxygen. If he had used oxygen in the experiment, methane would have decomposed into carbon dioxide and water, and ammonia would have decomposed into nitrogen and water.

On the other hand, since no ozone layer yet existed, no organic molecule could possibly have lived on earth because it was entirely unprotected against intense ultraviolet rays.

✦ In addition to a few amino acids essential for life, Miller's experiment also produced many organic acids with characteristics that are quite detrimental to the structures and functions of living things. If he had not isolated the amino acids and had left them in the same environment with these chemicals, their destruction or transformation into different compounds through chemical reactions would have been unavoidable. Moreover, a large number of right-handed amino acids also formed. The existence of these amino acids alone refuted the theory, even within its own reasoning, because right-handed amino acids are unable to function in the composition of living organisms and render proteins useless when they are involved in their composition.

To conclude, the circumstances in which amino acids formed in Miller's experiment were not suitable for life forms to come into being. The medium in which they formed was an acidic mixture that destroyed and oxidised any useful molecules that might have been obtained.

Evolutionists themselves actually refute the theory of evolution, as they are often wont to do, by advancing this experiment as "proof". If the experiment proves anything, it is that amino acids can only be produced in a controlled laboratory environment where all the necessary conditions have been specifically and consciously designed. That is, the experiment shows that what brings life (even the "near-life" of amino acids) into being cannot be unconscious chance, but rather conscious will – in a word, Creation. This is why every stage of Creation is a sign proving to us the existence and might of Allah.

The Miraculous Molecule: DNA

The theory of evolution has been unable to provide a coherent explanation for the existence of the molecules that are the basis of the cell. Furthermore, developments in the science of genetics and the discovery of the nucleic acids (DNA and RNA) have produced brand-new problems for the theory of evolution.

In 1955, the work of two scientists on DNA, James Watson and Francis Crick, launched a new era in biology. Many scientists directed their attention to the science of genetics. Today, after years of research, scientists have, largely, mapped the structure of DNA.

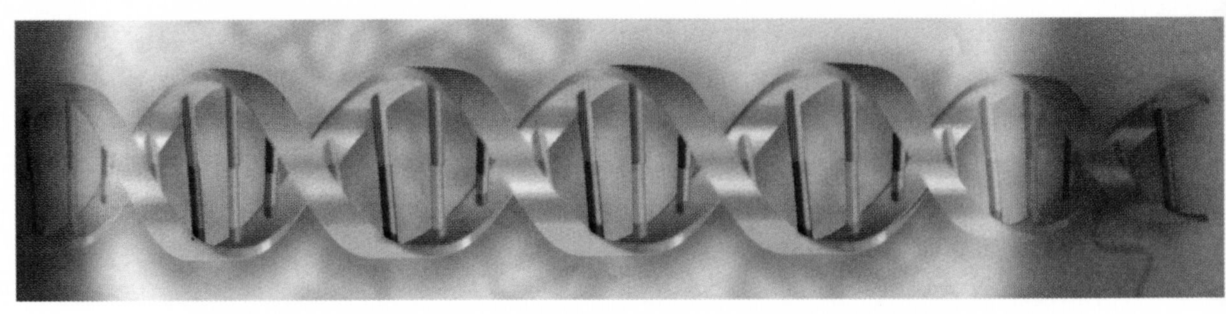

The molecule called DNA contains the complete construction plan of the human body.

Here, we need to give some very basic information on the structure and function of DNA:

The molecule called DNA, which exists in the nucleus of each of the 100 trillion cells in our body, contains the complete construction plan of the human body. Information regarding all the characteristics of a person, from the physical appearance to the structure of the inner organs, is recorded in DNA by means of a special coding system. The information in DNA is coded within the sequence of four special bases that make up this molecule. These bases are specified as A, T, G, and C according to the initial letters of their names. All the structural differences among people depend on the variations in the sequence of these bases. There are approximately 3.5 billion nucleotides, that is, 3.5 billion letters in a DNA molecule.

The DNA data pertaining to a particular organ or protein is included in special components called "genes". For instance, information about the eye exists in a series of special genes, whereas information about the heart exists in quite another series of genes. The cell produces proteins by using the information in all of these genes. Amino acids that constitute the structure of the protein are defined by the sequential arrangement of three nucleotides in the DNA.

At this point, an important detail deserves attention. An error in the sequence of nucleotides making up a gene renders the gene completely useless. When we consider that there are 200 thousand genes in the human body, it becomes more evident how impossible it is for the millions of nucleotides making up these genes to form by accident in the right sequence. An evolutionist biologist, Frank Salisbury, comments on this impossibility by saying:

> A medium protein might include about 300 amino acids. The DNA gene controlling this would have about 1,000 nucleotides in its chain. Since there are four kinds of nucleotides in a DNA chain, one consisting of 1,000 links could exist in 4^{1000} forms. Using a little algebra (logarithms), we can see that $4^{1000}=10^{600}$. Ten multiplied by itself 600 times gives the figure 1 followed by 600 zeros! This number is completely beyond our comprehension.[15]

The number 4^{1000} is equivalent to 10^{600}. We obtain this number by adding 600 zeros to 1. As 10 with 11 zeros indicates a trillion, a figure with 600 zeros is indeed a number that is difficult to grasp.

Evolutionist Prof. Ali Demirsoy was forced to make the following admission on this issue:

> In fact, the probability of the random formation of a protein and a nucleic acid (DNA-RNA) is inconceivably small. The chances against the emergence of even a particular protein chain are astronomic.[16]

In addition to all these improbabilities, DNA can barely be involved in a reaction because of its double-chained spiral shape. This also makes it impossible to think that it can be the basis of life.

Moreover, while DNA can replicate only with the help of some enzymes that are actually proteins, the synthesis of these enzymes can be realised only by the information coded in DNA. As they both depend on each other, either they have to exist at the same time for replication, or one of them has had to be "created" before the other. American microbiologist Jacobson comments on the subject:

> The complete directions for the reproduction of plans, for energy and the extraction of parts from the current environment, for the growth sequence, and for the effector mechanism translating instructions into growth – all had to be simultaneously present at that moment (when life began). This combination of events has seemed an incredibly unlikely happenstance, and has often been ascribed to divine intervention.[17]

The quotation above was written two years after the disclosure of the structure of DNA by James Watson and Francis Crick. Despite all the developments in science, this problem remains unsolved for evolutionists. To sum up, the need for DNA in reproduction, the necessity of the presence of some proteins for reproduction, and the requirement to produce these proteins according to the information in the DNA entirely demolish evolutionist theses.

Two German scientists, Junker and Scherer, explained that the synthesis of each of the molecules required for chemical evolution, necessitates distinct conditions, and that the probability of the compounding of these materials having theoretically very different acquirement methods is zero:

> Until now, no experiment is known in which we can obtain all the molecules necessary for chemical evolution. Therefore, it is essential to produce various molecules in different places under very suitable conditions and then to carry them to another place for reaction by protecting them from harmful elements like hydrolysis and photolysis.[18]

In short, the theory of evolution is unable to prove any of the evolutionary stages that allegedly occur at the molecular level.

To summarise what we have said so far, neither amino acids nor their products, the proteins making up the cells of living beings, could ever be produced in any so-called "primitive atmosphere" environment. Moreover, factors such as the incredibly complex structure of proteins, their right-hand, left-hand features, and the difficulties in the formation of peptide bonds are just parts of the reason why they will never be produced in any future experiment either.

Even if we suppose for a moment that proteins somehow did form accidentally, that would still have no meaning, for proteins are nothing at all on their own: they cannot themselves reproduce. Protein synthesis is only possible with the information coded in DNA and RNA molecules. Without DNA and RNA, it is impossible for a protein to reproduce. The specific sequence of the twenty different amino acids encoded in DNA determines the structure of each protein in the body. However, as has been made abundantly clear by all those who have studied these molecules, it is impossible for DNA and RNA to form by chance.

The Fact of Creation

With the collapse of the theory of evolution in every field, prominent names in the discipline of microbiology today admit the fact of creation and have begun to defend the view that everything is created by a conscious Creator as part of an exalted creation. This is already a fact that people cannot disregard. Scientists who can approach their work with an open mind have developed a view called "intelligent design". Michael J. Behe, one of the foremost of these scientists, states that he accepts the absolute being of the Creator and describes the impasse of those who deny this fact:

> The result of these cumulative efforts to investigate the cell – to investigate life at the molecular level – is a loud, clear, piercing cry of "design!" The result is so unambiguous and so significant that it must be ranked as one of the greatest achievements in the history of science. This triumph of science should evoke cries of "Eureka" from ten thousand throats.
>
> But, no bottles have been uncorked, no hands clapped. Instead, a curious, embarrassed silence surrounds the stark complexity of the cell. When the subject comes up in public, feet start to shuffle, and breathing gets a bit laboured. In private people are a bit more relaxed; many explicitly admit the obvious but then stare at the ground, shake their heads, and let it go like that. Why does the scientific community not greedily embrace its startling discovery? Why is the observation of design handled with intellectual gloves? The dilemma is that while one side of the [issue] is labelled intelligent design, the other side must be labelled God.[19]

Today, many people are not even aware that they are in a position of accepting a body of fallacy as truth in the name of science, instead of believing in Allah. Those who do not find the sentence "Allah created you from nothing" scientific enough can believe that the first living being came into being by thunderbolts striking a "primordial soup" billions of years ago.

As we have described elsewhere in this book, the balances in nature are so delicate and so numerous that it is entirely irrational to claim that they developed "by chance". No matter how much those who cannot set themselves free from this irrationality may strive, the signs of Allah in the heavens and the earth are completely obvious and they are undeniable.

Allah is the Creator of the heavens, the earth and all that is in between.

The signs of His being have encompassed the entire universe.

---

1. Charles Darwin, *The Origin of Species: By Means of Natural Selection or the Preservation of Favoured Races in the Struggle for Life*, London: Senate Press, 1995, p. 134.
2. Derek A. Ager. "The Nature of the Fossil Record." *Proceedings of the British Geological Association*, vol. 87, no. 2, (1976), p. 133.
3. T.N. George, "Fossils in Evolutionary Perspective", *Science Progress*, vol.48, (January 1960), p.1-3
4. Richard Monestarsky, Mysteries of the Orient, *Discover*, April 1993, p.40.
5. Stefan Bengston, *Nature* 345:765 (1990).
6. Earnest A. Hooton, *Up From The Ape*, New York: McMillan, 1931, p.332.
7. Stephen Jay Gould, Smith Woodward's Folly, *New Scientist*, 5 April, 1979, p. 44.
8. Charles E. Oxnard, The Place of Australopithecines in Human Evolution: Grounds for Doubt, *Nature*, No. 258, p. 389.
9. Richard Leakey, *The Making of Mankind*, London: Sphere Books, 1981, p. 116
10. Eric Trinkaus, Hard Times Among the Neanderthals, *Natural History*, No. 87, December 1978, p. 10, R.L. Holoway, "The Neanderthal Brain: What was Primitive?", *American Journal of Physical Anthrophology Supplement*, No. 12, 1991, p. 94
11. Ali Demirsoy, *Kalitim ve Evrim* (Inheritance and Evolution), Ankara: Meteksan Yayinlari 1984, p. 61
12. Ali Demirsoy, *Kalitim ve Evrim* (Inheritance and Evolution), Ankara: Meteksan Yayinlari 1984, p. 61
13. *Fabbri Britannica Science Encyclopaedia*, Vol. 2, No. 22, p. 519
14. Kevin McKean, *Bilim ve Teknik*, No. 189, p. 7
15. Frank B. Salisbury, "Doubts about the Modern Synthetic Theory of Evolution", *American Biology Teacher*, September 1971, p. 336.
16. Ali Demirsoy, *Kalitim ve Evrim* (Inheritance and Evolution), Ankara: Meteksan Publishing Co., 1984, p. 39.
17. Homer Jacobson, "Information, Reproduction and the Origin of Life", *American Scientist*, January, 1955, p.121.
18. Reinhard Junker & Siegfried Scherer, "Entstehung Gesiche Der Lebewesen", Weyel, 1986, p. 89.
19. Michael J. Behe, *Darwin's Black Box*, New York: Free Press, 1996, pp. 232-233.

WARNING

The chapter you are about to read reveals a crucial secret of your life. You should read it very attentively and thoroughly for it concerns a subject that is liable to make fundamental changes in your outlook on the external world. The subject of this chapter is not just a point of view, a different approach, or a traditional or philosophical thought: it is a fact which everyone, believing or unbelieving, must admit and which is also proven by science today.

A VERY DIFFERENT APPROACH TO MATTER

People who conscientiously and wisely contemplate their surroundings realise that everything in the universe – both animate and inanimate – must have been created. The question is "Who is the Creator of all these things?"

It is evident that **"the fact of creation"**, which reveals itself in every aspect of the universe, cannot be an outcome of the universe itself. For example, a bug cannot have created itself. The solar system cannot have created or organised itself. Neither plants, humans, bacteria, erythrocytes (red-blood corpuscles), nor butterflies can have created themselves. Also the possibility that all these could have originated "by chance" is not even imaginable.

We therefore arrive at the following conclusion: Everything that we see has been created, but nothing we see can themselves be "creators". The Creator is different from and superior to all that we see with our eyes, a superior power that is invisible but whose existence and attributes are revealed in everything that exists.

This is the point at which those who deny the existence of Allah demur. These people are conditioned not to believe in His existence unless they see Him with their eyes. These people, who disregard the fact of **"creation"**, are forced to ignore the actuality of "creation" manifest throughout the universe and try to prove that the universe and the living things in it have not been created. Evolutionary theory is an essential example of their vain endeavours to this end.

The basic mistake of those who deny Allah is shared by some people who do not really deny the existence of Allah but have a wrong perception of Him. They do not deny creation but have superstitious beliefs about "where" Allah is. Some think that Allah is up in the "sky". They tacitly imagine that Allah is behind a very distant planet and interferes with "worldly affairs" once in a while, or perhaps does not intervene at all. They imagine that He created the universe and then left it to itself, leaving people to determine their fates for themselves.

Still others have heard that it is written in the Qur'an that Allah is "everywhere" but they cannot conceive what exactly this means. They think that Allah surrounds everything like radio waves or like an invisible, intangible gas.

However, this and other beliefs that are unable to make clear **"where" Allah is** (and maybe because of that deny Him) are all based on a common mistake. They are prejudiced without any grounds for it and so are then moved to wrong opinions of Allah. What is this prejudice?

This prejudice is about the nature and characteristics of matter. We are so conditioned in our suppositions about the existence of matter that we never think whether it does exist or not or whether it is only a shadow. Modern science demolishes this prejudice and discloses a very important and revealing reality. In the following pages, we will try to clarify this great reality to which the Qur'an points.

THE WORLD OF ELECTRICAL SIGNALS

All the information that we have about the world in which we live is conveyed to us by our five senses. The world we know of consists of what our eyes see, our hands feel, our noses smell, our tongues taste, and our ears hear. We never think that the "external" world could be anything other than that which our senses present to us, as we have been dependent on only those senses since birth.

Modern research in many different fields of science points to a very different understanding and creates serious doubt about our senses and the world that we perceive with them.

The starting-point of this approach is that the notion of an "external world" shaped in our brain is only a response created in our brain by electrical signals. The redness of apples, the hardness of wood and, moreover, your mother, father, family, and everything that you own, your house, job, and the lines of this book, are comprised only of electrical signals.

Frederick Vester explains the point that science has reached on this subject:

Statements of some scientists posing that "man is an image, everything experienced is temporary and deceptive, and this universe is a shadow", seems to be proven by science in our day.[1]

The famous philosopher, George Berkeley commented on the subject as follows:

We believe in the existence of objects just because we see and touch them, and they are reflected to us by our perceptions. However, our perceptions are only ideas in our mind. Thus, objects we captivate by perceptions are nothing but ideas, and these ideas are essentially in nowhere but our mind... Since all these exist only in the mind, then

it means that we are beguiled by deceptions when we imagine the universe and things to have an existence outside the mind. So, none of the surrounding things have an existence out of our mind.[2]

In order to clarify the subject, let us consider our sense of sight, which provides us with the most extensive information about the external world.

How Do We See, Hear, and Taste?

The act of seeing is realised progressively. Light clusters (photons) travel from the object to the eye and pass through the lens at the front of the eye where they are refracted and fall upside-down on the retina at the back of the eye. Here, impinging light is turned into electrical signals that are transmitted by neurons to a tiny spot called the centre of vision in the back of the brain. This electrical signal is perceived as an image in this centre in the brain after a series of processes. The act of seeing actually takes place in this tiny spot in the posterior part of the brain, which is **pitch-dark and completely insulated from light**.

Now, let us reconsider this seemingly ordinary and unremarkable process. When we say, "we see", we are in fact seeing the effects of impulses reaching our eyes and induced in our brain, after they are transformed into electrical signals. That is, **when we say, "we see", we are actually observing electrical signals in our mind**.

All the images we view in our lives are formed in our centre of vision, which only comprises a few cubic centimetres of the volume of the brain. Both the book you are now reading and the boundless landscape you see when you gaze at the horizon fit into this tiny space. Another point that has to be kept in

Stimulations coming from an object are converted into electrical signals and cause effects in the brain. When we "see", we in fact view the effects of these electrical signals in our mind.

mind is that, as we have noted before, the brain is insulated from light; its inside is absolutely dark. The brain has no contact with light itself.

We can explain this interesting situation with an example. Let us suppose that in front of us there is a burning candle. We can sit opposite this candle and watch it at length. However, during this period, our brain never has any direct contact with the original light of the candle. Even as we see the light of the candle, the inside of our brain is completely dark. We watch a colourful and bright world inside our dark brain.

R. L. Gregory gives the following explanation about the miraculous aspects of seeing, something that we take so much for granted:

> **We are so familiar with seeing, that it takes a leap of imagination to realise that there are problems to be solved. But consider it. We are given tiny distorted upside-down images in the eyes, and we see separate solid objects in surrounding space. From the patterns of simulation on the retinas we perceive the world of objects, and this is nothing short of a miracle.[3]**

The same situation applies to all our other senses. Sound, touch, taste and smell are all transmitted to the brain as electrical signals and are perceived in the relevant centres in the brain.

The sense of hearing works in a similar manner to that of sight. The outer ear picks up sounds by the auricle and directs them to the middle ear. The middle ear transmits the sound vibrations to the inner ear and intensifies them. The inner ear translates the vibrations into electrical signals, which it sends into the brain. Just as with the eye, the act of hearing finally takes place in the centre of hearing in the brain. The brain is insulated from sound just as it is from light. Therefore, no matter how noisy it is outside, the inside of the brain is completely silent.

Nevertheless, even the subtlest sounds are perceived in the brain. This is so precise that the ear of a healthy person hears everything without any atmospheric noise or interference. In your brain, which is insulated from sound, you listen to the symphonies of an orchestra, hear all the noises of a crowded place, and perceive all the sounds within a wide frequency range, from the rustling of a leaf to the roar of a jet plane. However, if the sound level in your brain were to be measured by a sensitive device at that moment, it would be seen that a complete silence is prevailing there.

Our perception of odour is formed in a similar way. Volatile molecules emitted by things such as vanilla or a rose reach the receptors in the delicate hairs in the epithelium region of the nose and become involved in an interaction. This interaction is transmitted to the brain as electrical signals and perceived as smell. Everything that we smell, be it pleasant or unpleasant, is nothing but the brain's perception of the interactions of volatile molecules after they have been transformed into electrical signals. You perceive the scent of a perfume, a flower, a food that you like, the sea, or other odours you like or dislike, in your brain. The molecules themselves never reach the brain. Just as with sound and vision, what reach your brain simply electrical signals. In other words, all the odours that you have assumed – since you were born – to belong to external objects are just electrical signals that you feel through your sense organs.

Similarly, there are four different types of chemical receptors in the front part of a human's tongue. These pertain to the four tastes: salty, sweet, sour, and bitter. Our taste receptors transform these perceptions into electrical signals through a chain of chemical processes and transmit them to the brain. These signals are perceived as taste by the brain. The taste you experience when you eat a chocolate bar or a fruit that you like is the interpretation of electrical signals by the brain. You can never reach the object in the external world; you can never see, smell or taste the chocolate itself. For instance, if the taste nerves that travel to the brain are cut, the taste of things you eat will not reach your brain; you will completely lose your sense of taste.

At this point, we come across another fact: We can never be sure that what we experience when we taste a food and what another person experiences when he tastes the same food, or what we perceive when we hear a voice and what another person perceives when he hears the same voice are the same. Lincoln Barnett says that no one can know whether another person perceives the colour red or hears the C note the in same way as does he himself.[4]

Our sense of touch is no different from the others. When we touch an object, all information that will help us recognise the external world and objects are transmitted to the brain by the sense nerves on the skin. The feeling of touch is formed in our brain. Contrary to general belief, the place where we perceive the sense of touch is not at our finger-tips or on our skins but at the centre of touch perception in our brains. Because of the brain's interpretation of electrical stimuli coming to it from objects, we experience those objects differently such as that they are hard or soft, hot or cold. We derive all the details that help us recognise an object from these stimuli. Concerning this, the thoughts of two famous philosophers, B. Russell and L. Wittgenstein, are as follows:

> **For instance, whether a lemon truly exists or not and how it came to exist cannot be questioned and investigated. A lemon consists merely of a taste sensed by the tongue, an odour sensed by the nose, a colour and shape sensed by the eye; and only these features of it can**

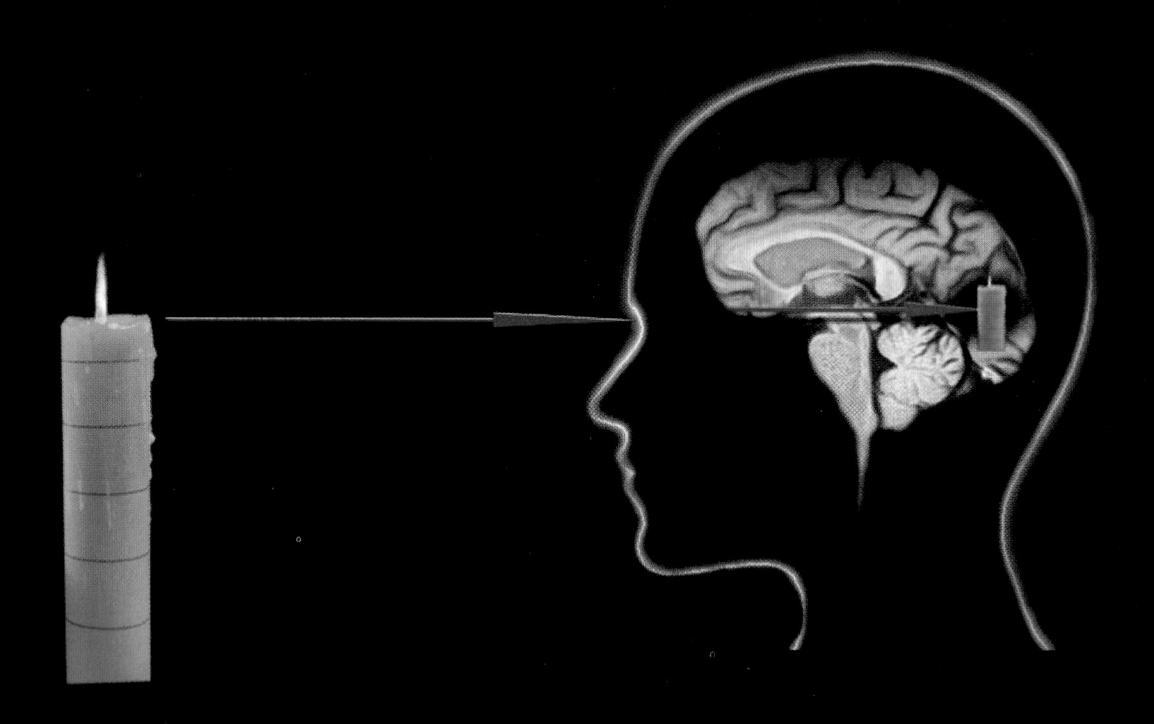

Even at the moment when we feel the light and heat of a fire, the inside of our brain is pitch dark and its temperature never changes.

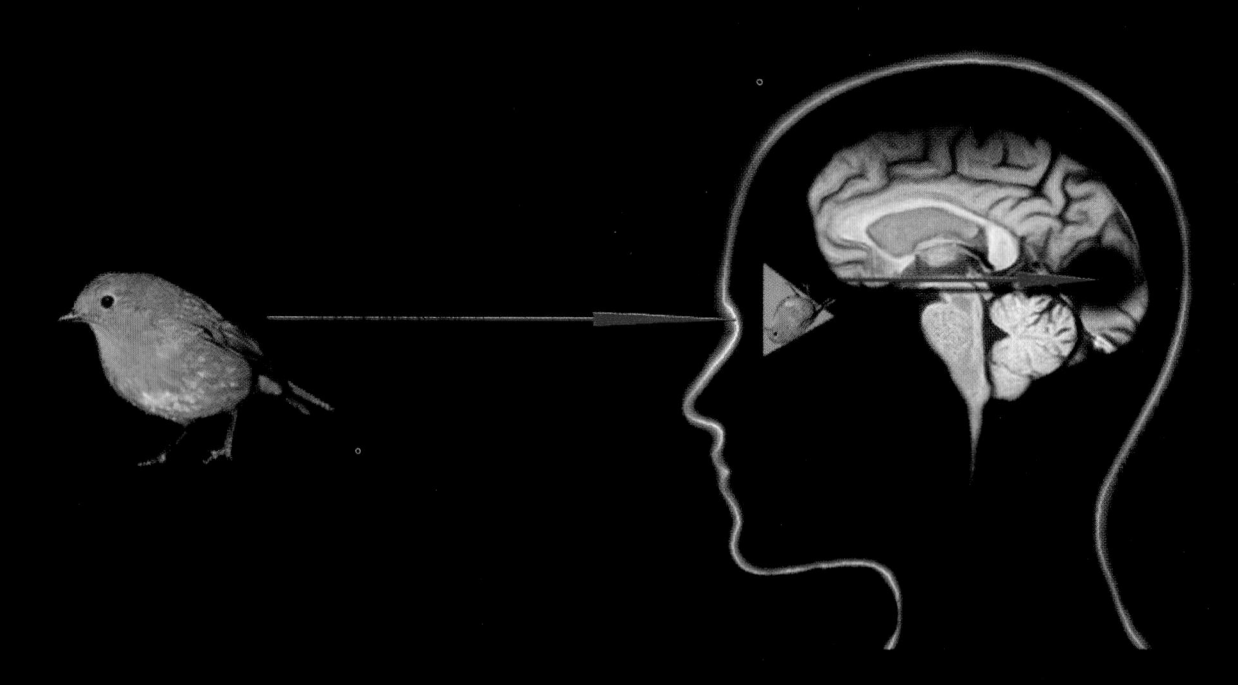

Bundles of light coming from an object falls upside-down on the retina. Here, the image is converted into electrical signals and transmitted to the centre of vision at the back of the brain. Since the brain is insulated from light, it is impossible for light to reach the centre of vision. This means that we view a vast world of light and depth in a tiny spot that is insulated from light.

be subject to examination and assessment. Science can never know the physical world.[5]

It is impossible for us to reach the physical world. All objects around us are a collection of perceptions such as seeing, hearing, and touching. By processing the data in the centre of vision and in other sensory centres, our brains, throughout our lives, **do not confront the "original" of the matter existing outside us but rather the copy formed inside our brain.** It is at this point that we are misled by assuming these copies are instances of real matter outside us.

"The External World" Inside Our Brain

From the physical facts described so far, we may conclude the following. Everything we see, touch, hear, and perceive as "matter", "the world" or "the universe" is only electrical signals occurring in our brain.

Someone eating a fruit does not confront the actual fruit but its perception in the brain. The object considered by the person a "fruit" actually consists of electrical impressions of the shape, taste, smell, and texture of the fruit in the brain. If the sight nerves travelling to the brain were to be severed suddenly, the image of the fruit would suddenly disappear. A disconnection in the nerve travelling from the sensors in the nose to the brain would completely interrupt the sense of smell. Put simply, the fruit is nothing but the brain's interpretation of electrical signals.

Another point to be considered is **the sense of distance**. Distance, for example the distance between you and this book, is only a feeling of space formed in your brain. Objects that seem to be distant in one person's view also exist in the brain. For instance, someone who watches the stars in the sky assumes that they are millions of light-years away from him. Yet, what he "sees" are really the stars inside himself, in his centre of vision. While you read these lines, you are, in truth, not inside the room you assume yourself to be in; on the contrary, the room is inside you. Your seeing your body makes you think that you are inside it. **However, you must remember that your body, too, is an image formed inside your brain.**

The same applies to all your other perceptions. For instance, when you think that you hear the sound of the television in the next room, you are actually experiencing the sound inside your brain. You can prove neither that a room exists next to yours, nor that a sound comes from the television in that room. Both the sound you think to be coming from metres away and the conversation of a person right next to you are perceived in a centre of hearing a few centimetres square in your brain. Apart from in this centre of perception,

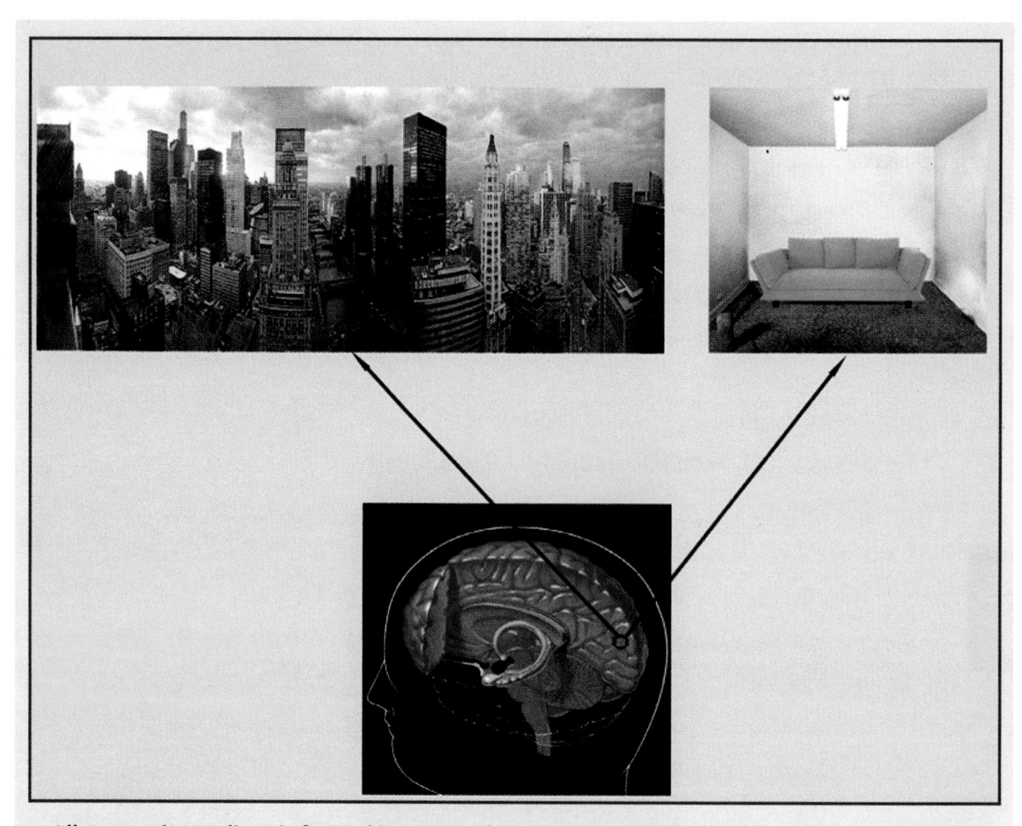

All we see in our lives is formed in a part of our brain called the "vision centre" which lies at the back of our brain, and which occupies only a few cubic centimetres. Both the book you are now reading and the boundless landscape you see when you gaze at the horizon fit into this tiny space. Therefore, we see objects not in their actual sizes existing outside, but in the sizes perceived by our brain.

no concept such as right, left, front or behind exists. That is, sound does not come to you from the right, from the left or from the air; **there is no direction from which sound comes.**

The smells that you perceive are like that too; none of them reaches you from a great distance. You suppose that the end-effects formed in your centre of smell are the smell of the objects in the external world. However, just as the image of a rose is in your centre of vision, so the smell of the rose is in your centre of smell; there is neither a rose nor an odour pertaining to it in the external world.

The "external world" presented to us by our perceptions is merely a collection of electrical signals reaching our brains. Throughout our lives, our brains process these signals and we live without recognising that we are mistaken in assuming that these are the original versions of things existing in the "external world". We are misled because we can never reach the matters themselves by means of our senses.

Moreover, again our brains interpret and attribute meaning to signals that we assume to be the "external world". For example, let us consider the sense of hearing. Our brains transform the sound waves in the "external world" into a symphony. That is to say, music is also a perception created by our brains. In the same manner, when we see colours, what reach our eyes are merely electrical signals of **different wavelengths**. Again our brains transform these signals into colours. **There are no colours in the "external world".** Neither is the apple red, nor is the sky blue, nor the trees green. They are as they are just because we perceive them to be so. **The "external world" depends entirely on the perceiver.**

The findings of modern physics show that the universe is a collection of perceptions. The following question appears on the cover of the well-known American science magazine New Scientist, which dealt with this matter in its 30 January 1999 issue: "Beyond Reality: Is the Universe Really a Frolic of Primal Information and Matter Just a Mirage?"

Even the slightest defect in the retina of the eye causes colour blindness. Some people perceive blue as green, some red as blue, and some perceive all colours as different tones of grey. At this point, it does not matter whether the object externally is coloured or not.

The prominent thinker Berkeley also addressed this fact:

> **At the beginning, it was believed that colours, odours, etc., "really exist", but subsequently such views were renounced, and it was seen that they only exist in dependence on our sensations.**[6]

In conclusion, the reason we see objects coloured is not because they are coloured or because they have an independent material existence outside ourselves. The truth of the matter is rather that **all the qualities we ascribe to objects are inside us and not in the "external world".**

So what remains of the "external world"?

Is the Existence of the "External World" Indispensable?

So far, we have been speaking repeatedly of an "external world" and a world of perceptions formed in our brains, the latter of which is what we see. However, since we can never actually reach the "external world", how can we be sure that such a world really exists?

Actually we cannot. Since each object is only a collection of perceptions and those perceptions exist only in the mind, it is more accurate to say that **the**

only world that really exists is the world of perceptions. The only world we know of is the world that exists in our mind: the one that is designed, recorded, and made vivid there; the one, in short, that is created within our mind. This is the only world of which we can be sure.

We can never prove that the perceptions we observe in our brain have material correlates. Those perceptions could conceivably be coming from an "artificial" source.

It is possible to observe this. False stimuli can produce an entirely imaginary "material world" in our brain. For example, let us imagine a very developed recording instrument in which all kinds of electrical signals could be recorded. First, let us transmit all the data related to a setting (including body image) to this instrument by transforming them into electrical signals. Second, let us imagine that the brain could survive apart from the body. Finally, let us connect the recording instrument to the brain with electrodes that will function as nerves and send the pre-recorded data to the brain. In this state, you would experience yourself living in this artificially created setting. For instance, you could easily believe that you are driving fast on a highway. It might never become possible to understand that you consist of nothing but your brain. This is because what is needed to form a world within your brain is not the existence of a real world but rather the stimuli. It is perfectly possible that these stimuli could be coming from an artificial source, such as a tape-recorder.

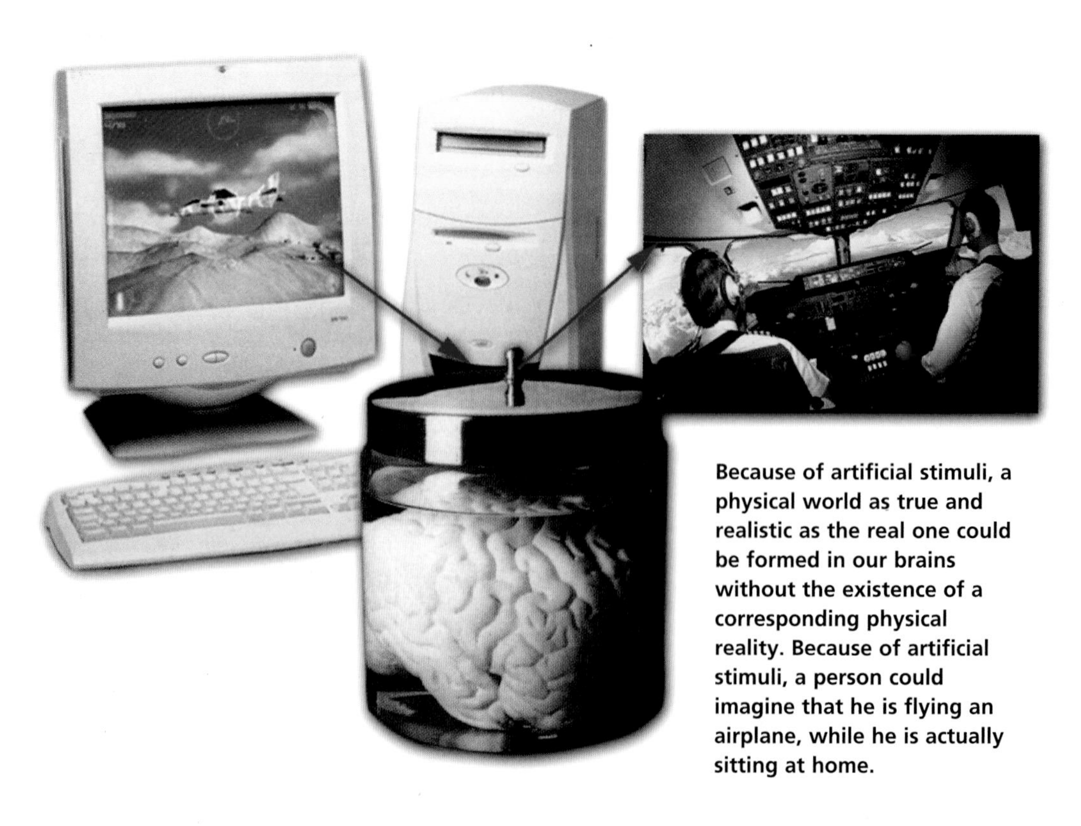

Because of artificial stimuli, a physical world as true and realistic as the real one could be formed in our brains without the existence of a corresponding physical reality. Because of artificial stimuli, a person could imagine that he is flying an airplane, while he is actually sitting at home.

In that connection, distinguished philosopher Bertrand Russell wrote:

As to the sense of touch when we press the table with our fingers, that is an electric disturbance on the electrons and protons of our fingertips, produced, according to modern physics, by the proximity of the electrons and protons in the table. If the same disturbance in our finger-tips arose in any other way, we should have the sensations, in spite of there being no table.[7]

It is indeed very easy for us to be deceived into believing perceptions, without any material correlates, to be real. We often experience this feeling in our dreams, in which we experience events, see people, objects and settings that seem completely real. However, they are all nothing but mere perceptions. There is no basic difference between the dream and the "real world"; both of them are experienced in the brain.

Who Is the Perceiver?

As we have related so far, there is no doubt that the world we think we inhabit and that we call the "external world" is perceived inside our brain. However, here arises the question of primary importance. If all physical events that we know are intrinsically perceptions, what about our brain? Since our brains are a part of the physical world just like our arms, legs, or any other objects, it also must be a perception just like all other objects.

An example about dreams will illuminate the subject further. Let us think that we see the dream within our brain in accordance with what has been said so far. In the dream, we will have an imaginary body, an imaginary arm, an imaginary eye, and an imaginary brain. If during our dream, we were asked, "where do you see?" we would answer "I see in my brain". The seer of the images is not the imaginary brain in the dream, but a "being" that is far "superior" to it.

We know that there is no physical distinction between the setting of a dream and the setting we call real life. So when we are asked in the setting we call real life the above question "where do you see", it would be just as meaningless to answer "in my brain" as in the example above. In both conditions, the entity that sees and perceives is not the brain, which is after all only a hunk of meat.

When we analyse the brain, we see that there is nothing in it but lipid and protein molecules, which also exist in other living organisms. This means that within the piece of meat we call our "brain", there is nothing to observe the images, to constitute consciousness, or to create the being we call "myself".

R. L. Gregory refers to a mistake people make in relation to the perception of images in the brain:

There is a temptation, which must be avoided, to say that the eyes produce pictures in the brain. A picture in the brain suggests the need of some kind of internal eye to see it – but this would need a further eye to see its picture... and so on, in an endless regress of eyes and pictures. This is absurd.[8]

This is the very point that puts materialists, who do not hold anything but matter to be true, in a quandary: to whom belongs "the eye inside" that sees, that perceives what it sees and reacts?

Karl Pribram also focused on this important question, about who the perceiver is, in the world of science and philosophy:

Since the Greeks, philosophers have been thinking about "the ghost in the machine", "the small man within the small man" etc. Where is "I", the person who uses his brain? Who is it that realises the act of knowing? As Saint Francis of Assisi said: "What we search for is the one that sees".[9]

Now, think of this: The book in your hand, the room you are in, in brief, all the images in front of you are seen inside your brain. Is it the atoms that see these images? Blind, deaf, unconscious atoms? Why did some atoms acquire this quality whereas some did not? Do our acts of thinking, comprehending, remembering, being delighted, being unhappy, and everything else consist of the electrochemical reactions between these atoms?

When we ponder these questions, we see that there is no sense in looking for will in atoms. It is clear that the being that sees, hears, and feels is a supra-material being. This being is "alive" and it is neither matter nor an image of matter. This being associates with the perceptions in front of it by using the image of our body.

This being is the "soul".

The aggregate of perceptions we call the "material world" is a dream observed by this soul. Just as the bodies we possess and the material world we see in our dreams have no reality, the universe we occupy and the bodies we possess also have no material reality.

The real being is the soul. Matter consists merely of perceptions viewed by the soul. The intelligent beings that write and read these lines are not each a heap of atoms and molecules and the chemical reactions between them, but a "soul".

The Real Absolute Being

All these facts bring us face to face with a very significant question. If the

The brain is a collection of cells made up of protein and fat molecules. It is formed of nerve cells called neurons. There is no power in this piece of meat to observe images, to constitute consciousness, or to create the being we call "myself".

thing we acknowledge to be the material world is merely comprised of perceptions seen by our soul, then what is the source of these perceptions?

In answering this question, we must consider the following: matter does not have a self-governing existence by itself. Since matter is a perception, it is something "artificial". That is, this perception must have been caused by another power, which means that it must have been created. Moreover, this creation must be continuous. If there were not a continuous and consistent creation, then what we call matter would disappear and be lost. This may be likened to a television on which a picture is displayed as long as the signal continues to be broadcast. So, who makes our soul see the stars, the earth, plants, people, our bodies and all else that we see?

It is very evident that there is a Creator, Who has created the entire material universe, that is, the sum of perceptions, and continues His creation ceaselessly. Since this Creator displays such a magnificent creation, He surely has eternal power and might.

This Creator introduces Himself to us. He has revealed a Book and through this Book has described Himself, the universe and the reason of our existence to us.

This Creator is Allah and the name of His book is the Qur'an.

The facts that the heavens and the earth, that is, the universe is not stable, that their presence is only made possible by Allah's creating them and that they will disappear when He ends this creation, are all explained in a verse as follows:

It is Allah Who sustains the heavens and the earth, lest they cease (to function): and if they should fail, there is none - not one - can sustain them thereafter: Verily He is Most Forbearing, Oft-Forgiving. (Surat al-Fatir: 41)

As we mentioned at the beginning, some people have no genuine understanding of Allah and so they imagine Him as a being present somewhere in the heavens and not really intervening in worldly affairs. The basis of this logic actually lies in the thought that the universe is an assembly of matter and Allah is "outside" this material world, in a far away place. In some false religions, belief in Allah is limited to this understanding.

However, as we have considered so far, matter is composed only of sensations. And the only real absolute being is Allah. That means that **only Allah is; all things except Him are shadow beings.** Consequently, it is impossible to conceive of Allah as separate and outside of this whole mass of matter. **Allah is surely "everywhere" and encompasses all.** This reality is explained in the Qur'an as follows;

Allah! There is no god but He, the Living, the Self-subsisting, Eternal. No slumber can seize Him nor sleep. His are all things in the heavens and on earth. Who is there can intercede in His presence except as He permits? He knows what (appears to His creatures as) before or after or behind them. Nor shall they compass aught of His knowledge except as He wills. His Throne extends over the heavens and the earth, and He feels no fatigue in guarding and preserving them for He is the Most High, the Supreme (in glory). (Surat al-Baqarah: 255)

That Allah is not bound by space and that He encompasses everything roundabout is stated in another verse as follows:

To Allah belong the east and the west: Whithersoever you turn, there is the face of Allah. For Allah is all-pervading, all-knowing. (Surat al-Baqarah: 115)

Since material beings are each a perception, they cannot see Allah; but Allah sees the matter He created in all its forms. In the Qur'an, this is stated thus: **"No vision can grasp Him, but His grasp is over all vision." (Surat al-An'am: 103)**

That is, we cannot grasp Allah's being with our eyes, but Allah has thoroughly encompassed our inside, outside, looks and thoughts. We cannot utter any word but with His knowledge, nor can we even take a breath.

While we watch these sensory perceptions in the course of our lives, the closest being to us is not any one of these sensations, but Allah Himself. The secret of the following verse in the Qur'an is concealed in this reality: "It is We

Who created man, and We know what dark suggestions his soul makes to him: for **We are nearer to him than (his) jugular vein.**" **(Surah Qaf: 16)** When a person thinks that his body is only made up of "matter", he cannot comprehend this important fact. If he takes his brain to be "himself", then the place that he accepts to be the outside is 20-30 cm away from him. However, when he understands that there is nothing such as matter, and that everything is imagination, notions such as outside, inside, far or near lose meaning. **Allah has encompassed him and He is "infinitely close" to him.**

Allah informs men that He is "**infinitely close**" to them with the verse "When My servants ask you concerning Me, **I am indeed close (to them).**" (Surat al-Baqarah: 186). Another verse relates the same fact: "We told you that **your Lord encompasses mankind round about.**" **(Surat al-Isra, 60)**.

Man is misled in thinking that the being closest to him is himself. Allah, in truth, is even closer to us than ourselves. He has called our attention to this point in the verse "Why is it not then that when it (soul) comes up to the throat, and you at that time look on, **We are nearer to him than you,** but you see not." **(Surat al-Waqi'ah: 83-85)**. As we are told in the verse, people live unaware of this phenomenal fact because they do not see it with their eyes.

Why is it not then that when it (soul) comes up to the throat, and you at that time look on, We are nearer to him than you, but you see not.
(Surat al-Waqia, 83-85)

On the other hand, it is impossible for man, who is nothing but a shadow being, to have power and will independent of Allah. The verse "But **Allah has created you and what you do!**" **(Surat as-Saffat: 96)** shows that everything we experience takes place under Allah's control. In the Qur'an, this reality is stated in the verse "**You did not throw, when you threw, it was Allah Who threw**" (Surat al-Anfal, 17) whereby it is emphasised that no act is independent of Allah. Since the human being is a shadow being, he himself does not perform the act of throwing. However, Allah gives this shadow being the feeling of self. In reality, Allah performs all acts. If someone takes the acts he does as his own, he evidently means to deceive himself.

This is the reality. A person may not want to concede this and may think of himself as a being independent of Allah; but this does not change a thing. Of course his unwise denial is again within Allah's will and wish.

Everything That You Possess Is Intrinsically Illusory

As may be seen clearly, it is a logical scientific fact that the "external world" has no material reality and that it is a collection of images Allah perpetually presents to our soul. Nevertheless, people usually do not include, or rather do do not want to include, everything in the concept of the "external world".

Think about this issue sincerely and boldly. You will realise that your house, furniture, car – which is perhaps recently bought, office, jewellery, bank account, wardrobe, spouse, children, colleagues, and everything else that you possess are in fact included in this imaginary external world projected to you. Everything you see, hear, or smell – in short – perceive with your five senses around you is a part of this "imaginary world": the voice of your favourite singer, the hardness of the chair you sit on, a perfume whose smell you like, the sun that keeps you warm, a flower with beautiful colours, a bird flying in front of your window, a speedboat moving swiftly on the water, your fertile garden, the computer you use at your job, or your hi-fi that has the most advanced technology in the world...

This is the reality, because the world is only a collection of images created to test man. People are tested all through their limited lives with perceptions having no reality. These perceptions are intentionally presented as appealing and attractive. This fact is mentioned in the Qur'an:

Fair in the eyes of people is the love of things they covet: Women and

If one ponders deeply on all that is said here, one will soon realise this amazing, extraordinary situation by oneself: that all the events in the world are but mere imagination...

sons; heaped-up hoards of gold and silver; horses branded (for blood and excellence); and (wealth of) cattle and well-tilled land. Such are the possessions of this world's life; but in nearness to Allah is the best of the goals (to return to). (Surat Ali 'Imran: 14)

Most people cast their religion away for the lure of property, wealth, heaped-up hoards of gold and silver, dollars, jewellery, bank accounts, credit cards, wardrobes full of clothes, last-model cars, in short, all the forms of prosperity that they either possess or strive to possess. They concentrate only on this world while forgetting the hereafter. They are deceived by the "fair and alluring" face of the life of this world, and fail to keep up prayer, give charity to the poor, and perform worship that will make them prosper in the hereafter. They say instead, "I have things to do", "I have ideals", "I have responsibilities", "I do not have enough time", "I have things to complete" and "I will do it in the future". They consume their lives trying to prosper only in this world. In the verse, **"They know but the outer (things) in the life of this world: but of the End of things they are heedless" (Surat ar-Rum: 7)**, this misconception is described.

The fact we describe in this chapter, namely that everything is an image, is very important for its implications that render all lusts and boundaries meaningless. The verification of this fact makes it clear that everything people possess or toil to possess – wealth acquired with greed, children of whom they boast, spouses whom they consider closest to them, friends, their dearest bodies, the social status which they believe to be a superiority, the schools they have attended, the holidays on which they have been – is nothing but mere illusion. Therefore, all the effort, the time spent, and the greed, prove unavailing.

This is why some people unwittingly make fools of themselves when they boast of their wealth and properties or of their "yachts, helicopters, factories, holdings, manors and lands" as if they really exist. Those well-to-do people who ostentatiously sail in their yachts, show off their cars, keep talking about their wealth, suppose that their posts rank them higher than everyone else and keep thinking that they are successful because of all this, should actually think what kind of a state they will find themselves in once they realise that success is nothing but an illusion.

These scenes are seen many times in dreams as well. In their dreams, they also have houses, fast cars, extremely precious jewels, rolls of dollars, and loads of gold and silver. In their dreams, they are also positioned in high ranks, own factories with thousands of workers, possess power to rule over many people, and dress in clothes that make everyone admire them. Just as someone who, on waking, boasted about his possessions in his dreams would be ridiculed, he is sure to be equally ridiculed for boasting of images he sees in this world. Both what he sees in his dreams and in this world are mere images in his mind.

Similarly, the way people react to events they experience in the world will make them feel ashamed when they realise the reality. Those who fiercely fight with each other, rave furiously, swindle, take bribes, commit forgery, lie, covetously withhold their money, do wrong to people, beat and curse others, rage aggressively, are full of passion for office and rank, are envious, and show off, will be disgraced when they realise that they have done all of this in a dream.

Since Allah creates all these images, the Ultimate Owner of everything is Allah alone. This fact is stressed in the Qur'an:

> **But to Allah belong all things in the heavens and on earth: And He it is that encompasses all things. (Surat an-Nisa: 126)**

It is great foolishness to cast religion away for the sake of imaginary passions and thus lose the eternal life which is meant to be an everlasting deprivation.

At this stage, one point should be understood. It is not said here that "the possessions, wealth, children, spouses, friends, rank you have with which you are being stingy, will vanish sooner or later, and therefore they do not have any meaning", but that "all the possessions you seem to have do not exist, but they are merely dreams composed of images which Allah shows you to test you". As you see, there is a big difference between the two statements.

Although one does not want to acknowledge this right away and would rather deceive oneself by assuming everything one has truly exists, one is finally to die and in the hereafter everything will be clear when we are recreated. On that day **"sharp is one's sight" (Surah Qaf: 22)** and we will see everything much more clearly. However, if we have spent our lives chasing after imaginary aims, we are going to wish we had never lived this life and say **"Ah! Would that (Death) had made an end of me! Of no profit to me has been my wealth! My power has perished from me!" (Surat al-Haqqah: 27-29)**

What a wise man should do, on the other hand, is to try to understand the greatest reality of the universe here in this world, while he still has time. Otherwise, he will spend all his life running after dreams and face a grievous penalty at the end. In the Qur'an, the final state of those people who run after illusions (or mirages) in this world and forget their Creator, is stated as follows:

> **But the unbelievers, their deeds are like a mirage in sandy deserts, which the man parched with thirst mistakes for water; until when he comes up to it, he finds it to be nothing: But he finds Allah (ever)**

with him, and Allah will pay him his account: and Allah is swift in taking account. (Surat an-Nur: 39)

Logical Defects of the Materialists

From the beginning of this chapter, it is clearly stated that matter does not have absolute being, as materialists claim, but is rather a collection of sense impressions Allah creates. Materialists resist this evident reality, which destroys their philosophy, in an extremely dogmatic manner and bring forward baseless anti-theses.

For example, one of the biggest advocates of materialist philosophy in the 20th century, an ardent Marxist, **George Politzer**, gave the "**bus example**" as the "greatest evidence" for the existence of matter. According to Politzer, philosophers who think that matter is only a perception also run away when they see a bus about to run them over and this is the proof of the physical existence of matter.[10]

When another famous materialist, Johnson, was told that matter is a collection of perceptions, he tried to "prove" the physical existence of stones by giving them a kick.[11]

A similar example is given by **Friedrich Engels**, the mentor of Politzer and founder, along with Marx, of dialectical materialism. He wrote, **"if the cakes we eat were mere perceptions, they would not stop our hunger"**.[12]

There are similar examples and some outrageous sentences such as **"you understand the existence of matter when you are slapped in the face"** in the books of famous materialists such as **Marx**, **Engels**, **Lenin**, and others.

The disorder in comprehension that gives way to these examples of the materialists is their interpreting the explanation of "matter is a perception" as "matter is a trick of light". They think that perception is limited to sight and that other faculties like touch have physical correlates. A bus knocking down a man makes them say "look, it crashed, therefore it is not a perception". They do not understand that all perceptions experienced during a bus crash, such as hardness, collision, and pain, are also formed in the brain.

The Example of Dreams

The best example to explain this reality is the dream. A person can experience very realistic events in dream. He can roll down the stairs and break his leg, have a serious car accident, become stuck under a bus, or eat a cake and be satiated. Similar events to those experienced in our daily lives are also experienced in dreams with the same persuasive sense of their reality, and arousing the same feelings in us.

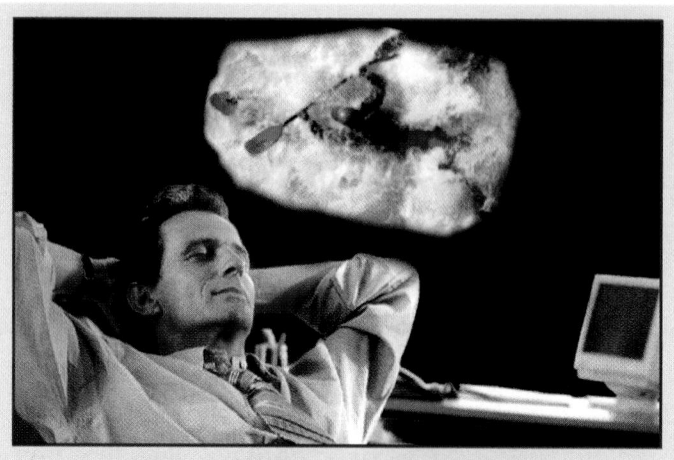

THE WORLD IN DREAMS

For you, reality is all that can be touched with the hand and seen with the eye. In your dreams you can also "touch with your hand and see with your eye", but in reality, then you have neither hand nor eye, nor is there anything that can be touched or seen. There is no material reality that makes these things happen except your brain. You are simply being deceived.
What is it that separates real life and dreams from one another? Ultimately, both forms of living are brought into being within the brain. If we are able to live easily in an unreal world during our dreams, the same can equally be true for the world we live in while awake. When we wake up from a dream, there is no logical reason not to think that we have entered a longer dream called "real life". The reason we consider our dream a fancy and the world 'real' is only a product of our habits and prejudices. This suggests that we may well be awoken from the life on earth, which we think we are living right now, just as we are awoken from a dream.

A person who dreams that he is knocked down by a bus can open his eyes in a hospital again in his dream and understand that he is disabled, but it is all a dream. He can also dream that he dies in a car crash, angels of death take his soul, and his life in the hereafter begins. (This latter event is experienced in the same manner in this life, which, just like the dream, is a perception.)

This person perceives very sharply the images, sounds, feelings of solidity, light, colours, and all other feelings pertaining to the event he experiences in his dream. The perceptions he perceives in his dream are as natural as the ones in "real" life. The cake he eats in his dream satiates him although it is a mere dream-sense perception, because being satiated is also a dream-sense perception. However, in reality, this person is lying in his bed at that moment. There are no stairs, traffic, or buses to consider. The dreaming person experiences and sees perceptions and feelings that do not exist in the external world. The fact that in our dreams, we experience, see, and feel events with no physical correlates in the "external world" very clearly reveals that the "external world" of our waking lives also consists absolutely of mere perceptions.

Those who believe in materialist philosophy, particularly **Marxists**, are enraged when they are told about this reality, the essence of matter. They quote examples from the superficial reasoning of **Marx**, **Engels**, or **Lenin** and make emotional declarations.

However, these persons must think that they can also make these declarations in their dreams. In their dreams, they can also read "*Das Kapital*", participate in meetings, fight with the police, be hit on the head, and feel the pain of their wounds. When asked in their dreams, they will think that what they experience in their dreams also consists of "absolute matter", just as they assume the things they see when they are awake are "absolute matter". However, whether it is in their dreams or in their daily lives, all that they see, experience, or feel consists only of perceptions.

The Example of Connecting the Nerves in Parallel

Let us consider the car crash example given by Politzer in which he talked of someone crushed by a car. If the crushed person's nerves travelling from his five senses to his brain, were connected to another person's, take Politzer's brain, with a parallel connection, at the moment the bus hit that person, it would also hit Politzer sitting at home at the same time. All the feelings experienced by that person having the accident would be experienced by Politzer, just like the same song listened to from two different loudspeakers connected to the same tape recorder. Politzer would feel, see, and experience the braking of the bus, the touch of the bus on his body, the images of a broken arm and blood, fractures, images of his entering the operation room, the hardness of the plaster cast, and the feebleness of his arm.

Every other person connected to the man's nerves in parallel would experience the accident from beginning to end just like Politzer. If the man in the accident fell into a coma, they would all fall into a coma. Moreover, if all the perceptions pertaining to the car accident were recorded in a device and if all these perceptions were transmitted to a person repeatedly, the bus would knock this person down many times.

So, which one of the buses hitting those people is real? The materialist philosophy has no consistent answer to this question. The right answer is that they all experience the car accident in all its details in their own minds.

The same principle applies to the cake and stone examples. If the nerves of the sense organs of Engels, who felt the satiety and fullness of the cake in his stomach after eating a cake, were connected to a second person's brain in parallel, that person would also feel full when Engels ate the cake and was satiated. If the nerves of Johnson, who felt pain in his foot when he delivered a sound kick to a stone, were connected to a second person in parallel, that person would feel the same pain.

So, which cake or which stone is the real one? The materialist philosophy again falls short of giving a consistent answer to this question. The correct and consistent answer is this: both Engels and the second person have eaten the cake in their minds and are satiated; both Johnson and the second person have fully experienced the moment of striking the stone in their minds.

Let us make a change in the example we gave about Politzer: let us connect the nerves of the man hit by the bus to Politzer's brain, and the nerves of Politzer sitting in his house to the brain of the man who is hit by the bus. In this case, Politzer will think that a bus has hit him although he is sitting in his house. The man actually hit by the bus will never feel the impact of the accident and think that he is sitting in Politzer's house. The very same logic may be applied to the cake and the stone examples.

As we see, it is not possible for man to transcend his senses and break free of them. In this respect, a man's soul can be exposed to all kinds of representations of physical events although it has no physical body and no material existence and lacks material weight. It is not possible for a person to realise this because he assumes these three-dimensional images to be real and is certain of their existence because, like everybody, he depends on perceptions experienced by his sensory organs.

The famous British philosopher David Hume expresses his thoughts on this fact:

> **Frankly speaking, when I include myself in what I call "myself", I always come across with a specific perception pertaining to hot or cold, light or shadow, love or hatred, sour or sweet or some other notion. Without the existence of a perception, I can never capture myself in a particular time and I can observe nothing but perception.**[13]

The Formation of Perceptions in the Brain is Not Philosophy But Scientific Fact

Materialists claim that what we have been saying here is a philosophical view. However, to hold that the "external world", as we call it, is a collection of perceptions is not a matter of philosophy but a plain scientific fact. How the image and feelings form in the brain is taught in medical schools in detail. These facts, proven by 20th-century science particularly physics, clearly show that matter does not have an absolute reality and that, in a sense, everyone is watching the "monitor in his brain".

Everyone who believes in science, be he an atheist, Buddhist, or someone who holds any other view, has to accept this fact. A materialist might deny the existence of a Creator yet he cannot deny this scientific reality.

The inability of Karl Marx, Friedrich Engels, Georges Politzer and others to comprehend such a simple and evident fact is still startling, although the level of scientific understanding of their times was perhaps insufficient. In our time, science and technology are highly advanced and recent discoveries make it easier to comprehend this fact. Materialists, on the other hand, are flooded with the fear of both comprehending this fact, even partially, and realising how definitely it demolishes their philosophy.

The Great Fear of the Materialists

For a while, no substantial response came from materialist Turkish circles on the subject brought up in this book, that is, the fact that matter is a mere perception. This gave us the impression that our point had not been made so clear and that it needed further explanation. Yet, before long, it was revealed that materialists felt quite uneasy about the popularity of this subject, and felt a great fear of it.

For some time, materialists have been loudly proclaiming their fear and panic in their publications, conferences and panels. Their agitated and hopeless discourses imply that they are suffering a severe intellectual crisis. The scientific collapse of the theory of evolution, the so-called basis of their philosophy, had already come as a great shock to them. Now, they come to realise that they start to lose matter itself, which is a greater mainstay for them than Darwinism, and they are experiencing an even greater shock. They declare that this issue is the "biggest threat" to them and that it totally "demolishes their cultural fabric".

One of those who expressed most outspokenly the anxiety and panic felt by materialist circles was Renan Pekunlu, an academician as well as writer of the *Bilim ve Utopya* (Science and Utopia) periodical which has assumed the task of defending materialism. Both in his articles in *Bilim ve Utopya* and in the panels he attended, Pekunlu presented the book *Evolution Deceit* by Harun Yahya as the number one "threat" to materialism. What disturbed Pekunlu even more than the chapters that invalidated Darwinism was the part you are currently reading. To his readers and audience, the latter of whom were only a handful, Pekunlu delivered the message, "do not let yourselves be carried away by the indoctrination of idealism and keep your faith in materialism". He quoted Vladimir I. Lenin, the leader of the bloody communist revolution in Russia, as reference. Advising everyone to read Lenin's century-old book titled

Turkish materialist writer Rennan Pekunlu says that "the theory of evolution is not so important, the real threat is this subject", because he is aware that this subject nullifies matter, the only concept in which he has faith.

Materialism and Empirio-Criticism, Pekunlu repeated the counsels of Lenin, "do not think over this issue, or you will lose track of materialism and be carried away by religion". In an article he wrote in the aforementioned periodical, he quoted the following lines from Lenin:

Once you deny objective reality, given us in sensation, you have already lost every weapon against fideism, for you have slipped into agnosticism or subjectivism – and that is all that fideism requires. A single claw ensnared, and the bird is lost. And our Machists have all become ensnared in idealism, that is, in a diluted, subtle fideism; they became ensnared from the moment they took "sensation" not as an image of the external world but as a special "element". It is nobody's sensation, nobody's mind, nobody's spirit, nobody's will.[14]

These words clearly demonstrate that the fact which Lenin, in alarm, realised and wanted to take out both of his mind and the minds of his "comrades", also disturbs contemporary materialists in a similar way. However, Pekunlu and other materialists suffer a yet greater distress; because they are aware that this fact is now being put forward in a far more explicit, certain and convincing way than 100 years ago. It is for the first time in world history that this subject is being explained in such an irresistible way.

Nevertheless, the general picture is that a great number of materialist scientists still take a very superficial stand against the fact that "matter is nothing but an illusion". The subject explained in this chapter is **one of the most important and most exciting subjects** that one can ever come across in one's life. There is no chance of them having faced such a crucial subject before. Still, the reactions of these scientists or the manner they employ in their speeches and articles hint at how shallow and superficial their comprehension is.

The reactions of some materialists to the subject discussed here show that their blind adherence to materialism has caused some kind of harm to their logic. For this reason, they are far removed from comprehending the subject. For instance, Alaattin Senel, also an academician and writer for *Bilim ve Utopya*, expressed similar sentiments as Rennan Pekunlu saying, **"Forget the collapse of Darwinism, the really threatening subject is this one"**. Sensing that his own philosophy has no basis, he made demands such as "prove what you say!"

More interestingly, this writer has himself written lines revealing that he cannot grasp this fact, which he considers a menace.

For instance, in an article in which he discussed this subject exclusively, Senel accepts that the external world is perceived in the brain as an image. However, he then goes on to claim that images are divided into two: those having physical correlates and those that do not, and that images pertaining to the external world have physical correlates. In order to support his assertion, he gives "the example of the telephone". In summary, he wrote: "I do not know whether the images in my brain have correlates in the external world or not, but the same thing applies when I speak on the phone. When I speak on the telephone, I cannot see the person I am speaking to but I can have this conversation confirmed when I later see him face to face."[15]

By saying so, this writer actually means the following: "If we doubt our perceptions, we can look at the matter itself and check its reality." However, this is an evident misconception, because it is impossible for us to reach the matter itself. **We can never get out of our mind and know what is "outside".** Whether the voice on the telephone has a correlate or not can be confirmed by the person on the other end. However, this confirmation is also imagery, which is experienced in the mind.

These people also experience the same events in their dreams. For instance, Senel may also see in his dream that he speaks on the telephone and then have this conversation confirmed by the person to whom he spoke. Pekunlu may in his dream feel himself facing "a serious threat" and advising people to read century-old books of Lenin. However, no matter what they do, these materialists can never deny that the events they have experienced and the people they have talked to in their dreams are nothing but perceptions.

Who, then, will confirm whether the images in the brain have correlates or not? The shadow beings in the brain? Without doubt, it is impossible for materialists to find a source of information that can yield data concerning the outside of the brain and confirm it.

Conceding that all perceptions are formed in the brain, but assuming that one can step "out" of this and have the perceptions confirmed by the real external world, reveals that the intellectual capacity of the person is limited and that his reasoning is distorted.

However, any person with a normal level of understanding and reasoning can easily grasp these facts. Every unbiased person knows, in relation to all that we have said, that it is not possible for him to test the existence of the external world with his senses. Yet, it appears that blind adherence to materialism distorts the reasoning capacity of people. For this reason, contemporary materialists display severe logical flaws in their reasoning just like their mentors who tried to "prove" the existence of matter by kicking stones or eating cakes.

It also has to be said that this is not an astonishing situation, because inability to understand is a common trait of all unbelievers. In the Qur'an, Allah particularly states that they are **"a people without understanding" (Surat al-Ma'idah: 58)**

Materialists Have Fallen into the Biggest Trap in History

The atmosphere of panic sweeping through materialist circles in Turkey, of which we have here mentioned only a few examples, shows that materialists face utter defeat, which they have never met before in history. That matter is simply a perception has been proven by modern science and it is put forward in a very clear, straightforward and forceful way. It only remains for materialists to see and acknowledge the collapse of the entire material world in which they blindly believe and on which they rely.

Materialist thought has always existed throughout the history of humanity. Being very assured of themselves and the philosophy they believe in, materialists revolted against Allah Who created them. The scenario they formulated maintained that matter has no beginning or end, and that all these could not possibly have a Creator. Because of their arrogance, they denied Allah and took refuge in matter, which they held to have real existence. They were so confident in this philosophy that they thought that it would never be possible to put forth an explanation proving the contrary.

That is why the facts told in this book regarding the real nature of matter surprised these people so much. What has been told here destroyed the very basis of their philosophy and left no ground for further discussion. Matter, upon which they based all their thoughts, lives, their arrogance and denial, vanished all of a sudden. **How can materialism exist when matter does not?**

One of the attributes of Allah is His plotting against the unbelievers. This is stated in the verse "They plot and plan, and Allah too plans; but **Allah is the best of planners.**" (Surat al- Anfal: 30)

Allah entrapped materialists by making them assume that matter exists and, so doing, humiliated them in an unseen way. Materialists deemed their possessions, status, rank, the society to which they belong, the whole world and everything else to really exist and grew arrogant against Allah by relying on these. They revolted against Allah by being boastful and added to their unbelief. While so doing, they totally relied on matter. Yet, they are so lacking in understanding that they fail to think that Allah encompasses them round about. Allah announces the state to which the unbelievers are led as a result of their thick-headedness:

Or do they intend a plot (against you)? But those who defy Allah are themselves involved in a plot! (Surat at-Tur: 42)

This is most probably their biggest defeat in history. While growing arrogant, materialists have been tricked and suffered a serious defeat in the war they waged against Allah by bringing up something monstrous against Him. The verse "Thus have We placed leaders in every town, its wicked men, to plot therein: but **they only plot against their own souls, and they perceive it not**" announces how unconscious these people who revolt against their Creator are, and how they will end up (Surat al- An'am: 123). In another verse the same fact is related as:

Fain would they deceive Allah and those who believe, but they only deceive themselves, and realise (it) not! (Surat al-Baqarah: 9)

While the unbelievers try to plot, they do not realise a very important fact which is stressed by the words "they only deceive themselves, and realise (it) not!" in the verse. This is the fact that everything they experience is an imagination designed to be perceived by them, and all plots they devise are simply images formed in their brain just like every other act they perform. Their folly has made them forget that they are all alone with Allah and, hence, they are entrapped in their own devious plans.

No less than those unbelievers who lived in the past, those living today face a reality that will shatter their devious plans at their foundations. With the verse "**...feeble indeed is the cunning of Satan**" (Surat an-Nisa: 76), Allah says that these plots were doomed to end in failure the day they were hatched. He gives good tidings to believers with the verse "**...not the least harm will their cunning do you.**" (Surat Ali 'Imran: 120)

In another verse Allah says: "But **the unbelievers, their deeds are like a mirage in sandy deserts,** which the man parched with thirst mistakes for water; until when he comes up to it, he finds it to be nothing." (Surat an-Nur: 39). Materialism, too, becomes a "mirage" for the rebellious just as it is stated in this verse; when they have recourse to it, they find it to be nothing but an illusion. Allah has deceived them with such a mirage, and beguiled them into perceiving this whole collection of images as real. All those "eminent" people, professors, astronomers, biologists, physicists, and all others regardless of their rank and post are simply deceived like children, and are humiliated because they took matter as their god. Assuming a collection of images to be absolute, they based their philosophy and ideology on it, became involved in serious discussions, and adopted so-called "intellectual" discourse. They deemed themselves wise enough to offer an argument about the truth of the universe and, more importantly, to dispute about Allah with their limited intelligence. Allah explains their situation in the following verse:

And (the unbelievers) plotted and planned, and Allah too planned, and the best of planners is Allah. (Surat Ali 'Imran: 54)

It may be possible to escape from some plots; however, this plan of Allah against the unbelievers is so firm that there is no way of escape from it. No matter what they do or to whom they appeal, they can never find a helper other than Allah. As Allah informs in the Qur'an, **"they shall not find for them other than Allah a patron or a helper."** (Surat an-Nisa: 173)

Materialists never expected to fall into such a trap. Having all the means of the 20th century at their disposal, they thought they could grow obstinate in their denial and drag people to disbelief. Allah describes this everlasting mentality of unbelievers and their end as follows in the Qur'an:

They plotted and planned, but We too planned, even while they perceived it not. Then see what was the end of their plot! This, that We destroyed them and their people, all (of them). (Surat an-Naml: 50-51)

This, on another level, is what the verses come to mean: materialists are made to realise that everything they own is but an illusion, and therefore **everything they possess has been destroyed**. As they witness their possessions, factories, gold, dollars, children, spouses, friends, rank and status, and even their own bodies, all of which they deem to exist, slipping away from their hands, they are **"destroyed"** in the words of the 51st verse of Surat an-Naml. At this point, they are no more material entities but souls.

No doubt, realising this truth is the worst possible situation for materialists. The fact that everything they possess is only an illusion is tantamount, in their own words, to "death before dying" in this world.

This fact leaves them alone with Allah. With the verse, **"Leave Me alone, (to deal) with the (creature) whom I created (bare and) alone"**, Allah calls us to attend to the fact that each human being is, in truth, all alone in His presence. (Surat al- Muddaththir: 11). This remarkable fact is repeated in many other verses:

And behold! You come to us bare and alone as We created you for the first time: you have left behind you all (the favours) which We bestowed on you... (Surat al-An'am: 94)

And each one of them will come to Him on the Day of Resurrection, alone. (Surah Maryam: 95)

This, on another level, is what the verses indicate: those who take matter as their god have come from Allah and returned to Him. They have submitted their wills to Allah whether they want or not. Now they wait for the day of judgement when everyone of them will be called to account, however unwilling they may be to understand it.

Conclusion

The subject we have explained so far is one of the greatest truths that you will ever be told in your lifetime. Proving that the whole material world is in reality a **"shadow being"**, this subject is the key to comprehending the being of Allah and His creation and of understanding that He is the only absolute being.

The person who understands this subject realises that the world is not the sort of place it is thought by most people to be. The world is not an absolute place with a true existence as supposed by those who wander aimlessly about the streets, get into fights in pubs, show off in luxurious cafes, brag about their property, or who dedicate their lives to hollow aims. The world is only a collection of perceptions, an illusion. All of the people we have cited above are only shadow beings who watch these perceptions in their minds; yet, they are not aware of this.

This concept is very important for it undermines the **materialist philosophy** that denies the existence of Allah and causes it to collapse. This is the reason why materialists like **Marx**, **Engels**, and **Lenin** felt panic, became enraged, and warned their followers "not to think about" this concept when they were told about it. These people are so mentally deficient that they cannot even comprehend that perceptions are formed inside the brain. They assume that the world they watch in their brain is the "external world" and cannot comprehend obvious evidence to the contrary.

This unawareness is the outcome of the little wisdom Allah has given the disbelievers. As Allah says in the Qur'an, the unbelievers "**have hearts wherewith they understand not,** eyes wherewith they see not, and ears wherewith they hear not. They are like cattle – nay more misguided, for they are heedless (of warning)." (Surat al-A'raf: 179)

You can explore beyond this point by using the power of your personal reflection. For this, you have to concentrate, devote your attention, and ponder on the way you see the objects around you and the way you feel their touch. If you think heedfully, you can feel that the intelligent being that sees, hears, touches, thinks, and reads this book at this moment is only a soul and watches the perceptions called "matter" on a screen. The person who comprehends this is considered to have moved away from the domain of the material world that deceives a major part of humanity, and to have entered the domain of true existence.

This reality has been understood by a number of theists or philosophers throughout history. Islamic intellectuals such as Imam Rabbani, Muhyiddin Ibn al-'Arabi and Mawlana Jami realised this from the signs of the Qur'an and by using their reason. Some Western philosophers like George Berkeley have grasped the same reality through reason. Imam Rabbani wrote in his Maktubat (Letters) that the whole material universe is an "illusion and supposition (perception)" and that the only absolute being is Allah:

> **Allah... The substance of these beings which He created is but nothingness... He created all in the sphere of senses and illusions... The existence of the universe is in the sphere of senses and illusions, and it is not material... In reality, there is nothing in the outside except the Glorious Being, (Who is Allah).[16]**

Imam Rabbani explicitly stated that all images presented to man are only illusions, and that they have no originals in the "outside".

> **This imaginary cycle is portrayed in imagination. It is seen to the extent that it is portrayed, yet, with the mind's eye. In the outside, it seems as if it is seen with the head's eye. However, the case is not so. It has neither a designation nor a trace in the outside. There is no circumstance to be seen. Even the face of a person reflected in a mirror is like that. It has no constancy in the outside. No doubt, both its constancy and image are in the IMAGINATION. Allah knows best.[17]**

Mawlana Jami stated the same fact, which he discovered by following the signs of the Qur'an and by using his wit: "**Whatever there is in the universe are senses and illusions.** They are either like reflections in mirrors or shadows".

However, the number of those who have understood this fact throughout history has always been limited. Great scholars such as Imam Rabbani have written that it might not be wise to tell this fact to the masses because most people are not able to grasp it.

In the age in which we live, this has been made an empirical fact by the body of evidence put forward by science. The fact that the universe is a shadow being is described in such a concrete, clear, and explicit way for the first time in history.

For this reason, the **21st century will be a historical turning-point** when people will generally comprehend the divine realities and be led in crowds to Allah, the only Absolute Being. The materialistic creeds of the 19th century will be relegated to the trash-heaps of history, Allah's being and creating will be grasped, spacelessness and timelessness will be understood, humanity will break free of the centuries-old veils, deceits and superstitions confusing them.

It is not possible for this unavoidable course to be impeded by any shadow being.

RELATIVITY OF TIME AND REALITY OF FATE

Everything related so far demonstrates that "three-dimensional space" does not exist in reality, that it is a prejudice completely founded on perceptions and that one leads one's whole life in "spacelessness". To assert the contrary would be to hold a superstitious belief far removed from reason and scientific truth, for there is no valid proof of the existence of a three-dimensional material world.

This refutes the primary assumption of the materialist philosophy that underlies evolutionary theory, the assumption that matter is absolute and eternal. The second assumption upon which materialistic philosophy rests is the supposition that time is absolute and eternal. This is as superstitious as the first.

The Perception of Time

What we perceive as time is, in fact, a method by which one moment is compared to another. We can explain this with an example. For instance, when a person taps an object, he hears a particular sound. When he taps the same object five minutes later, he hears another sound. The person perceives that there is an interval between the first sound and the second and he calls this interval "time". Yet at the time he hears the second sound, the first sound he heard is no more than an imagination in his mind. It is merely a bit of information in his memory. The person formulates the concept of "time" by **comparing the moment in which he lives with what he has in his memory. If this comparison is not made, there can be no concept of time.**

Similarly, a person makes a comparison when he sees someone entering a room through a door and sitting in an armchair in the middle of the room. By the time this person sits in the armchair, the images related to the moments he opens the door, walks into the room, and makes his way to the armchair are compiled as bits of information in the brain. The perception of time occurs when one compares the man sitting in the armchair with those bits of information.

In brief, **time comes to exist as a result of the comparison made between some illusions stored in the brain.** If man did not have memory, then his brain would not make such interpretations and therefore would never have formed the concept of time. The only reason why someone determines himself to be thirty years old is because he has accumulated information pertaining to those thirty years in his mind. If his memory did not exist, then he would not think of the existence of such a preceding period and he would only experience the single "moment" in which he lives.

The Scientific Explanation of Timelessness

Let us try to clarify the subject by quoting various scientists' and scholars' explanations of the subject. Regarding the subject of time flowing backwards, the famous intellectual and Nobel laureate professor of genetics, François Jacob, states the following in his book *Le Jeu des Possibles* (The Possible and the Actual):

> **Films played backwards make it possible for us to imagine a world in which time flows backwards. A world in which milk separates itself from the coffee and jumps out of the cup to reach the milk-pan; a world in which light rays are emitted from the walls to be collected in a trap (gravity center) instead of gushing out from a light source; a world in which a stone slopes to the palm of a man by the astonishing cooperation of innumerable drops of water making the stone possible to jump out of water. Yet, in such a world in which time has such opposite features, the processes of our brain and the way our memory compiles information, would similarly be functioning backwards. The same is true for the past and future and the world will appear to us exactly as it currently appears.**[18]

Since our brain is accustomed to a certain sequence of events, the world operates not as is related above and we assume that time always flows forward. However, this is a decision reached in the brain and is relative. In reality, we can never know how time flows or even whether it flows or not. This is an indication of the fact that **time is not an absolute fact but just a sort of perception.**

The relativity of time is a fact also verified by one of the most important physicists of the 20th century, Albert Einstein. Lincoln Barnett, writes in his book *The Universe and Dr. Einstein*:

> **Along with absolute space, Einstein discarded the concept of absolute time – of a steady, unvarying inexorable universal time flow, streaming from the infinite past to the infinite future. Much of the obscurity that has surrounded the Theory of Relativity stems from man's reluctance to recognize that sense of time, like sense of color, is a form of perception. Just as space is simply a possible order**

of material objects, so time is simply a possible order of events. The subjectivity of time is best explained in Einstein's own words. "The experiences of an individual" he says, "appear to us arranged in a series of events; in this series the single events which we remember appear to be ordered according to the criterion of 'earlier' and 'later'. There exists, therefore, for the individual, an I-time, or subjective time. This in itself is not measurable. I can, indeed, associate numbers with the events, in such a way that a greater number is associated with the later event than with an earlier one.[19]

Einstein himself pointed out, as quoted in Barnett's book: "space and time are forms of intuition, which **can no more be divorced from consciousness** than can our concepts of colour, shape, or size." According to the Theory of General Relativity: **"time has no independent existence apart from the order of events by which we measure it."[20]**

Since time consists of perception, it depends entirely on the perceiver and is therefore relative.

The speed at which time flows differs according to the references we use to measure it because there is no natural clock in the human body to indicate precisely how fast time passes. As Lincoln Barnett wrote: "Just as there is no such thing as color without an eye to discern it, so an instant or an hour or a day is nothing without an event to mark it."[21]

The relativity of time is plainly experienced in dreams. Although what we see in our dreams seems to last for hours, in fact, it only lasts for a few minutes, and even a few seconds.

Let us think about an example to clarify the subject further. Let us assume that we were put in a room with a single window that was specifically designed and we were kept there for a certain period. Let there be a clock in the room from which we can see the amount of time that has passed. At the same time, let it be that we see from the window of the room the sun rising and setting at certain intervals. A few days later, the answer we would give to the question about the amount of time we spent in the room would be based both on the information we had collected by looking at the clock from time to time and on the computation we had made by referring to how many times the sun rose and set. For example, we estimate that we spent three days in the room. However, if the person who put us in that room said that we spent only two days in the room and that the sun we had seen from the window was produced artificially by a simulation machine and that the clock in the room was regulated specially to work faster, then the calculation we had done would have no meaning.

This example confirms that the information we have about the rate of passage of time is based on relative references. The relativity of time is a scientific fact also proven by scientific methodology. **Einstein's Theory of General Relativity** maintains that the speed of time changes depending on the speed of the object and its position in the gravitational field. As speed increases, time is shortened and compressed: it slows down as if coming to the point of "stopping".

Let us explain this with an example given by Einstein. Imagine two twins, one of whom stays on earth while the other goes travelling in space at a speed close to that of light. When he comes back, the traveller will see that his brother has grown much older than he has. The reason is that time flows much slower for the person who travels at speeds near the speed of light. Let us consider a space-travelling father and his earth-bound son. If the father were twenty-seven years old when he set out and his son three; when the father came back to earth thirty years later (earth time), the son would be thirty-three years old while his father would only be thirty.[22] This relativity of time is not caused by the deceleration or acceleration of clocks, or the deceleration of a mechanical spring. It is rather the result of the differentiated operation periods of the entire system of material existence, which goes as deep as sub-atomic particles. In other words, for the person experiencing it, the shortening of time is not experienced as if acting in a slow-motion picture. In such a setting where time shortens, one's heartbeats, cell replications, and brain functions, etc, all operate slower than those of the slower-moving person on earth. Nevertheless, the person goes on with his daily life and does not notice the shortening of time at all. Indeed the shortening does not even become apparent until comparison is made.

Relativity in the Qur'an

The conclusion to which we are led by the findings of modern science is that **time is not an absolute fact as supposed by materialists, but only a relative perception.** What is most interesting is that this fact, undiscovered until the 20th century by science, was revealed to mankind in the Qur'an fourteen centuries ago. There are various references in the Qur'an to the relativity of time.

It is possible to see in many verses of the Qur'an the scientifically-proven fact that time is a psychological perception dependent on events, the setting, and conditions. For instance, a person's entire life is a very short time as we are informed in the Qur'an:

On the Day when He will call you, and you will answer (His Call)

with (words of) His Praise and Obedience, and you will think that you have stayed (in this world) but a little while! (Surat al-Isra: 52)

And on the Day when He shall gather them together, (it will seem to them) as if they had not tarried (on earth) longer than an hour of a day: they will recognise each other. (Surah Yunus: 45)

Some verses indicate that people perceive time differently and that sometimes people can perceive a very short period as a very lengthy one. The following conversation of people held during their judgement in the hereafter is a good example of this:

He will say: "What number of years did you stay on earth?" They will say: "We stayed a day or part of a day, but ask those who keep account." He will say: "You stayed not but a little, if you had only known!" (Surat al-Muminun: 112-114)

In some other verses Allah states that time may flow at different paces in different settings:

Yet, they ask you to hasten on the punishment! But Allah will not fail in His promise. Verily a day in the sight of your Lord is like a thousand years of your reckoning. (Surat al-Hajj: 47)

The angels and the spirit ascend unto Him in a day the measure whereof is (as) fifty thousand years. (Surat al-Ma'arij: 4)

He rules (all) affairs from the heavens to the earth: in the end will (all affairs) ascend to Him in a day the measure of which is a thousand years of what you count. (Surat al-Sajda, 5)

These verses are clear expressions of the relativity of time. That this result, which was only recently understood by scientists in the 20th century, was communicated to man 1,400 years ago in the Qur'an is an indication of Allah's revelation of the Qur'an, Who encompasses the whole of time and space.

Many other verses of the Qur'an reveal that time is a perception. This is particularly evident in the stories. For instance, Allah has kept the Companions of the Cave, a group of believing people mentioned in the Qur'an, in a deep sleep for more than three centuries. When they awoke, these people thought that they had stayed in that state but a little while, and could not reckon how long they had slept:

Then We drew (a veil) over their ears, for a number of years, in the Cave, (so that they heard not). Then We raised them up that We might know which of the two parties would best calculate the time that they had tarried. (Surat al-Kahf: 11-12)

Such (being their state), We raised them up (from sleep), that they might question each other. Said one of them, "How long have you stayed (here)?" They said, "We have stayed (perhaps) a day, or part of a day." (At length) they (all) said, "Allah (alone) knows best how long you have stayed here..." (Surat al-Kahf: 19)

The situation told in the verse below is also evidence that time is in truth a psychological perception.

Or (take) the similitude of one who passed by a hamlet, all in ruins to its roofs. He said, "How shall Allah bring it (ever) to life, after (this) its death?" but Allah caused him to die for a hundred years, then raised him up (again). He said: "How long did you tarry (thus)?" He said: (Perhaps) a day or part of a day." He said: "Nay, you have tarried thus a hundred years; but look at your food and your drink; they show no signs of age; and look at your donkey. And that We may make of you a sign unto the people, look further at the bones, how We bring them together and clothe them with flesh." When this was shown clearly to him, he said: "I know that Allah has power over all things." (Surat al-Baqara: 259)

The above verse clearly emphasises that Allah, Who created time, is unbound by it. Man, on the other hand, is bound by time, which Allah ordains. As in the verse, man is even incapable of knowing how long he slept. In such a state, to assert that time is absolute (just as materialists, in their distorted thinking, do) is very unreasonable.

Destiny

This relativity of time clears up a very important matter. Relativity is so variable that a period appearing billions of years' duration to us may last only a second in another perspective. Moreover, an enormous period of time extending from the world's beginning to its end may not even last a second but just an instant in another dimension.

This is the very essence of the concept of destiny – a concept that is not well understood by most people, especially materialists who deny it completely. Destiny is Allah's perfect knowledge of all events past or future. A majority of people question how Allah can already know events that have not yet been experienced and this leads them to fail in understanding the authenticity of destiny. However, "events not yet experienced" are only so **for us**. Allah is not bound by time or space for He Himself has created them. For this reason, **past, future, and present are all the same to Allah; for Him everything has already taken place and finished.**

In *The Universe and Dr. Einstein*, Lincoln Barnett explains how the Theory of General Relativity leads to this conclusion. According to Barnett, the universe can be **"encompassed in its entire majesty only by a cosmic intellect"**.[23] The will that Barnett calls "the cosmic intellect" is **the wisdom and knowledge of Allah, Who prevails over the entire universe.** Just as we can easily see a ruler's beginning, middle, and end, and all the units in between as a whole, Allah knows the time we are subject to as if it were a single moment right from its beginning to its end. People, however, experience incidents only when their time comes and they witness the destiny Allah has created for them.

It is also important to draw attention to the shallowness of the distorted understanding of destiny prevalent in our society. This distorted belief of fate is a superstition that Allah has determined a "destiny" for every man but that these destinies can sometimes be changed by people. For instance, people make superficial statements about a patient who returns from death's door such as "he defeated his destiny". No-one is able to change his destiny. The person who returned from death's door, didn't die precisely because he was destined not to die at that time. It is, ironically, the destiny of those people who deceive themselves by saying "I defeated my destiny" that they should say so and maintain such a mindset.

Destiny is the eternal knowledge of Allah and for Allah, Who knows time like a single moment and Who prevails over the whole of time and space; everything is determined and finished in destiny. We also understand from what He relates in the Qur'an that time is one for Allah: some incidents that appear to us to happen in the future are related in the Qur'an in such a way as if they had already taken place long before. For instance, the verses that describe the accounts that people must give to Allah in the hereafter are related as events which occurred long ago:

And the trumpet is blown, and all who are in the heavens and all who are in the earth swoon away, save him whom Allah wills. Then it is blown a second time, and behold them standing waiting! And the earth shone with the light of her Lord, and the Book is set up, and the prophets and the witnesses are brought, and it is judged between them with truth, and they are not wronged... And those who disbelieve are driven unto hell in troops... And those who feared their Lord are driven unto Paradise in troops" (Surat az-Zumar: 68-73)

Some other verses on this subject are:

And every soul came, along with it a driver and a witness. (Surat al-Qaf: 21)

And the heaven is cloven asunder, so that on that day it is frail. (Surat al-Haqqah: 16)

And because they were patient and constant, He rewarded them with a garden and (garments of) silk. Reclining in the (garden) on raised thrones, they saw there neither the sun's (excessive heat) nor excessive cold. (Surat al-Insan: 12-13)

And Hell is placed in full view for (all) to see. (Surat an-Nazi'at: 36)

But on this day the believers laugh at the unbelievers (Surat al-Mutaffifin: 34)

And the sinful saw the fire and apprehended that they have to fall therein: no means did they find to turn away therefrom. (Surat al-Kahf: 53)

As may be seen, occurrences that are going to take place after our death (from our point of view) are related in the Qur'an as past events already experienced. Allah is not bound by the relative time frame in which we are confined. Allah has willed these things in timelessness: people have already performed them and all these events have been lived through and are ended. He imparts in the verse below that every event, big or small, is within the knowledge of Allah and recorded in a book:

In whatever business you may be, and whatever portion you may be reciting from the Qur'an, and whatever deed you (mankind) may be doing, We are witnesses thereof when you are deeply engrossed therein. Nor is hidden from your Lord (so much as) the weight of an atom on the earth or in heaven. And not the least and not the greatest of these things but are recorded in a clear record. (Surah Yunus: 61)

The Worry of the Materialists

The issues discussed in this chapter, namely the truth underlying matter, timelessness, and spacelessness, are indeed extremely clear. As expressed before, these are definitely not any sort of philosophy or way of thought, but **scientific outcomes that are impossible to deny**. In addition to its being a technical reality, the evidence also admits of no other rational and logical alternatives on this issue: **the universe** is an **illusory entity** with all the matter composing it and all the creatures living in it. It is a collection of perceptions.

Materialists have a hard time understanding this issue. For instance, if we return to Politzer's bus example: although Politzer technically knew that he could not step out of his perceptions he could only admit it in certain cases.

That is, for Politzer, events take place in the brain until the bus crash, but as soon as the bus crash takes place, things go out of the brain and gain a physical reality. The logical defect of this point is very clear. Politzer has made the same mistake as the materialist Johnson who said, "I hit the stone, my foot hurts, therefore it exists". Politzer could not understand that the shock felt after the impact of the bus was merely a perception as well.

The subliminal reason why materialists cannot comprehend this subject is their fear of what they will face when they comprehend it. Lincoln Barnett tells us that some scientists "discerned" this subject:

> **Along with philosophers' reduction of all objective reality to a shadow-world of perceptions, scientists have become aware of the alarming limitations of man's senses.**[24]

Any reference made to the fact that matter and time are perceptions arouses great fear in the materialist, because these are the only notions he relies on as absolute beings. He, in a sense, takes them as idols to worship; because he thinks that matter and time (through evolution) created him.

When he feels that the universe in which he thinks he is living, the world, his own body, other people, other materialist philosophers by whose ideas he is influenced, and, in short, everything is a perception, he feels overwhelmed by a horror at it all. Everything he depends on, believes in, and has recourse to suddenly vanishes. He feels a taste of the desperation which he will really experience on the day of judgement, as described in the verse "That day shall they (openly) show (their) submission to Allah; and **all their inventions left them in the lurch.**" **(Surat an-Nahl: 87)**

From then on, this materialist tries to convince himself of the reality of matter, and makes up "evidence" for this end. He hits his fist on the wall, kicks stones, shouts, yells, but can never escape from the reality.

Just as they want to dismiss this reality from their minds, they also want other people to discard it. They are also aware that if people in general know the true nature of matter, the primitive nature of their own philosophy and the ignorance of their worldview will be bared for all to see, and there will be no ground left on which they can found their views. These fears are the reasons why they are so disturbed at the facts related here.

Allah states that the fears of the unbelievers will be intensified in the hereafter. On the day of judgement, they will be addressed thus:

> **One day shall We gather them all together. We shall say to those who ascribed partners (to Us): "Where are the partners whom you (invented and) talked about?" (Surat al-An'am: 22)**

After that, unbelievers will witness their possessions, children and their intimates, whom they had assumed to be real and had ascribed as partners to Allah, leaving them and vanishing. Allah informs us of this in the verse **"Behold! How they lie against their own selves! But the (lie) which they invented left them in the lurch." (Surat al-An'am: 24).**

The Gain of Believers

While the fact that matter and time are perceptions alarms materialists, the opposite holds true for believers. People of faith become very glad when they perceive the secret behind matter, because this reality is the key to all questions. With this key, all secrets are unlocked. One comes easily to understand many issues that one previously had difficulty in understanding.

As said before, the questions of death, paradise, hell, the hereafter, changing dimensions, and questions such as "Where is Allah?" "What was before Allah?" "Who created Allah?" "How long will life in the grave last?" "Where are heaven and hell?" and "Where do heaven and hell currently exist?" are easily answered. It will be understood with what kind of order Allah created the entire universe from out of nothing, so much so that, with this secret, **the questions of "when?" and "where?" become meaningless** because there are no time and no space left. When spacelessness is grasped, it will be understood that hell, heaven and earth are all actually **the same place**. If timelessness is grasped, it will be understood that everything takes place at **a single moment**: nothing is waited for and time does not go by, because everything has already happened and finished.

With this secret delved, **the world becomes like heaven for a believer.** All distressful material worries, anxieties, and fears vanish. The person grasps that the entire universe has a single sovereign, that He changes the entire physical world as He pleases and that all one has to do is to turn to Him. He then submits himself entirely to Allah **"to be devoted to His service"**. (Surat Ali 'Imran: 35)

To comprehend this secret is the greatest gain in the world.

With this secret, another very important reality mentioned in the Qur'an is unveiled: that **"Allah is nearer to man than his jugular vein"** (Surah Qaf: 16). As everybody knows, the jugular vein is inside the body. What could be nearer to a person than his inside? This situation can easily be explained by the reality of spacelessness. This verse also can be much better comprehended by understanding this secret.

This is the plain truth. It should be well established that there is no helper and provider for man other than Allah. **There is nothing but Allah;** He is the only absolute being with Whom one can seek refuge, to Whom one can appeal for help and count on for reward.

Wherever we turn, there is the presence of Allah.

---

1 Frederick Vester, *Denken, Lernen, Vergessen*, vga, 1978, p.6

2 George Politzer, *Principes Fondamentaux de Philosophie*, Editions Sociales, Paris, 1954, pp.38-39-44

3 R.L.Gregory, *Eye and Brain: The Psychology of Seeing*, Oxford University Press Inc., New York, 1990, p.9

4 Lincoln Barnett, *The Universe and Dr.Einstein*, William Sloane Associate, New York, 1948, p.20

5 Orhan Hançerlioglu, *Düsünce Tarihi (The History of Thought)*, Istanbul: Remzi Bookstore, 6.ed., September, 1995, p.447

6 V.I.Lenin, *Materialism and Empirio-criticism*, Progress Publishers, Moscow, 1970, p.14

7 Bertrand Russell, *ABC of Relativity*, George Allen and Unwin, London, 1964, pp.161-162

8 R.L.Gregory, *Eye and Brain: The Psychology of Seeing*, Oxford University Press Inc. New York, 1990, p.9

9 Karl Pribram, David Bohm, Marilyn Ferguson, Fritjof Capra, *Holografik Evren 1(Holographic Universe 1)*, translated by Ali Çakiroglu, Kuraldisi Publishing, Istanbul: 1996, p37

10 George Politzer, *Principes Fondamentaux de Philosophie*, Editions Sociales, Paris 1954, p.53

11 Orhan Hançerlioglu, *Düsünce Tarihi (The History of Thought)*, Istanbul: Remzi Bookstore, 6.ed., September, 1995, p.261

12 George Politzer, *Principes Fondamentaux de Philosophie*, Editions Sociales, Paris 1954, p.65

13 Paul Davies, *Tanri ve Yeni Fizik, (God and The New Physics)*, translated by Murat Temelli, Im Publishing, Istanbul 1995, pp.180-181

14 Rennan Pekünlü, "Aldatmacanin Evrimsizligi", (Non-Evolution of Deceit) *Bilim ve Ütopya*, December, 1998, (V.I.Lenin, Materialism and Empirio-criticism, Progress Publishers, Moscow, 1970, pp.334-335)

15 Alaettin Senel, "Evrim Aldatmacasi mi?, Devrin Aldatmacasi mi?", (Evolution Deceit or Deceit of the Epoch?) *Bilim ve Ütopya*, December 1998

16 *Imam Rabbani Hz. Mektuplari* (Letters of Rabbani), Vol.II, 357. Letter, p.163

17 *Imam Rabbani Hz. Mektuplari* (Letters of Rabbani), Vol.II, 470. Letter, p.1432

18 François Jacob, *Le Jeu des Possibles*, University of Washington Press, 1982, p.111

19 Lincoln Barnett, *The Universe and Dr.Einstein*, William Sloane Associate, New York, 1948, pp. 52-53

20 Lincoln Barnett, *The Universe and Dr.Einstein*, William Sloane Associate, New York, 1948, p.17

21 Lincoln Barnett, *The Universe and Dr.Einstein*, William Sloane Associate, New York, 1948, p.58.

22 Paul Strathern, *The Big Idea: Einstein and Relativity*, Arrow Books, 1997, p. 57

23 Lincoln Barnett, *The Universe and Dr.Einstein*, William Sloane Associate, New York, 1948, p.84

24 Lincoln Barnett, *The Universe and Dr.Einstein*, William Sloane Associate, New York, 1948, pp.17-18

CONCLUSION

All the living beings and systems we have covered in this book clearly establish that Allah created the entire universe and all the beings therein. Every being, including man, owes its life to Allah. He is the One Who gives them life and keeps them alive until a certain date. It is Allah Who feeds them, protects them and, when they fall ill, restores them to health.

The signs of Allah's creation, only a few of which we tried to review in the book, are so manifest that any conscientious person with insight can easily see and accept the facts referred to above. However, one's reaching that point, i.e., accepting that one is surrounded with evidence that demonstrates Allah's creation of the universe, is not enough. In the Qur'an, Allah refers to those people who accept His existence yet are still not on the right way:

Say: 'Who provides for you out of heaven and earth? Who controls hearing and sight? Who brings forth the living from the dead and the dead from the living? Who directs the whole affair?' They will say, 'Allah.' Say, 'So will you not have taqwa?' That is Allah, your Lord, the Truth, and what is there after truth except misguidance? So how have you been distracted? (Surah Yunus: 31-32)

The type of human mentioned in the verse is quite important: those people answer all the questions they are asked about the existence and attributes of Allah, and accept that Allah creates everything. Yet, still Allah warns them "So will you not have taqwa?" or "So how have you been distracted?"

This shows us that to accept the being of Allah does not mean having been saved from "error". Satan does not reject the being of Allah but rebels against Him. A person may confirm the existence of Allah under the influence of some traditional convictions, without fully grasping its meaning. The human type described above is like that. Such people confirm Allah's existence only verbally, yet do not reflect on this major matter or comprehend the essence of it. In the Qur'an, this state is described as follows: **"They do not measure Allah with His true measure. Allah is All-Strong, Almighty." (Surat al-Hajj, 74)**

On the other hand, the person who measures Allah with His true measure is very different from the above-mentioned type. Such a person perceives that the entire universe is created for a purpose. The purpose of his creation is to see the fact of creation and Allah's signs, which are observable in every corner of the universe, to revere its Owner, to submit to Him and serve Him. Allah communicates this fact as: **"I only created jinn and man to worship Me." (Surat adh-Dhariyat, 56)**. All the signs in the universe serve the purpose of reminding man of his duty to serve Allah:

> **"That is Allah, your Lord. There is no god but Him, the Creator of everything. So worship Him. He is responsible for everything." (Surat al-An'am, 102),**

It is Allah Who creates man from a drop of fluid, brings him up, feeds him, gives him hearing and sight, and restores him to health when he becomes sick. Do not forget that Allah creates the body's incredible immune system, medicines, the knowledge of medicine, and doctors. Therefore, man should serve Him alone, worship and obey only Him.

The most explicit indication of a man's keeping his duty to Allah is his fearing Him. Those who only confirm Allah verbally are those who do fear Him. A person, who truly has faith in Allah, is afraid of opposing Him and, because of seeing His signs throughout the universe, comes to perceive His might and omnipotence.

In addition, a person who has faith in Allah learns another fact from His Book: this world is a temporary creation. Man will stay here but only for a very short time. Then, in accordance with the verse **"O Man! You are toiling laboriously towards your Lord but meet Him you will!" (Surat al-Inshiqaq: 6)** he will return to Allah. He will start his eternal life in the hereafter in the new form that He will give him. Whether he will spend his life in the hereafter in Paradise in eternal bliss, or in Hell in eternal torment, depends on his deeds in this world. If he obeys Allah, serves Him and follows His path in this world, he will be rewarded with Allah's approval (good pleasure), and paradise. If he rebels against Allah, he will only find disgrace and exceeding torment in Hell.

This is the greatest truth of the world and nothing can be more important for anybody than this.

As we stated in the beginning, some people are liable to close their eyes to this truth, and not to confirm the being of Allah, or to affirm Him only verbally, and forget about the hereafter. This situation is described in the Qur'an in Prophet Yusuf's speech: **"Allah alone is qualified to judge. His order is to worship none but Him. That is in truth the straight and upright religion, but most of mankind simply do not know." (Surah Yusuf: 40)**. In another verse, Allah says **"...But most people do not know it. They know an outward aspect of the life of this world but are heedless of the hereafter." (Surat ar-Rum: 6-7)**. As stated in the verse, these people only know the "outward aspect of the life of this world". For instance, they may know exchange rates or fashion very well. However, they cannot see Allah's signs which everywhere, and cannot grasp Allah's might. They may seem to be accepting Allah's existence verbally, but this is a very crooked form of 'belief'. As stated in a verse, **"you have made Him into something to cast disdainfully behind your backs!" (Surah Hud: 92)**

These people are not aware of Allah and the hereafter in a real sense. For this reason, the social order they have adopted is a system based on ignorance of Allah and disregarding His existence. However "cultivated" these people, who are heedless of Allah, might seem, they are in truth deeply ignorant and this is why a society made up of these people is called "an ignorant society" in the Qur'an.

The members of this society cannot conceive of Allah by their own efforts. For this reason, Allah has revealed the Qur'an to men as a **"guidance" (Surat al-Baqarah: 2)**. The Qur'an communicates to people the facts of which they are unaware and invites them to know Allah and serve Him. Dissemination of the Qur'an among people will be, in accordance with Allah's command, through those who believe in it, that is, the believers. With regard to the numerous orders of Allah concerning the communication of religion, believers are responsible for conveying the message of the Qur'an to other people, and summoning them to the right path of Allah.

In this book, we tried to explain some subjects in the Qur'an to which Allah calls our attention. We attempted to call attention to only a few of Allah's infinite signs in the universe, and make them more noticeable. We sought to put light on those great facts which are unrealised by the ignorant society which has forgotten Allah. At this point, there are two options awaiting the person who has read this book or any other book written for the purpose of inviting to Qur'an's way:

The first is to be guided to Allah's way. He creates us, and so we are responsible for serving Him. A person may ponder this fact at any time, any day in his life and give up his old ways, which he passed without knowing Allah. He asks forgiveness of Allah and he starts a new life guided by Him.

The second option is to close this book and continue on his way as if nothing has happened. In this case, the person will go on living like "some people" who are unaware of Allah, and will keep on complying with the system of the ignorant society in which he lives.

The first option is the path that will take one to eternal bliss and salvation. The second has only pain, desperation, disappointment and punishment at its end.

The choice is for man to make...

Also by Harun Yahya

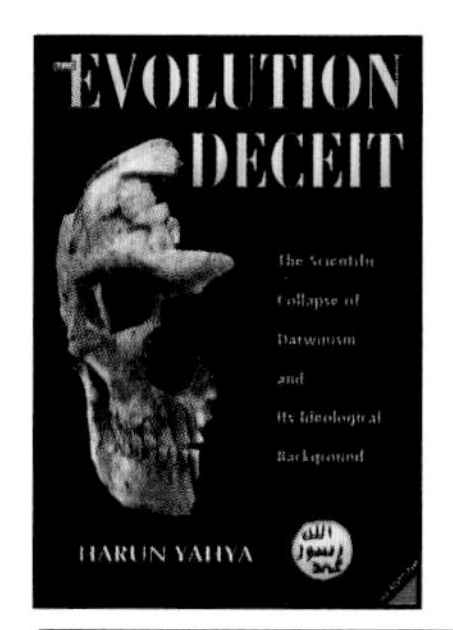

Many people think that Darwin's Theory of Evolution is a proven fact. Contrary to this conventional wisdom, recent developments in science completely disprove the theory. The only reason Darwinism is still foisted on people by means of a worldwide propaganda campaign lies in the ideological aspects of the theory. All secular ideologies and philosophies try to provide a basis for themselves by relying on the theory of evolution. This book clarifies the scientific collapse of the theory of evolution in a way that is detailed but easy to understand. It reveals the frauds and distortions committed by evolutionists to "prove" evolution. Finally it analyzes the powers and motives that strive to keep this theory alive and make people believe in it.

Anyone who wants to learn about the origin of living things, including mankind, needs to read this book.

238 PAGES WITH 166 PICTURES IN COLOUR

Have you ever thought that you were non-existent before you were born and suddenly appeared on Earth? Have you ever thought that the peel of a banana, melon, watermelon or an orange each serve as a quality package preserving the fruit's odour and taste?

Man is a being to which Allah has granted the faculty of thinking. Yet a majority of people fail to employ this faculty as they should... The purpose of this book is to summon people to think in the way they should and to guide them in their efforts to think.

128 PAGES WITH 137 PICTURES IN COLOUR

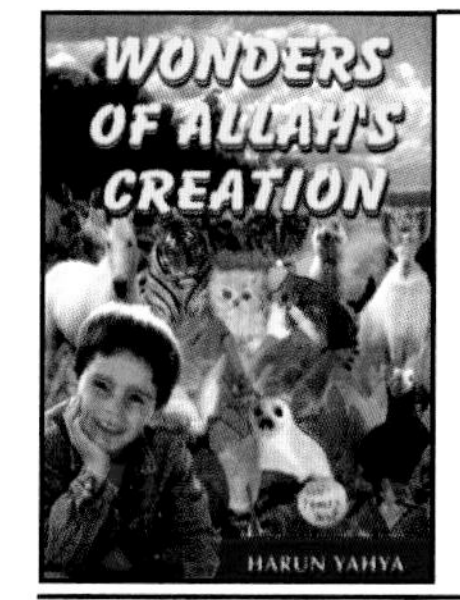

Children!

Have you ever asked yourself questions like these: How did our earth come into existence? How did the moon and sun come into being? Where were you before you were born? How did oceans, trees, animals appear on earth? How do your favourite fruits –bananas, cherries, plums– with all their bright colours and pleasant scents grow in black soil? How does a little tiny bee know how to produce delicious honey? How can it build a honeycomb with such astonishingly regular edges? Who was the first human being? Your mom gave birth to you. Yet the first human being could not have had parents. So, how did he come into existence?" In this book you will find the true answers to these questions.

144 PAGES WITH 282 PICTURESIN COLOUR

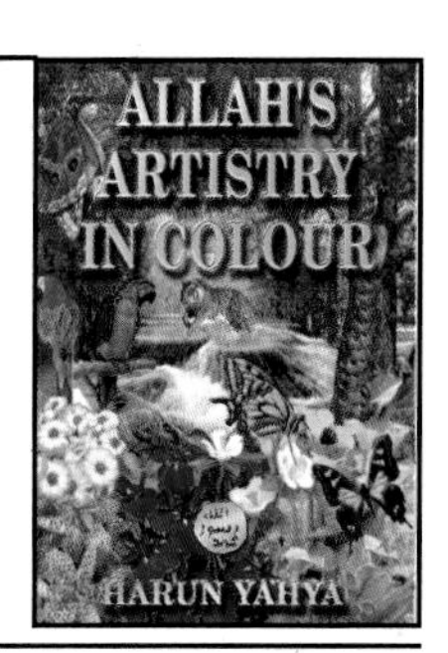

Colours, patterns, spots, even lines of each living being existing in nature have a meaning. For some species, colours serve as a communication tool; for others, they are a warning against enemies. Whatever the case, these colours are essential for the well-being of living beings. An attentive eye would immediately recognise that not only the living beings, but also everything in nature are just as they should be. Furthermore, he would realise that everything is given to the service of man: the comforting blue colour of the sky, the colourful view of flowers, the bright green trees and meadows, the moon and stars illuminating the world in pitch darkness together with innumerable beauties surrounding man.

160 PAGES WITH 215 PICTURES IN COLOUR

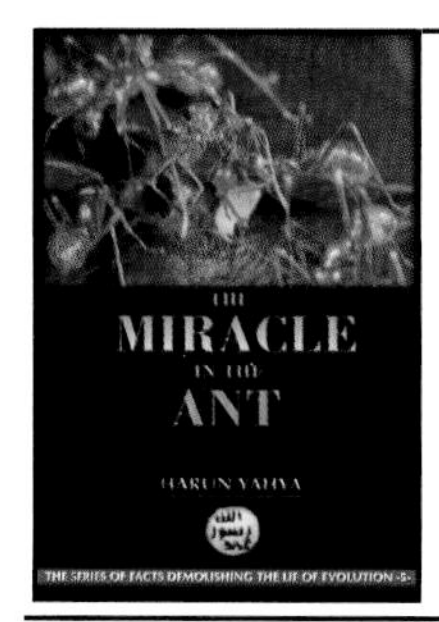

The evidence of Allah's creation is present everywhere in the universe. A person comes across many of these proofs in the course of his daily life; yet if he does not think deeply, he may wrongly consider them to be trivial details. In fact in every creature there are great mysteries to be pondered.

These millimeter-sized animals that we frequently come across but don't care much about have an excellent ability for organization and specialization that is not to be matched by any other being on earth. These aspects of ants create in one a great admiration for Allah's superior power and unmatched creation.

165 PAGES WITH 104 PICTURES IN COLOUR

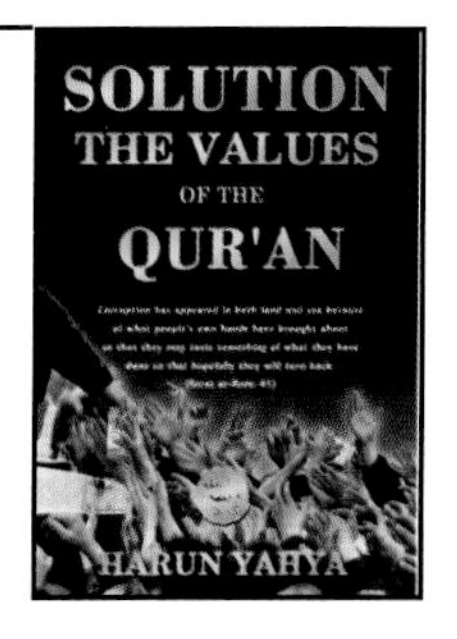

People who are oppressed, who are tortured to death, innocent babies, those who cannot afford even a loaf of bread, who must sleep in tents or even in streets in cold weather, those who are massacred just because they belong to a certain tribe, women, children, and old people who are expelled from their homes because of their religion... Eventually, there is only one solution to the injustice, chaos, terror, massacres, hunger, poverty, and oppression: the morals of the Qur'an.

208 PAGES WITH 276 PICTURES IN COLOUR

Never plead ignorance of Allah's evident existence, that everything was created by Allah, that everything you own was given to you by Allah for your subsistence, that you will not stay so long in this world, of the reality of death, that the Qur'an is the Book of truth, that you will give account for your deeds, of the voice of your conscience that always invites you to righteousness, of the existence of the hereafter and the day of account, that hell is the eternal home of severe punishment, and of the reality of fate.

112 PAGES WITH 74 PICTURES IN COLOUR

One of the major reasons why people feel a profound sense of attachment to life and cast religion aside is the assumption that life is eternal. Forgetting that death is likely to put an end to this life at any time, man simply believes that he can enjoy a perfect and happy life. Yet he evidently deceives himself. The world is a temporary place specially created by Allah to test man. That is why, it is inherently flawed and far from satisfying man's endless needs and desires. Each and every attraction existing in the world eventually wears out, becomes corrupt, decays and finally disappears. This is the never-changing reality of life.

This book explains this most important essence of life and leads man to ponder the real place to which he belongs, namely the Hereafter.

224 PAGES WITH 144 PICTURES IN COLOUR

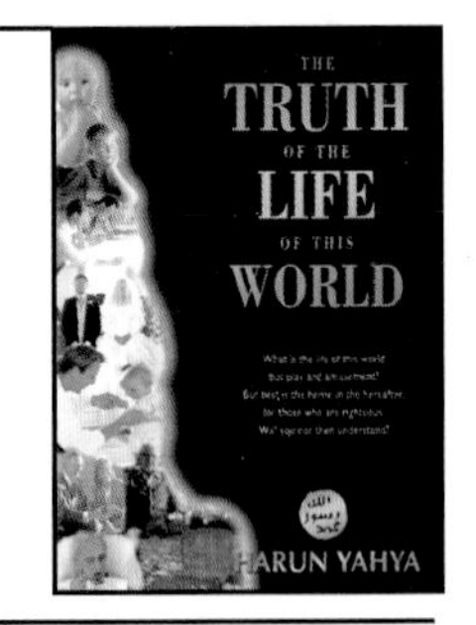

Many societies that rebelled against the will of Allah or regarded His messengers as enemies were wiped off the face of the earth completely... All of them were destroyed–some by a volcanic eruption, some by a disastrous flood, and some by a sand storm...

Perished Nations examines these penalties as revealed in the verses of the Quran and in light of archaeological discoveries.

149 PAGES WITH 73 PICTURES IN COLOUR

In a body that is made up of atoms, you breathe in air, eat food, and drink liquids that are all composed of atoms. Everything you see is nothing but the result of the collision of electrons of atoms with photons.

In this book, the implausibility of the spontaneous formation of an atom, the building-block of everything, living or non-living, is related and the flawless nature of Allah's creation is demonstrated.

139 PAGES WITH 122 PICTURES IN COLOUR

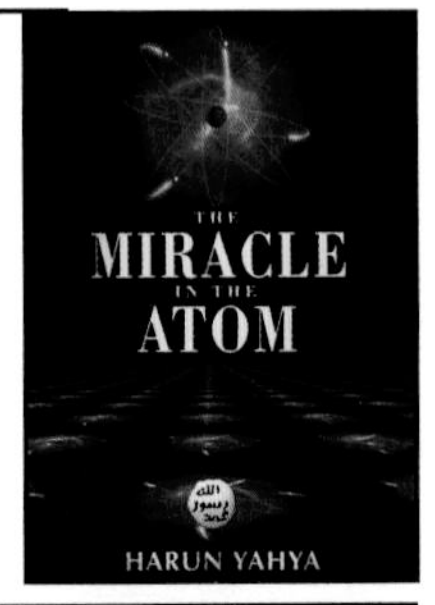

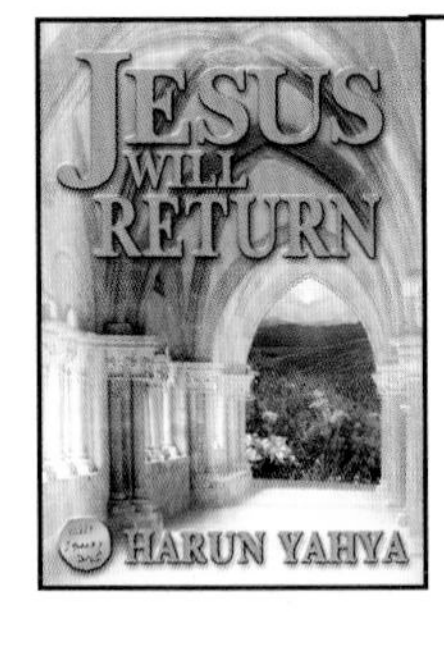

In the Qur'an, there is an explicit reference to the "second coming of the Jesus to the world" which is heralded in a hadith. The realisation of some information revealed in the Qur'an about Jesus can only be possible by Jesus' second coming...

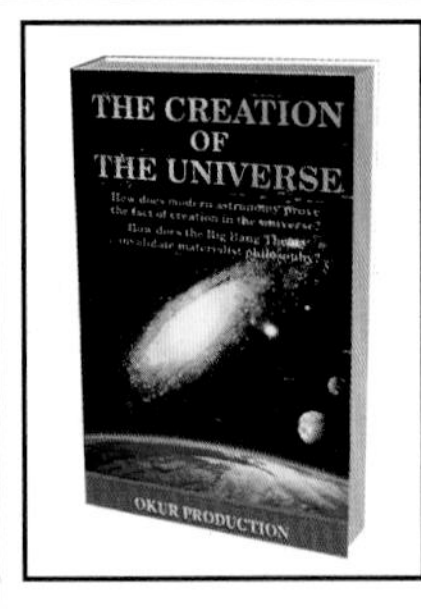

VHS VIDEO CASSETTES

They said 'Glory be to You! We have no knowledge except what You have taught us. You are the All-Knowing, the All-Wise.'
(Surat al-Baqarah: 32)